THE MAMMALS

By the same author

THE TEN-SPINED STICKLEBACK

THE BIOLOGY OF ART

MEN AND SNAKES (with Ramona Morris)

MEN AND APES (with Ramona Morris)

THE MAMMALS

A guide to the living species

by

Desmond Morris

Curator of Mammals, Zoological Society of London

HARPER & ROW, PUBLISHERS

NEW YORK AND EVANSTON

PREFACE

The range and variety of living mammals is enormous and, at first sight, bewildering. There seem to be scores of different antelopes, hundreds of kinds of monkeys, thousands of species of bats and countless rats and mice. If one wants to "get to know" the mammals, it is difficult to decide where to begin.

Two approaches are commonly used. One method simplifies the problem by dealing with a number of representative examples selected from the various groups. The other takes a closer look at the mammals found in one particular region—an island, county, state, or country. But neither system is entirely satisfactory. In both cases the reader becomes acutely aware of the species that escape the net. It is not possible to appreciate fully those that are being described and discussed unless they can be visualized against the backcloth of all their various relatives throughout the world.

There are, of course, too many species for it to be feasible to include descriptions of all of them in a single book of normal proportions, but they can at least be classified and listed. An inventory of this sort can be used as a kind of map for navigating one's thoughts around the vast network of inter-related species. It is rather surprising that no such list has been published in the past and it is pleasant to be able to correct this omission in the present volume.

Great care has been taken to ensure that this list is as accurate and up to date as possible. It includes not only the scientific and popular names of the various animals, but also their geographical distribution and, in each case, a reference to one or more technical works where further details can be found.

On the basis of our present knowledge there would appear to be 4,237 species of mammals living today and from these a representative cross-section of 300 types has been selected for more detailed treatment. Each of these is allocated a full page, with a photograph and brief descriptive text.

The book has a dual purpose and it is hoped that it will appeal at two levels. For the general reader the illustrations and their accompanying texts will provide a broad introduction to the mammals, with the species-inventory acting as a vital guide in the background. For the zoologist, on the other hand, the list itself will be the primary interest, with the illustrations as supplementary material to bring it to life. With this double function in mind, the language of the descriptive texts has been kept at a popular level, but no simplifications of any kind have been made in the case of the taxonomic list.

I am extremely grateful to the following for their painstaking assistance in the preparing of the descriptive texts for the illustrated species:

Michael Boorer (Education Officer, Zoological Society of London).

Malcolm Lyall-Watson (Department of Zoology, Westfield College, London University).

Jacqueline Nayman (Assistant Education Officer, Zoological Society of London).

I am also very indebted to Dr. F. C. Fraser, Mr. R. W. Hayman, Mr. J. E. Hill and

5

Miss J. E. King of the Natural History Museum, for checking my species list and for making valuable suggestions and criticisms. Mr. Hayman and Mr. Hill dealt with the land mammals. The aquatic mammals were checked by Dr. Fraser (Cetaceans) and Miss King (Seals). Mr. Hayman also read the species texts and made many valuable comments. No one could ask for a more expert scrutiny.

My thanks are also due to Mr. Leonard Cutts of Hodder and Stoughton for his continual encouragement during the writing of this volume, to my wife, Ramona, for her patience and help during the many hours when *The Mammals* monopolized my thoughts, and to Mrs. Mary Haynes for valuable assistance in preparing part of the typescript.

In addition I would like to express my gratitude to Granada Television and the Zoological Society of London who generously made available the majority (148 and 115 respectively) of the 300 photographs. Certain other institutions and photographers have kindly supplied individual pictures and I would also like to record my debt to them (see page 433).

Finally, a word about the origin of this book. It began several years ago as a result of a magnanimous gesture by Granada TV. In 1956 that company collaborated with the Zoological Society of London in setting up a joint TV and Film Unit at the London Zoo. This unit produced many animal programmes during its seven-year life at the Zoo and during the process a large number of still photographs were taken. Granada realized the scientific value of this photographic collection and generously made it available for publication. Unfortunately it was not possible to obtain new photographs of all the species required, but the Zoological Society kindly agreed to supply as many as possible of the missing illustrations from their own extensive photographic library. As I had already been busy for some time assembling a comprehensive "working list" of mammals, it seemed an ideal development to combine the list with the photographs and to produce a general guide to the mammalia. I only hope that you will enjoy using it as much as I have enjoyed compiling it.

DESMOND MORRIS
Regent's Park, 1964.

6

CONTENTS

FOREWORD

by Fairfield Osborn
President, New York Zoological Society

It has so happened that, in recent years, books published about birds have considerably exceeded in number those that provide basic information concerning mammals. This, no doubt, is principally due to the widespread cult of bird-watching, but who is to say that one form of animal life is of greater interest than another? In any event, a void in present-day mammalian literature is largely filled by Desmond Morris's notable accomplishment.

In THE MAMMALS, he provides, for the first time, a major listing of the known species of mammals of the world. These the author considers to number 4,237.* The general list has been arrived at by consulting the works of accepted authorities in each area, as shown in a useful graph. When the inevitable clashes have occurred, decisions of priority have been made, a task of no small consequence.

The detailed or statistical sections of the book are, of course, of greatest interest to the technical mammalogist, but for the more general reader 300 typical species, at least one in each Order, have been selected for short general accounts, each illustrated with a photograph of a living animal. In this way, the book serves a double purpose. It is technical and at the same time one that can be read with benefit by innumerable people who are interested in animal life.

This book is of particular value because the whole plan and scope of the mammals of the world are presented. No one can read it without being impressed anew with the amazing effects of evolutionary forces during some 150 million years that have resulted in creatures marked by extraordinary differences—from a two-inch bat to a hundred-foot Blue Whale—yet all sharing one major characteristic, the capacity to suckle their young.

Many years ago the New York Zoological Society published a classification of *Present Day Mammals* which, by comparison with Dr. Morris's work, was elementary. Yet for many years this little book was a useful working tool, especially for the student and beginner. Dr. Morris's book will prove of far greater worth and will reach a wider audience of both zoologists and laymen because of its scope and comprehensiveness. Dr. Morris as well as the Zoological Society of London may well be proud of this fine addition to the literature of mammalogy.

---

* For reasons of space the bat and rodent orders, 981 species and 1,729 species respectively, are given by genera only, with the number of known species listed for each.

INTRODUCTION

THE NATURE AND EVOLUTION OF MAMMALS

By definition a mammal is an animal that feeds its young with milk secreted from special organs, on the body of the mother, called mammary glands. But, although this is the officially accepted diagnostic feature of the group, it is not, in fact, the character we use to identify an unknown animal as a member of the class Mammalia.

Confronted with an unfamiliar creature with four limbs we would, in practice, look first to see if it had a hairy or furry coat. We would probably call it a reptile if it was covered with scales, a bird if it was feathered, or a mammal if it was hairy. This is the vital clue we look for in the first instance. Fortunately, it is just as reliable because hairiness and the possession of mammary glands are inevitably linked.

This is because, when hair was in the process of evolving, there developed with it, as part of a temperature-controlling system, certain simple but numerous skin glands. The hair kept the animal warm, and the secretion of the glands kept it cool, or made its coat glossy. It was from some of these glands that the mammary glands developed. It follows that no animal could have evolved mammary glands unless it had an insulating coat of hair in the first place.

It would seem, therefore, that mammals first stood on their own four feet as a distinct group, not as model parents feeding their young with their own bodies, but as animated thermostats.

In order to understand the reasons for such a development, it is necessary to look at the immediate ancestors of the mammals, the early reptilians. With the acquisition of a tough scaly skin, the reptiles had solved the problem of spreading their range away from the vicinity of water and had conquered the drier areas of the land. But they depended—and still do depend—on a suitable external temperature for efficient living.

If the environment became too hot, they were forced to hide from the sun's rays; or, if it became too cold, they became sluggish and even torpid. Clearly there were fresh fields and golden opportunities for any forms that could control heat loss or heat gain. A variable, insulatory coat was the answer and it was developed independently by two groups of reptiles. In one case it evolved as feathers, giving rise to birds; in the other case as hair, leading to the mammals.

In both instances the body-covering could be adjusted to produce greater heat gain or greater heat loss. Each unit of the body covering—each feather or hair—was provided with muscles that raised or lowered it. With this movement, the insulating power of the coat could be increased or decreased according to the external heat and the internal state of the animal. These changes could be put into operation in a few seconds, the coat of hair or feathers being made thicker or thinner immediately the animal experienced a change in temperature.

In the case of mammals, an additional long-term system was also developed. This was

9

geared, not to sudden minute-to-minute fluctuations, but to the major seasonal changes, a generally heavier coat growing as winter approached and then a lighter one replacing it in the spring.

It has already been mentioned that the outer surface of mammals not only sprouted hairs, but also possessed certain skin glands. If we look at living reptiles we find that their surfaces boast no such glands. Their skins are dry. It seems likely, therefore, that the early reptilian forms which gave rise to the mammals must still have retained, from their amphibian ancestors, some sort of skin secretions and that these were modified and perfected in new roles as sebaceous or sweat glands.

The sebaceous glands associated with each hair secreted an oily substance that lubricated the fur and waterproofed it. The sweat glands secreted water, taken from the blood stream, and the evaporation of this liquid from the exposed surface of the animal had a dramatic cooling effect. This cooling device, combined with panting and the full erection of the fur to expose the skin, formed the efficient heat loss mechanism of the mammal.

The heat retention properties of the insulating coat of hair, combined with this heat reduction system, gave the early mammals the great advantage of a high, constant body temperature. This was important in two ways. It not only enabled the animals concerned to spread over a wider range and into a greater variety of habitats, but it also enabled them to develop much more sensitive physiological systems. Metabolism became more efficient and the "hairy reptiles" more active and energetic.

Increased reaction speed, however, demanded improved circulatory and respiratory systems and a bigger, more complex brain. All these demands were met. A drastic change in the blood system, eliminating the inefficient mixing of venous and arterial blood, was evolved. This provided the more complex brain with a supply of higher quality blood. The development of a muscular diaphragm, separating the thorax from the abdomen, enabled the lungs to obtain increased oxygen intake. The evolving mammal was then capable of getting more oxygen quickly, of supplying purer oxygenated blood to the improved brain and setting in motion, with more efficient metabolism, actions and reactions superior to those of its reptilian rivals.

All this led to a more active, alert and intelligent animal. But an animal equipped in this way had to have more efficient limbs to carry out its improved actions. The reptilian legs, sticking out on either side of the body, were no longer good enough. They had to be pulled round and tucked under the body, supporting its weight more easily while propelling the animal forward. They also became much longer in relation to the body size and, as the brain worked faster, so did the body move faster. A high-speed action machine was in production.

But to produce a delicate piece of machinery that will operate with precise efficiency, a great deal of care has to be taken in the early stages of construction and the early stages of the life of the individual reptilian ancestor were too crude and too haphazard to suit the developing mammal. Mammals, as Romer once said, went in for "quality not quantity" in this respect. Reptiles laid many eggs and left the young animals more or less to their fate. But the mammalian trend was for fewer and fewer offspring with more and more attention paid to them.

Two main developments occurred. One was to abandon egg-laying altogether and to produce live young. The most successful mammals retained these offspring inside the mother's womb until an advanced stage of development was reached. This was done with the aid of a new structure called the placenta—a connection between the mother and the developing embryo, through which it could receive prolonged nourishment.

The other development has already been mentioned—the evolution, from the already existing skin glands, of the specialized mammary glands. These gave an even greater prolongation of the period of maternal nourishment to the growing offspring. In this way, the more complex organism was able to mature gradually and safely during its early stages.

Here then we have the mammal's formula for success—a more efficient, more sensitive body, a complex brain, constant high temperature, athletic limbs, fewer offspring with longer dependence on their parents and, above all, *activity and intelligence.*

But, at the start of the mammalian story, these trends and developments were occurring during the great boom in reptilian monsters. The dinosaurs towered over the land and dominated the scene by sheer power.

The first signs of the mammalian break-away from the pure reptilian stock appear in the Jurassic period, approximately 150 million years ago. The prototype mammals developed, not from the end-products of the reptile epoch, but during its early days. Then, for a period of 80 million years the ancestral mammals were forced to hide and cringe in corners—small insignificant creatures—held in check by the reptile giants that roamed the surface of the earth. Only with the mysterious downfall of the dinosaurs, and the end of the golden age of the reptilian fauna, were the mammals able to emerge and take control.

This period of severe competition was probably a blessing in disguise, however, for it must have forced the archi-mammals to improve more and more on the special developments they had started. By the time the reptilian crash came, at the end of the Mesozoic era, they were more eligible candidates to seize the throne. This they started to do approximately 70 million years ago, at the beginning of the Tertiary period, and so began the golden age of mammals. They spread and grew and multiplied until, in a rich variety of thousands of forms, they came to dominate the globe.

But there were still plenty of survival problems for them to solve. For no sooner had the dreaded scourge of the giant reptiles been removed and the great radiation of mammals gained impetus than new enemies began to appear. New killers prowled the earth and this time they were more cunning in their methods—for they were mammals themselves.

The flesh-eating reptiles may have driven the early mammals into corners and forced them to develop their special survival attributes, but the new and more skilful mammalian killers that arose out of the ashes, as it were, alongside the vast body of the radiating mammalian fauna, were a force to be reckoned with in more extreme terms. To survive this onslaught, special defence methods had to be evolved.

The sensory equipment became more and more subtle—better eyes, keener hearing, more sensitive noses. The motor equipment was tuned up—longer and still longer legs for the fleeing ungulates, with fewer and fewer toes; heavy balancing tails for the leapers and jumpers; huge digging claws for the burrowers; parachute skin membranes between the legs for the flying phalangers, flying lemurs and flying squirrels.

Some of the mammals fortified themselves against attack, rather as the giant reptiles had done before them, with enormous bodies and tough, thick skins—the rhinos, the hippos and the elephants. Some of the smaller species also armoured themselves, but to be successful they had to go to greater lengths—the porcupines, the spiny mice and spiny rats, the hedgehogs, the tenrecs and the echidnas all developed outer coverings of sharp prickles that succeeded in making them less tasty mouthfuls. The pangolins developed a new kind of scaliness, from modified hairs. The armadillos became encased in a hard bony shell and took on the role of the "tortoises" of the mammal world. A number of the small carnivores avoided attacks from other killers by resorting to chemical warfare. Powerful glands were developed in the anal region that could exude or squirt foul-smelling liquids, the skunks of the New World and the striped weasels of the Old World being the most advanced operators of this device. Coupled with this development, as often occurs, there developed brightly contrasted body markings, acting as conspicuous warning signals. For nearly all other species, however, the hair colours remained dull and inconspicuous, mostly shades of brown or grey. Special camouflage modifications evolved in many instances, the dull coats becoming even less obvious because of spotting, blotching, banding, or striping. These markings were particularly frequent among the forest-dwelling mammals. The open-country species tended to be plainer and the desert forms both plain and pale.

Predator pressures only accounted for one aspect of mammalian radiation. Another, equally important force at work was food competition. In their search to find food as well as to avoid becoming it, mammals became drastically modified in a number of ways. The ant-eating specialists that arose in the various groups evolved long, curved claws for tearing open the ant-hills, and extended, pointed snouts with enormously lengthy tongues that could lap up the ants easily and quickly. The killers developed immensely powerful jaws and necks and sharp claws. The grass and leaf munchers evolved elaborate alimentary systems to cope with large quantities of the rather poor quality food. The fish-eaters became streamlined swimmers, the winged insect-catchers became high-speed fliers, and the timid hiders and burrowers became energetic and elaborate hoarders.

In the fight for food and the struggle for self-protection new regions were conquered and re-conquered. The air, the trees, the plains, the swamps, the rivers, the earth and the sea were all invaded and, as we have seen, changes in both structure and behaviour accompanied these moves. New feeding habits influenced many aspects of mammalian design, but none so much as dentition. Mammalian teeth became much more differentiated than those of their reptilian ancestors. Instead of rows of similar sharp spikes, they split up into characteristic groups—the incisors, the canines, the pre-molars and the molars. The exact arrangement differs strikingly and consistently between mammalian types and provides a valuable basis for classification. New locomotion habits—evolved either in connection with avoiding predators or obtaining food—also influenced the structure of modern mammals in a number of ways, but principally the limb design. These differences and specializations have also been of major importance in classifying the various mammalian groups.

Reproductively, the mammals are a fairly homogeneous group, with the notable exceptions of the monotremes and the marsupials. The monotremes have retained the reptilian character of laying eggs and they have not developed a very efficient milk delivery system. The marsupials are excellent nipple-feeders, but they have failed to evolve successful internal nourishment for the developing embryo. It crawls into the world as a minute blob and clambers its way towards the pouch-protected nipples, guiding itself through its mother's fur by a sense of smell. Once there it clings to the nipple and starts to feed. Living, as it were, in a "womb with a view" the infant can now slowly develop.

Neither the monotremes nor the marsupials are particularly brainy, as mammals go, and it has been suggested that this is connected with these rather inefficient reproductive arrangements. The typical modern mammal, with placental connections with the mother during the early stages of development, can take its time to grow its giant brain, the delicate and complex structure being well nourished during its vital early phases of development. When the young placental mammal emerges into the world it is already a more advanced and perfected organism. During a prolonged period of parental protection and feeding it gains valuable experience of the hostile world around it. Its actions and reactions, more flexible and adjustable than those of other animals, become finely tuned to the variations and fluctuations of the environment.

From its parents it will have inherited many valuable instinctive actions and reactions. From its own experiences of the outside world as it has been maturing it will have learnt many ways of modifying these responses to its own advantage. It will be uniquely endowed with an extremely high level of curiosity; it will investigate, explore, manipulate the unfamiliar until it can either control it or learns to abandon it.

During this process of maturation the young mammal will be fitting itself into the social system of its species. In many cases, when it has been weaned, it will be driven away by its no longer parentally inclined mother or father and will have to establish a new territory of its own. This it will have to patrol and defend against other members of its species. Eventually it may come to share it with a member of the opposite sex, or it may remain solitary and meet the opposite sex only briefly for mating itself.

In other cases, the young animal will not be driven away as it grows older, but will stay in the family group to become a member of the social hierarchy. Large social gatherings of mammals are not rare. They can be found in most orders and are usually organized according to a rigid scale of dominance and subordination. As the young mammal grows older and stronger, he will work his way steadily up the dominance scale of the social hierarchy. The older members of the group will die off and eventually he himself may take the lead and become the boss animal, the overlord. He may then be the prime mover in deciding when the group will move on, stop to feed, sleep, run or defend itself. He will almost certainly have the pick of the females and will find himself in charge of a large harem. The more solitary, territorial mammals are more inclined to form pairs than establish harems, but in many cases there is a combination of the two systems. In these instances, a powerful male establishes his territory and collects as many females on to it as he can. Like a true territorial male, he will not tolerate any other males, but like a hierarchical male, he collects a large social group around him. The difference is that, apart from himself, the group is all female.

Some mammals breed all the year round, the females experiencing breeding cycle after breeding cycle, each period of heat, or oestrous, leading to fertilization, pregnancy, birth, lactation and then another period of heat. Such females are said to be poly-oestrous, having many cycles each year. Others, especially those living in the climatically more variable temperate zones, are monoestrous. That is, they experience only one breeding season during the year, lactation being followed by a sexually inactive period during which the reproductive organs lie dormant. During this non-reproductive period a female mammal is said to be anoestrous. The social organizations mentioned above may be constant throughout the year, where polyoestrous species are concerned, or they may vary dramatically with the seasons, in the case of monoestrous forms. In the latter case mammals may be more or less solitary, or loosely arranged in foraging groups, during the non-reproductive period. Then, when the breeding season arrives, changes in day-length and temperature start to influence the output of reproductive hormones, and a whole new pattern of social behaviour swings into operation as an accompaniment to the physiological changes in the reproductive systems of both sexes. Males may become more aggressive, more territorial. Both sexes may feel the urge to migrate to different ground. They may become less fearful of predators, less interested in the search for food. After the short season is over, they will return again to their non-reproductive moods and their feeding grounds, taking with them a new generation.

Social organization in mammals is often established by fighting to settle disputes, but very frequently such problems are solved by the use of nothing more than the threat of fighting. Many species have evolved a less damaging "cold war" technique consisting of a sign language of threats, counter-threats, submissions, appeasements and greetings. These signals indicate the mood of the displaying animal and tell his companions or rivals exactly what he *will* do, if the signal is not responded to in the appropriate way. If a powerful male can threaten powerfully and a weak male can only threaten weakly, then the system is as valid as actual combat and is far less dangerous to the species. It means that the species will not be reducing its own numbers unnecessarily and yet will be able to work out an efficient social organization in which the vital rules of selective survival can still operate.

The language of mammals comprises visual, auditory, tactile and chemical signals. The visual signals can be clearly observed in the facial expressions of higher primates, and in the ear, lip and tail postures and movements of members of the dog family and many other groups, to mention only a few examples. Auditory signals are extremely varied, from the shrill twittering of marmosets and the squeaking of rodents, to the roaring of lions and the trumpeting of elephants. Most auditory signals are the result of highly modified respiration responses and are produced by the larynx, but quite a number are produced by percussive means: beavers slap their tails on the water, apes beat their chests or hollow trees, rabbits and certain rodents thump the ground with their back feet. Tactile signals are limited largely to parental and mating acts and are of a fairly simple kind although, in the case of mutual grooming and cleaning, the friendly

14

contact established is of great importance as a social communication and must be considered as a tactile signal. Chemical language is of extreme importance to most mammals. Unfortunately man is an exceptional mammal in this respect and he therefore finds it difficult to appreciate or analyse the complex "language of smells" that seems to exist for all the more typical "big-nosed" mammals. Certainly many species have complex scent glands on different parts of the body: on the flanks (hamsters), in the middle of the back (hyraxes, peccaries), on the wrists and the shoulders (lemurs), under the eyes (certain antelopes and deer), in the anal region (many carnivores and others), on the feet (muntjacs and others), on the snout (capybaras), and so on. These glands may exude their chemical products without effort, or by being contracted, or by being rubbed against part of the environment. In the latter case, scent markings are left behind by the mammal concerned. By rubbing against different landmarks in his territory or home range, he can deposit his personal odour all over it. Like mammary glands, most scent glands have probably evolved from simpler sweat or sebaceous glands. In addition, deposits of urine and faeces may be employed as scent-markers. These products may be placed in special areas of the territory, signalling the presence of its owner to others of its species. Many of the olfactory signals are, in fact, aggressive, others are sexual and still others are associated with individual or family recognition. When mammals meet they do not usually look at one another, they smell one another. They may smell one another's mouths and noses, or, more frequently, one another's anal regions. In this way, they can evaluate the mood and condition of the stranger in some detail, but we still need to know a great deal more about the exact nature of the information that is conveyed in olfactory communication.

Mammals that have spread into the colder regions of the world solve their winter problems either by migrating to warmer regions, or by hibernating. Migrating is something more of a problem for earthbound mammals than it is for air-free birds. As a result, only very few birds hibernate and not many mammals migrate. The more common, hibernating mammals are in a sense reverting to an ancestral reptilian solution to the problem. They are abandoning their modern, progressive qualities of thermostatic control and high-activity level and are becoming torpid, cold-bodied slumberers. There are many degrees of hibernation, from heavy but reasonably normal slumbering that can be interrupted easily for a wintry snack, to complete torpor. In some parts of the world, it is the height of summer that becomes unbearable and then a condition known as aestivation may occur. This is similar in most respects to the condition of hibernation, the mammal passing through a period of extreme drought, heat, or food scarcity, in a passive, slumbering state.

Even when they are fully active, mammals resort to long periods of daily rest and sleep. In some species, such as the elephants, this never lasts for more than a few hours at a time. At the other end of the scale, the tiny shrews similarly can only rest for brief periods before having to resume the quest for food. Most mammals, however, sleep for one or two long periods every 24 hours. Those that sleep during the day and are active at night are called nocturnal mammals; those that are day-active only are called diurnal; and those that are active during the morning and evening, but sleep during the dead of night and during the height of day, are called crepuscular. In popular thinking, mammals

15

are usually divided up into day-time and night-time creatures, but the truth is that the vast majority of them are crepuscular.

During their inactive periods many of them lie up in specially prepared dens, nests, or lairs. These may be as simple as the fork of a tree, or a depression in the ground, or as elaborate as the bed of an Orang-utan or the nest of a Harvest Mouse.

A successful individual in the world of mammals may live as long as 60 to 70 years if it is an elephant, 40 to 50 if it is a rhinoceros or a hippopotamus, 30 to 40 if it is one of the cattle, 20 to 30 if it is a typical ungulate, a large carnivore, or a large primate, 10 to 20 if it is a large rodent, a small carnivore, or a small primate, and under 10 years if it is a small rodent or an insectivore. From these figures it is obvious that the bigger the mammal the longer it lives. On this basis it is clear that, as a mammal, man has artificially stretched out his life span to such an abnormal extent that he can not only hope to live for twice as long as he should, but is also the longest-lived of all mammals. Even the elephant cannot compete.

THE CLASSIFICATION OF MAMMALS

An animal classification performs two functions. It hands out labels and it illuminates evolutionary relationships. Unfortunately, labelling is a static concept and evolution a dynamic one. As a result there has been a certain amount of confusion.

Classifications of animals existed, of course, long before evolutionary ideas were developed. The lists of creatures were then nothing more than collections of titles, useful for referring to this or that animal without ambiguity. By an international use of Latin or Greek it was possible for each form of life to be given not only a local, popular name, but also a world-wide scientific name.

In order that everyone should agree about the names to be allocated, a strict rule of priorities was observed. The first person to describe, technically and in detail, the features of a particular animal was allowed to give it its official name. The date of the publication of his description was all-important. If, years later, another publication dealing with the same animal was unearthed and its date proved to be even slightly earlier than the accepted one, then the name would have to be changed. These rules still apply and this is why most taxonomic publications today state not only the year of publication, but also the month and the day.

Many such changes have been made in the course of time. As far as mammals are concerned, a book published a century ago will probably contain more obsolete names than valid ones. But establishing the correct priorities is only one reason for this. A second reason concerns the change in attitude of biologists following the Darwinian upheaval. As soon as it was accepted that one animal form could evolve into another it became clear that any rigid, static type of classification was bound to be artificial. Each kind of animal had, at some point in the past, been something else and would, at some point in the future, be something else again. At any one moment in time, different groups of animals could, therefore, be at any stage in the gradual process of change. Some would be distinct forms, with no close relatives; others would be just about to split up into effectively different units. How could a classification system embody this concept and yet remain rigid enough to act as a useful naming and labelling device?

The basic unit of biological classification is the species. In pre-evolutionary thinking a species was accepted as valid if it differed in some slight but distinct way from its closest relatives. In post-evolutionary thinking, however, a species had to be not only different, but also reproductively independent from its relatives. For example, when an animal population is successful and spreads its range into, say, a desert region, it is likely to adapt to this new way of life by becoming lighter in colour, as generation follows generation. If the pale desert form becomes separated from the darker forest form and the two groups breed separately, more and more changes may take place as the adaptations improve. If the two populations now meet again they may or may not interbreed. If the differences are still slight, then the populations will be able to re-mingle. If they are greater, the two forms will now live alongside one another but without mixing. If the latter occurs, then a new species has come into being and must be named as such. If they intermingle, then, despite their distinctive differences in appearance, they are still members of the same species and are referred to only as different races. It could be that the visible differences are only very slight and yet the two forms do not mix. No matter how minor these distinctions may be, however, the fact that they result in reproductive isolation means that there are two good species. Very striking superficial differences, on the other hand, may not necessarily mean that one is dealing with separate species. Even though the animals may look very unlike one another, if they interbred freely and naturally in the wild state they are considered only as racial types of a single species.

Some animals that have a very wide geographical distribution may exist in many different sizes and colours, each one grading into the next, across the whole range. Such a series, called a cline, may vary so gradually from one type to another that it is impossible to decide where to split it up into races. In the western extreme of the range it may be a very dark brown; in the middle, a paler reddish-brown; farther on a reddish-grey and, in the east, a very pale grey. The dark brown race and the pale grey race will be easy to name and distinguish when they are the only two known, but as more and more of the intermediates are discovered the distinction becomes less and less clear-cut. When the whole spectrum of a cline is known in detail, it becomes almost pointless to try to name any segment of it at all. For this reason the idea of giving labels to different races is becoming less and less popular. Their variations are described and the significance of the clinal changes discussed. The various forms are then simply lumped together as a single breeding complex—a single good species.

It is obvious how the development of this idea must have thrown confusion into the camp of the old-style classification experts. They enjoyed splitting animals up into as many species as possible. For some of them, founding a new species had almost become an obsession. Every new skin or skull was eagerly searched for some tiny difference from similar ones already known. If there were larger spots, broader teeth, longer claws—anything that was measurably different, they proudly pronounced a new discovery, named it and published their description. During the last century not hundreds, but literally thousands of "new species" were named in this way, without any regard for the

17

significance, or lack of significance, of the minute differences that were so laboriously recorded. What was happening, of course, was that specimens were being brought into the museums from different parts of the range of each species and, because the intermediates were not known, there were no nicely graded series to expose the folly and stop the rot from going any farther. It reached a point where animals, carefully recorded as belonging to widely separate species, might, on checking back to their source of origin, be found to have come from the same litter!

As more and more specimens became available and as the concept of reproductively isolated species became accepted, so the tide was turned and the "splitters", as they were called, were replaced by the modern "lumpers". They set about the task of cleaning up the enormous mess and sank name after meaningless name into oblivion.

For anyone outside the technical world of zoological taxonomy this situation can lead to all kinds of difficulties. Books published in different decades carry different scientific names for the same animals. Where is one to turn for a final statement? How can one decide ultimately what to call a particular creature? With the priorities of various names still being argued over and the process of lumping still going on, as more and more information becomes available, how can one be sure that one is using the correct name for a species that is really valid?

The answer is that it is necessary, when compiling a technical list, to mention in detail all the old rejected names and their authorities and to list the various related species that have been recorded but are now being abandoned by lumping. This means that many species in a "check list" take up at least half a page and often much more. As there are 4,237 species of living mammals accepted at the moment, this would mean that such a list for all the mammals would cover, at the very least, 2,000 pages.

No such work exists, but there are detailed check lists for different regions of the world and for certain groups of mammals. By selecting the latest and best of these technical works and carefully pooling their information it has been possible to produce for the present volume a much more condensed "working list" covering all the living species of mammals.

This was only feasible in a general work such as this if each species was restricted to a single line of text. On to that line the currently accepted scientific name, the best popular name and the approximate geographical range are recorded. It is not possible to include the rejected scientific names, the alternative popular names, or the precise range of the species, but, in order to make these available to the serious student, a symbol is added at the end of each species-line indicating the technical authority, or authorities, from which the scientific name has been taken. Detailed references and a key to these symbols are given on page 21.

As a result of this procedure every species mentioned in this book can have its credentials checked and evaluated and yet the list is concise and reasonably uncomplicated for the general reader.

In two cases, the bats and the rodents, it has been impossible, for reasons of space, to list all the species separately. There are so many recorded bats and rats that even with the condensed system they would need a whole book to themselves. However, in both instances every genus has been listed and the number of species in each one is given. Where a genus has only a single species then space permits it to be named in full.

With the other seventeen orders of mammals every single species is given. If an animal name does not appear in the list it can mean one of three things. Either the name has been pre-dated and therefore replaced, or it has turned out to be no more than a race of one of the species listed, or it belongs to an animal that was not discovered until after the book went to press. There is one other possibility, but I hope it will not apply—namely that in my researches a species has been overlooked. Every effort has been made to avoid this and I would like to reiterate my gratitude to the officials of the Natural History Museum for their assistance in this matter.

Taxonomic Authorities

Up to this point I have been discussing the basic unit of classification—the species. But what of the higher levels? The mammals as a whole are regarded as a class—the Class Mammalia. This is divided into nineteen orders—the Carnivores, Order Carnivora, for example. Each order is divided further into a number of families—the Cats, Family Felidae, for example. Then again each family is split into a number of genera, such as the Big Cats—Genus *Panthera*—and each genus into its species—the Lion, *Panthera leo*.

Where the situation is more complicated at a particular level, additional sub-divisions are brought into play—suborders, superfamilies, subfamilies and so on. In some instances these sub-divisions may seem rather more complicated than is warranted by the number of species listed. This is because the taxonomic system has been devised to encompass both living and extinct mammals, but the latter have been omitted from the present work.

In 1945 George Gaylord Simpson published an important work in which he presented an excellent classification of the mammals, at the higher levels. I have followed this in almost every detail above the level of the genus. I have also followed it for the *sequence* of the genera, but for decisions concerning the generic names themselves and also the species names I have turned to more specialized studies.

My aim has been to select the most erudite and up-to-date works for the various geographical regions and then to combine them in the sequence laid down by Simpson. The world map on page 27 shows how this was done. The land masses have been divided up into eleven sections. These areas have been determined by the scope of the different studies. In some, but not all cases they are natural biological regions.

At first sight this appears to be a fairly simple process of addition of information, but difficulties did arise. Firstly, some species extended their range over several of the basic regions. If the different authorities disagreed, it became necessary to disregard all but one of them. This meant a scale of preferences. In a similar way, several of the authorities overlapped one another's regions and once again preferences had to be established for the duplicated areas.

A second problem was that in certain geographical sections even the best authority available was taxonomically weak. This could lead to the following situation: Supposing a genus used to be recorded as having ten species in region A and ten in B. Region A is then studied in great detail by a good modern taxonomist and the ten doubtful species are reduced by sensible lumping to, say, three. Region B does not get this treatment. The genus must today, therefore, be listed as having a total of thirteen species, when it probably has far fewer. Nothing can be done about this until the poorly studied regions are re-worked. All we can do for the moment is to assemble the best information available, admitting as we do so that it is uneven in quality and noting the areas where improvement is needed. Luckily this only applies in one or two regions. (The respective merits of the various authors and a scale of preferences is given on page 26.)

A partial solution to this last problem is to extract from the recent literature revision studies of special groups, or of parts of regions. This has been done in a few cases but where this course has been taken the earlier major reference is always given, so that it remains possible to trace the species with only a handful of technical works.

In addition, one or two major mammalian *group* studies have been used in those areas where they are superior to the regional studies. Also, newly discovered mammals that have not yet been included in major works have been listed against their special paper references.

As this volume is a general work and not a technical taxonomy no attempt has been made to introduce new terms or modify existing names. Such procedure would be out of place and only add further confusion.

For the general reader the list gives the best and the most up-to-date names and groupings available from the specialized literature. For the zoologist it provides a complete inventory, the source of every part of which can be traced and checked in detail. The use of letters (A to S) for the nineteen orders and numbers for the species in each order makes it possible to refer to each mammal by means of a simple numerical designation (e.g. *Lagenorhynchus obliquidens*, the Pacific White-sided Dolphin=K55). This should prove of value in various contexts such as the numbering of mammalian card index systems, photographic collections, etc.

The specific authorities used are shown in the table that follows.

CLASSIFICATION ABOVE THE GENUS LEVEL

Author	Date	Reference
SIMPSON, G. G.	1945	The principles of classification and a classification of mammals. Bull. Amer. Mus. Nat. Hist. 85, p. 1–350.

CLASSIFICATION OF GENERA AND SPECIES

PRINCIPAL REGIONAL WORKS

Symbol	Authors	Date	Title and Reference	Region
EM	ELLERMAN, J. R. and MORRISON-SCOTT, T. C. S.	1951	Checklist of Palaearctic and Indian Mammals. 1758–1946 B.M. (Nat. Hist.), London. p. 1–810	Europe, Asia and N. Africa
EMH	ELLERMAN, J. R., MORRISON-SCOTT, T. C. S. and HAYMAN, R. W.	1953	Southern African Mammals. 1758–1951. B.M. (Nat. Hist.), London. p. 1–363	S. Africa
LH	LAURIE, E. M. O. and HILL, J. E.	1954	List of Land Mammals of New Guinea, Celebes and Adjacent Islands. 1758–1952. B.M. (Nat. Hist.), London. p. 1–175	New Guinea and Celebes
C1	CABRERA, A.	1957	Catalogo de los Mamiferos de America del Sur. Vol. 1. Rev. Mus. Argent. Cienc. Nat. Zool. 4, p. 1–307	S. America
C2	CABRERA, A.	1961	ditto—Vol. 2. p. 308–732	S. America
HK	HALL, E. R. and KELSON, K. R.	1959	Mammals of North America. (2 vols.) Ronald Press, N.Y. p. 1–1083	N. America, Cen. America, and W. Indies
GG	GOODWIN, G. G. and GREENHALL, A. M.	1961	A review of the bats of Trinidad and Tobago. Bull. Amer. Mus. Nat. Hist. 122, p. 191–301	Trinidad and Tobago
IT	IREDALE, T. and TROUGHTON, E. le G.	1934	A checklist of the mammals recorded from Australia. Mem. Austral. Mus., Sydney. 6, p. 1–122	Australia and Tasmania
CH	CHASEN, F. N.	1940	A handlist of Malaysian mammals. Bull. Raffles Mus. 15, p. 1–209	Malaya, Sumatra, Java and Borneo
TAY	TAYLOR, E. H.	1934	Philippine Land Mammals. Manila: Monog. 30 of Bur. Sci. p. 1–548	Philippines
A	ALLEN, G. M.	1939	A Checklist of African Mammals. Bull. Mus. Comp. Zool., Harvard. 83, p. 1–763	Africa and Madagascar
HU	HUTTON, F. W.	1904	Index Faunae Novae Zealandiae. Phil. Inst. Canterbury, New Zealand	New Zealand

CLASSIFICATION OF GENERA AND SPECIES

SUPPLEMENTARY WORKS

Symbol	Authors	Date	Title and Reference
AN	ANDERSEN, K.	1912	Catalogue of the Chiroptera in the collection of the British Museum. Second Edition. 1. Megachiroptera. London. p. 1–854
B	BOURRET, R.	1951	Une nouvelle chauvre-souris du Tonkin, *Rhinomegalophus paradoxolphus*. Bull. Mus. Hist. Nat. Paris (2) 23, p. 607–609
CON	CONISBEE, L. R.	1953	A list of the names proposed for genera and subgenera of recent mammals. 1904–1951. B.M. (Nat. Hist.), London. p. 1–109
D	DEKEYSER, P. L.	1943	Description d'un type de Crocidure africaine d' A. Milne-Edwards: Crocidura bloyeti. Bull. Mus. Hist. Nat. Paris (2) 15 (4). p. 155–157
DLH	HARRISON, D. L.	1956	A new flat-headed bat of the genus *Platymops* Thomas from S.E. Sudan. Ann. Mag. Nat. Hist. (12) 9. p. 549–552
DO	DORST, J.	1947	Une nouvelle chauvre-souris de l'Indochine française. Bull. Mus. Hist. Nat. Paris (2) 19 (6). p. 436–437
E1	ELLERMAN, J. R.	1940	The Families and Genera of Living Rodents. B.M. (Nat. Hist.), London. Vol. 1. p. 1–689
E2	ELLERMAN, J. R.	1941	ditto—Vol. 2. p. 1–690
E3	ELLERMAN, J. R.	1949	ditto—Vol. 3. Part 1. p. 1–210
EM55	ELLERMAN, J. R. and MORRISON-SCOTT, T. C. S.	1955	Supplement to Chasen (1940), A Handbook of Malaysian Mammals. B.M. (Nat. Hist.), London. p. 1–66
FCF	FRASER, F. C.	1963	(Personal Communication)
FP	FRASER, F. C. and PURVES, P. E.	1960	Hearing in Cetaceans. Bull. Brit. Mus. (Nat. Hist.) Zool. 7, p. 1–140
FR1	FRASER, F. C.	1956	A new Sarawak dolphin. Sarawak Mus. J. 7, p. 478–503
FR2	FRASER, F. C.	1960	A specimen of the genus *Feresa* from Senegal. Bull. Inst. franc. Afr. noire. 22A, p. 699–707
FS	FUNAIOLI, U. and SIMONETTA, A. M.	1960	Spedizione biologica in Somalia, 1959, Risultati zoologico, II. Carnivora. Monit. Zool. Ital. 68, p. 58–79

Symbol	Authors	Date	Title and Reference
GHL	GUTH, C., HEIM DE BALSAC, H. and LAMOTTE, M.	1960	Recherches sur la morphologie de *Micropotamogale lamottei* et l'evolution des Potamogalinae. Mammalia, Paris 24, p. 190–217
H	HAYMAN, R. W.	1936	On a collection of mammals from the Gold Coast. Proc. Zool. Soc. London (1935), p. 915–937
H1	HAYMAN, R. W.	1958	A new genus and species of West African Mongoose. Ann. Mag. Nat. Hist. 13 (1), p. 448–452
H2	HAYMAN, R. W.	1962	A new genus and species of African rodent. Rev. Zool. Bot. Africaine 65, p. 129–138
HB	HEIM DE BALSAC, H.	1943	Mission Th. Monod.—Genre nouveau de Rongeur (Gerbillinae) de Mauritanie. Bull. Mus. Hist. Nat. Paris (2) 15 (5), p. 287–288
HB1	HEIM DE BALSAC, H.	1954	Un genré inédit et inattendu de mammifère (Insectivore Tenrecidae) d'Afrique Occidentale. C.R. Acad. Sci. Paris 239, p. 102–104
HB2	HEIM DE BALSAC, H.	1956	Un Soricidae inédit et aberrant du Kasai exige le création d'un Genre nouveau. (Mamm., Insectivores). Rev. Zool. Bot. Africaine 54, p. 137–146
HB3	HEIM DE BALSAC, H.	1956	Diagnoses de *Crocidura* inédites d'Afrique Occidentale. Mammalia, Paris 20, p. 131–139
HB4	HEIM DE BALSAC, H.	1957	Insectivores Soricidae du Mont Cameroun. Zool. Jahrb. (Syst) 85, p. 607–618
HB5	HEIM DE BALSAC, H.	1958	La réserve naturelle intégrale du Mont Nimba. XIV. Mammifères insectivores. Mèm. Inst. Franc. Afr. Noire 53, p. 301–337
HBA	HEIM DE BALSAC, H. and AELLEN, V.	1958	Les Soricidae de basse Côte-d'Ivoire. Rev. Suisse Zool. 65, p. 921–956
IS	SANDERSON, I. T.	1940	The mammals of the North Cameroons forest area. Trans. Zool. Soc. London 24, p. 623–725
JEH	HILL, J. E.	1961	Fruit Bats from the Federation of Malaya. Proc. Zool. Soc. London 136, p. 629–642
K1	KING, J. E.	1959	A note on the specific name of the Kerguelen Fur Seal. Mammalia, Paris 23, p. 381
K2	KING, J. E.	1960	Sealions of the genera *Neophoca* and *Phocarctos*. Mammalia, Paris 24, p. 445–456
KU	KUHN, H. J.	1960	*Genetta (Paragenetta) lehmanni*, eine neue Schleichkatze aus Liberia. Saugetierk. Mitt. 8, p. 154–160

		SUPPLEMENTARY WORKS—*continued*	
Symbol	*Authors*	*Date*	*Title and Reference*
L	LAWRENCE, B.	1939	Collections from the Philippine Islands. Bull. Mus. Comp. Zool. Harvard, Mass. 86, p. 28–73
MK	MILLER, G. S. and KELLOGG, R.	1955	List of North American Recent mammals. Bull. U.S. Nat. Mus. 205, p. 1–954
O1	OSMAN HILL, W. C.	1953	Primates. Comparative Anatomy and Taxonomy. I. Strepsirhini. p. 1–798. Edinburgh: University Press
O2	OSMAN HILL, W. C.	1955	ditto—II. Haplorhini: Tarsioidea. p. 1–374
O3	OSMAN HILL, W. C.	1957	ditto—III. Pithecoidea, Platyrrhini. p. 1–354
O4	OSMAN HILL, W. C.	1960	ditto—IV. Cebidae, Part A. p. 1–523
O5	OSMAN HILL, W. C.	1962	ditto—V. Cebidae, Part B. p. 1–537
OH	OSMAN HILL, W. C.	1952	The external and visceral anatomy of the Olive Colobus Monkey (*Procolobus verus*). Proc. Zool. Soc. London 122, p. 127–186
OL	OLIVER, W. R. B.	1937	*Tasmacetus shepherdi*: a new genus and species of Beaked Whale from New Zealand. Proc. Zool. Soc. London 107, B. p. 371–381
P	POHLE, H.	1943	*Scotonycteris ophiodon*. sp. n., eine neue Art epomophoroider Flughunde. Sitz. Ber. Ges. naturf. Fr. Berl. (1942) 1–10 (1943), p. 78–87
RCA	ANDREWS, R. C.	1911	A new porpoise from Japan. Bull. Amer. Mus. Nat. Hist. 30, p. 31–51
S	SCHEFFER, V. B.	1958	Seals, Sealions and Walruses. A review of the Pinnipedia. Oxford University Press. p. 1–179
SA	SANBORN, C. C.	1952	Philippine Zoological Expedition 1946–7: Mammals. Fieldiana, Zool. 33, p. 89–158
SA1	SANBORN, C. C.	1953	Mammals from Mindanao, Philippine Islands, collected by the Danish Philippine Expedition, 1951–2. Vidensk. Medd. dansk naturh. Foren. Kbh. 115, p. 283–288
SL	SCOTT, H. H. and LORD, C. E.	1926	Studies in Tasmanian Mammals, living and extinct. XIII. The Eared Seals of Tasmania. Papers and Proc. R. Soc. Tasmania, Hobart for 1925. p. 75–78, p. 185–194
SM	SCHALDACH, W. J. and MCLAUGHLIN, C. A.	1960	A new genus and species of glossophagine bat from Colima, Mexico. Contr. Sci. Los Angeles 37, p. 1–8

24

Symbol	Authors	Date	Title and Reference
T	TROUGHTON, E. G.	1957	Furred Animals of Australia. Angus and Robertson, Sydney. p. 1–376
TA1	TATE, G. H. H.	1947	On the anatomy and classification of the Dasyuridae (Marsupialia). Bull. Amer. Mus. Nat. Hist. 88, p. 97–156
TA2	TATE, G. H. H.	1948	Studies in the Peramelidae (Marsupialia). Bull. Amer. Mus. Nat. Hist. 92, p. 313–346
TA3	TATE, G. H. H.	1948	Studies on the anatomy and phylogeny of the Macropodidae (Marsupialia). Bull. Amer. Mus. Nat. Hist. 91, p. 233–352
TA4	TATE, G. H. H.	1951	The rodents of Australia and New Guinea. Bull. Amer. Mus. Nat. Hist. 97, p. 183–430
TA5	TATE, G. H. H.	1951	The wombats (Marsupialia, Phascolomyidae). Amer. Mus. Novit. 1525, p. 1–18
TAR	TATE, G. H. H. and ARCHBOLD, R.	1941	New rodents and marsupials from New Guinea. Amer. Mus. Novit. 1101, p. 1–9
VB1	VAN BEMMEL, A. C. V.	1949	Revision of the rusine deer in the Indo-Australian Archipelago. Treubia 20 (2), p. 191–262
VB2	VAN BEMMEL, A. C. V.	1953	One of the rarest deer in the world. Beaufortia, Amsterdam 27, p. 1–5

(The principal regional works have been listed approximately in order of priority. The supplementary works have been listed alphabetically according to their letter symbols, for easy reference.)

The Principal Regional Authorities

Ellerman and Morrison-Scott (EM), Ellerman, Morrison-Scott and Hayman (EMH) and Laurie and Hill (LH) are of the highest order as taxonomic works and have been followed in almost every detail. They are models of modern classification and have been given preference wherever they have come into conflict with other authorities.

Cabrera's work (C1 and C2) on South American mammals is excellent in most respects and, although it is puzzling in one or two details, it is followed throughout. It clashes slightly with Hall and Kelson's North American study. Where this happens Cabrera is given preference.

Hall and Kelson's recent work (HK) is extremely detailed. It omits nothing—in fact, it admits rather too much. Where in doubt, they have included a dubious species instead of cutting it out. They have an unfortunate tendency to score many minor island forms as separate species, and I have been reluctantly forced to include these even though, in many instances, I doubt their validity (see especially the raccoons). In general, however, this is a valuable and important study.

Between them, Cabrera and Hall and Kelson cover the whole of the New World, including the West Indies, with the omission only of Trinidad and Tobago. Luckily, Goodwin and Greenhall (GG), in their very recent publication on the bats of these islands, have included a list of all the mammal species found there and so can be used to complete the American region.

Iredale and Troughton (IT) deal comprehensively with the Australian region, but in certain respects are guilty of old-fashioned splitting. This has been corrected in the present volume for certain groups by using the more recent reviews by Tate (TA). He has published papers on four important marsupial families, the Dasyuridae, the Peramelidae, the Phascolomidae and the Macropodidae and these have been followed in each case. A later work by Troughton (T) has been used as a source for recently discovered Australian species.

Chasen (CH) fills the gap in South Asia between Ellerman and Morrison-Scott's Palaearctic study (EM) and Laurie and Hill's New Guinea work (LH). Chasen's work is valuable but in some respects inadequate. It has been provided with an important supplement by Ellerman and Morrison-Scott (EM55) in which various modifications are suggested and these have been followed. Chasen is also over-ruled wherever a species overlaps from either the Palaearctic (EM) region or the New Guinea (LH) region.

Taylor (TAY) is the latest complete study on Philippine species. It suffers badly from splitting. This region is seriously in need of a new treatment. A partial study by Sanborn (SA) has, however, been of some help in dispensing with certain obviously valueless species.

Allen's (A) African check list is, like Taylor's work, full of meaningless splitting. He has listed every named form with little attempt at a critical evaluation. Fortunately

Ellerman and Morrison-Scott's Palaearctic work (EM) extends into North Africa, and Ellerman, Morrison-Scott and Hayman (EMH) have dealt with South Africa, so that it is only necessary to resort to Allen in Central Africa and Madagascar. Like the Philippines, this region would amply repay a ruthless taxonomic reassessment.

New Zealand is an almost mammal-free zone (with the exception of species recently introduced by man). It can only boast three truly native mammals (two bats and a rat). The best authority for these is Hutton (HU).

Supplementary Authorities

In addition to the above principal regional works, the following studies have been used to obtain supplementary information.

For primates, Osman Hill's major works (O1, O2, O3, O4, O5) have been used wherever the regional work was weak. In the case of American primates, his volumes are also quoted, but, where they disagree with Cabrera, modifications have been made and the appropriate Cabrera symbol added (e.g. O4/C1). For rodents, Ellerman's major work (E1, E2, E3) has been used as a basis, but has been modified in regions where good new studies have been made. For seals, Scheffer's recent publication (S) has been followed, but has been modified in a similar way.

Van Bemmel's revision (VB1) of certain Asiatic deer has been helpful in improving Taylor's list of these poorly known species.

Finally, in the case of newly-discovered species, a small number of original papers on specific genera or species has been used.

Further brief details and comments are given in the separate sections dealing with the various orders of mammals.

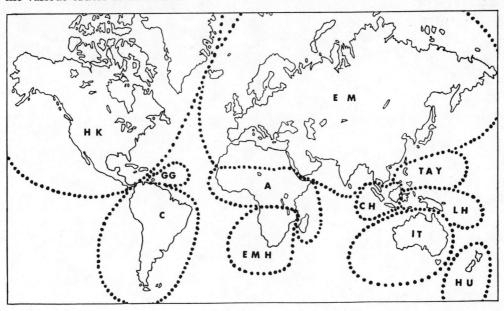

Please Note

When using the classification lists it should be remembered that the geographical range quoted has had to be condensed into only a few words. In the New World this is comparatively easy. No American species inhabits both North and South America without also occurring in Central America. The designation North and South America therefore automatically includes Central America.

Europe, Africa and Australia are straightforward enough in this context, but Asia is more complex. To lump Sumatra, Java, Borneo, etc., with the mainland under the general heading of "Asia" would have meant losing a great deal of valuable zoogeographical information. On the other hand, to include all the smaller islands of the archipelago would have been impossible. The compromise arrived at was to designate the mainland of the Continent and its smaller offshore islands as "Asia" and to treat as separate areas, between Asia and Australia, the following: Sumatra, Java, Borneo, the Philippines, Celebes and New Guinea. Minor islands are omitted, except where they are the sole region where a particular species is found. (A similar rule has also been applied in other parts of the world, where certain species have extremely localized ranges.)

Picture References

Finally, it should be noted that, for convenience, the number of each of the 300 illustrated species is shown in bold figures in the classification lists, with a small arrow (►) beside it.

THE MAMMALIAN ORDERS

THE MAMMALIAN ORDERS

There are nineteen orders of mammals and they are now dealt with in turn. In each case, the basic features characterizing the members of the order will be given. Where it is of particular interest, their geographical distribution as a group will be mapped. Their principal sub-divisions will be outlined and there will then follow a detailed, comprehensive classification. Finally, in each instance, a limited number of representative species will be illustrated and described.

As regards this last point, it will be noticed that some groups have been more favoured with illustrations than others, in relation to the numbers of living species in the various cases. Groups that benefit in this way are, for example, the primates and the carnivores. Amongst those which suffer are the insectivores and the bats. This is largely because there is so little visual variety amongst many insectivores and bats and such a wealth of it in primates and carnivores. It is also partly the result of the present work being written at a zoo, where very few insectivores or bats are ever exhibited.

A comparative chart of the number of species, genera and families in each of the orders is given on page 32 and following it, on page 33, a similar chart showing crude geographical distributions. It can be seen at a glance that, as far as number of species and geographical distribution are concerned, the rodents and the bats are well in the lead. (Man has, of course, been omitted from the primate distribution chart.) Minor groups are the monotremes, the flying lemurs, the elephants, the hyraxes, the sirenians and, with only a single species, the aardvark order.

The total number of mammalian species (4,237) is far lower than most authorities believed. When poorly known areas, such as the Philippines and Central Africa, have been re-studied in detail there will probably be even fewer.

THE NUMBERS OF SPECIES AND GROUPS
OF LIVING MAMMALS

	Order	No. of species	No. of genera	No. of families
A.	MONOTREMES	6	3	2
B.	MARSUPIALS	248	80	8
C.	INSECTIVORES	374	62	8
D.	FLYING LEMURS	2	1	1
E.	BATS	981	180	17
F.	PRIMATES	193	58	11
G.	EDENTATES	32	14	3
H.	PANGOLINS	7	1	1
I.	LAGOMORPHS	66	9	2
J.	RODENTS	1,729	363	32
K.	CETACEANS	92	38	10
L.	CARNIVORES	252	95	7
M.	SEALS	32	21	3
N.	AARDVARK	1	1	1
O.	ELEPHANTS	2	2	1
P.	HYRAXES	6	2	1
Q.	SIRENIANS	4	2	2
R.	ODD-TOED UNGULATES	16	5	3
S.	EVEN-TOED UNGULATES	194	80	9
	Total:	4,237 species	1,017 genera	122 families

GEOGRAPHICAL DISTRIBUTION OF THE MAMMALIAN ORDERS

	EUROPE	AFRICA	ASIA	NORTH AMERICA	SOUTH AMERICA	AUSTRALASIA	
MONOTREMES						●	1
MARSUPIALS				●	●	●	3
INSECTIVORES	●	●	●	●	●		5
FLYING LEMURS			●				1
BATS	●	●	●	●	●	●	6
PRIMATES		●	●		●		3
EDENTATES				●	●		2
PANGOLINS		●	●				2
LAGOMORPHS	●	●	●	●	●		5
RODENTS	●	●	●	●	●	●	6
CETACEANS	●	●	●	●	●	●	6
CARNIVORES	●	●	●	●	●		5
SEALS	●	●	●	●	●	●	6
AARDVARK		●					1
ELEPHANTS		●	●				2
HYRAXES		●	●				2
SIRENIANS		●	●	●	●	●	5
ODD-TOED UNGULATES		●	●		●		3
EVEN-TOED UNGULATES	●	●	●	●	●		5
	8	15	15	11	13	7	

33

B

A. MONOTREMES

The monotremes are confined to Australia, Tasmania and New Guinea. The six species are of two basic types—the echidnas and the platypus. The name monotreme means literally "one hole", a special feature of this group being the possession of a single posterior opening—the cloaca—through which urine, faeces and eggs (or sperm) all pass. This is a typically reptilian character, as is their habit of laying eggs with tough, leathery shells.

Adult monotremes are completely toothless. There are no external ears. The body temperature control is comparatively inefficient, fluctuations of 5°C. being common.

Monotremes have no close relatives. They are the least mammalian of the mammals and undoubtedly arose from stock that was separated from the mainstream of mammalian evolution at a very early stage.

Male monotremes are unique in possessing poison spurs on their hind legs. Little is known about the action of these weapons except that for some reason they appear to function only in the breeding season.

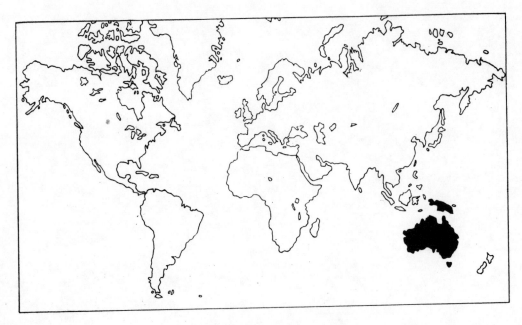

A. Order MONOTREMATA.   Monotremes.

Family TACHYGLOSSIDAE.   Echidnas.

1	*Tachyglossus aculeatus.*	**Australian Echidna.**	Australia. (IT)
2 ►	*Tachyglossus setosus.*	**Tasmanian Echidna.**	Tasmania. (IT)
3 ►	*Zaglossus bruijni.*	**Bruijn's Echidna.**	New Guinea. (LH)
4	*Zaglossus bartoni.*	**Barton's Echidna.**	New Guinea. (LH)
5	*Zaglossus bubuensis.*	**Bubu Echidna.**	New Guinea. (LH)

Family ORNITHORHYNCHIDAE.   Platypus.

6 ► *Ornithorhynchus anatinus.*   **Duck-billed Platypus.**   E. Australia and Tasmania. (IT)

The bold figures denote the species illustrated and discussed in the following pages

36

TASMANIAN ECHIDNA

Tachyglossus setosus

(Tasmania)

The Echidna, or Spiny Anteater, is one of the strangest of living mammals. It possesses a number of reptilian characters—a bony shoulder girdle, poor temperature control, the ability to fast for long periods, a cloacal opening, the laying of a thin-shelled large-yolked egg, and the use of poison in self-defence.

The name Echidna means "Adder" and arose from the discovery that the spurs on the hind legs of the male are connected to poison glands. The milky fluid contained in these glands is not, however, particularly dangerous and the more basic method of self-defence of the Echidna is to dig itself rapidly into the ground until only its sharp spines are protruding above the surface.

In the winter the Echidna hibernates. On emerging, it sheds its fur and spines and grows a new coat. It lives in rough, rocky country and is usually only seen in the early morning or late evening digging for ants, grubs, termites and beetles. It has the typical ant-eating adaptations of powerful claws, a tube-like probing snout, and a long extensible tongue covered in thick mucous. It has a small mouth and no teeth and has to crush larger food objects between its front feet before eating them.

At the beginning of each mating season the female develops a small pouch into which she later transfers the single egg. The mammary glands discharge directly into the pouch, there being no nipples, and the milk is sucked off the hairs by the young Echidna.

The closely related Australian Echidna has a smaller body, a longer more slender snout, larger spines and is less hairy.

A 3

BRUIJN'S ECHIDNA

Zaglossus bruijni

(New Guinea)

There are three species of echidna to be found in New Guinea: Bruijn's, Barton's (*Zaglossus bartoni*) and the Bubu Echidna (*Zaglossus bubuensis*). Bruijn's Echidna is the most common of the three, the other two being confined, as far as is known at present, to the highlands of north-eastern New Guinea. They are larger and heavier than the better known Australian and Tasmanian forms and are even stronger in appearance. The snout or "beak" is even longer and is downward curved and tapering. The fur is dense and almost hides the short spines. The colour varies considerably, from light to dark brown.

They are said to live in burrows in rocky country and like the Australo-Tasmanian echidnas they feed mainly on ants. Although their total length is only 30 inches their sticky tongues are as much as 12 inches long. The name of the genus *Zaglossus* in fact means "very-tongued" (Greek *za*–very, *glossa*–tongue). All echidnas have greatly enlarged salivary glands that keep these active tongues constantly sticky. The total adult body weight is 35 lb.

A strange feature of Bruijn's Echidna is the shortness of its front claws. Those of the Tasmanian Echidna shown on the previous page are the typical long, powerful structures that one associates with a species specialized in digging. It is odd that Bruijn's Echidna, also a digger, should apparently lack the tools for the job.

In captivity echidnas live for many years and quickly adapt to a basic diet of raw minced meat, raw eggs and milk.

38

DUCK-BILLED PLATYPUS

Ornithorhynchus anatinus

(Eastern Australia and Tasmania)

Like the Echidnas, the Duck-billed Platypus is a primitive egg-laying mammal which still retains certain reptilian characters, but unlike its spiny relatives the female has no pouch and must incubate the eggs as if she were a bird.

Fully-grown, a male Platypus measures about 22 inches in length and weighs a little more than 4 lb. The female is slightly smaller than the male. They have the short, dense, soft fur typical of many aquatic mammals. The tail is broad and flattened like a beaver's and each of the feet bears five, clawed digits connected by a web. The soft, rubbery bill contains no teeth; diagonal horny ridges are used for crushing the food.

The Platypus is found in a wide range of aquatic habitats from tropical streams at sea-level to cold lakes at an altitude of 6,000 feet, but it is always found in water that has a muddy substratum. It feeds on shrimps, larvae, earthworms and tadpoles which it collects in cheek pouches as it sieves through the mud with its bill. Communal burrows are excavated in mud banks. At breeding time, the pregnant female builds a special solitary burrow with a grass-lined den in which she lays two eggs. These are incubated for about 2 weeks, the mother curling her body tightly round them after plugging up the den entrance. The young feed by sucking the milk from the hair surrounding the mother's mammary glands.

Like the Echidna, the hind leg of the male bears a poison spur, but the Platypus has few natural enemies apart from a fish known as the Giant Perch.

B. MARSUPIALS

The marsupials are found today in Australia, Tasmania, New Guinea, Timor, Celebes, South America, Central America and the south of North America. There are 176 species in the Australasian region and 72 species in the American region.

The name marsupial means literally "pouched-one", the most striking of these creatures' special features being the possession of a protective pouch of skin around the female's nipples. In all cases the young are born at a very early stage of development, crawl into the pouch and attach themselves to the nipples. They remain there for some weeks or even months, feeding and growing, shielded from the outside world.

The marsupial reproductive system is unusual in a number of ways. The females have two uteri and a double vagina. The males have a forked penis. Their testes are situated not behind, but in front of the penis. Typically the developing embryo has no placental connection with its mother.

The teeth of marsupials are numerous. There are no "milk teeth", there being only one set throughout life.

These animals are small-brained creatures of comparatively low intelligence. In competition with the quicker, more efficient placental mammals they have fared badly.

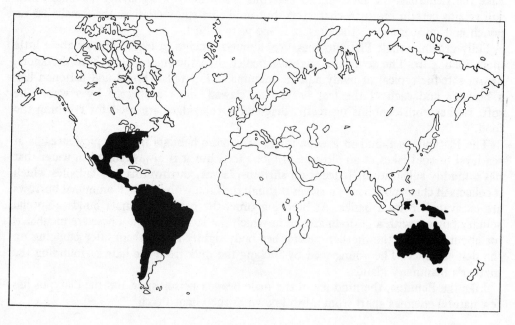

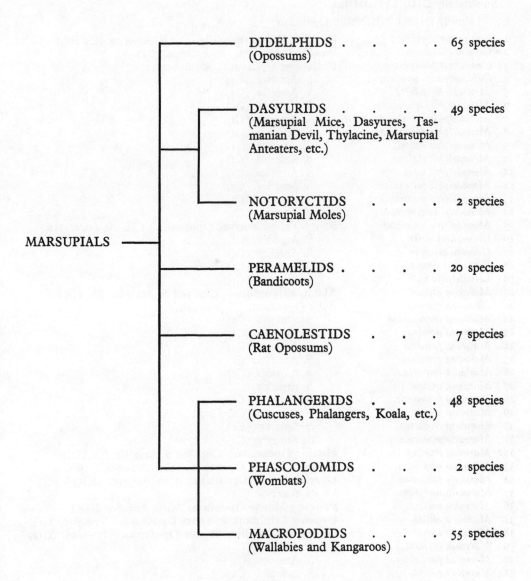

MARSUPIALS —

DIDELPHIDS . . . . 65 species
(Opossums)

DASYURIDS . . . . 49 species
(Marsupial Mice, Dasyures, Tasmanian Devil, Thylacine, Marsupial Anteaters, etc.)

NOTORYCTIDS . . . 2 species
(Marsupial Moles)

PERAMELIDS . . . . 20 species
(Bandicoots)

CAENOLESTIDS . . . 7 species
(Rat Opossums)

PHALANGERIDS . . . 48 species
(Cuscuses, Phalangers, Koala, etc.)

PHASCOLOMIDS . . . 2 species
(Wombats)

MACROPODIDS . . . 55 species
(Wallabies and Kangaroos)

B. Order MARSUPIALIA.   Marsupials.

Superfamily DIDELPHOIDEA.

Family DIDELPHIDAE.   Opossums.

1	*Caluromys derbianus.*	**Derbian Opossum.** Cen. and S. America. (CI HK)
2 ►	*Caluromys lanatus.*	**Woolly Opossum.** S. America. (CI)
3	*Caluromys philander.*	**Philander Opossum.** S. America. (CI)
4	*Caluromysiops irrupta.*	S. America. (CI)
5	*Monodelphis adusta.*	S. America. (CI)
6	*Monodelphis americana.*	S. America. (CI)
7	*Monodelphis brevicaudata.*	S. America. (CI)
8	*Monodelphis domestica.*	S. America. (CI)
9	*Monodelphis henseli.*	S. America. (CI)
10	*Monodelphis scalops.*	S. America. (CI)
11	*Monodelphis sorex.*	S. America. (CI)
12	*Monodelphis touan.*	S. America. (CI)
13	*Monodelphis unistriata.*	S. America. (CI)
14	*Monodelphis dimidiata.*	S. America. (CI)
15	*Monodelphis melanops.*	**Short-Tailed Murine Opossum.** Cen. America. (HK)
16	*Dromiciops australis.*	S. America. (CI)
17	*Glironia criniger.*	S. America. (CI)
18	*Glironia venusta.*	S. America. (CI)
19	*Lestodelphis halli.*	S. America. (CI)
20	*Marmosa alstoni.*	**Alston's Opossum.** Cen. and S. America. (CI/HK)
21	*Marmosa cinerea.*	**Ashy Opossum.** S. America. (CI)
22	*Marmosa constantiae.*	S. America. (CI)
23	*Marmosa domina.*	S. America. (CI)
24	*Marmosa fuscata.*	S. America. (CI)
25	*Marmosa germana.*	S. America. (CI)
26	*Marmosa impavida.*	S. America. (CI)
27	*Marmosa incana.*	S. America. (CI)
28	*Marmosa juninensis.*	S. America. (CI)
29	*Marmosa lepida.*	S. America. (CI)
30	*Marmosa leucastra.*	S. America. (CI)
31	*Marmosa mapiriensis.*	S. America. (CI)
32 ►	*Marmosa murina.*	**Murine Opossum.** Cen. and S. America. (CI/HK)
33	*Marmosa mexicana.*	**Mexican Mouse Opossum.** Cen. America. (HK)
34	*Marmosa canescens.*	**Greyish Mouse Opossum.** Cen. America. (HK)
35	*Marmosa noctivaga.*	S. America. (CI)
36	*Marmosa invicta.*	**Panama Mouse Opossum.** Cen. America. (HK)
37	*Marmosa mitis.*	**Greater Trinidadian Mouse Opossum.** Trinidad. (GG)
38	*Marmosa carri.*	**Lesser Trinidadian Mouse Opossum.** Trinidad. (GG)
39	*Marmosa ocellata.*	S. America. (CI)
40	*Marmosa parvidens.*	S. America. (CI)
41	*Marmosa phaea.*	S. America. (CI)
42	*Marmosa quichua.*	S. America. (CI)
43	*Marmosa rapposa.*	S. America. (CI)
44	*Marmosa regina.*	S. America. (CI)
45	*Marmosa robinsoni.*	Cen. and S. America. (CI/HK)
46	*Marmosa rubra.*	S. America. (CI)
47	*Marmosa scapulata.*	S. America. (CI)
48	*Marmosa aceramarcae.*	S. America. (CI)
49	*Marmosa agilis.*	S. America. (CI)

50	*Marmosa agricolai.*	S. America. (CI)
51	*Marmosa dryas.*	S. America. (CI)
52	*Marmosa elegans.*	S. America. (CI)
53	*Marmosa emiliae.*	S. America. (CI)
54	*Marmosa grisea.*	S. America. (CI)
55	*Marmosa marica.*	S. America. (CI)
56	*Marmosa microtarsus.*	S. America. (CI)
57	*Marmosa pusilla.*	S. America. (CI)
58	*Marmosa unduaviensis.*	S. America. (CI)
59	*Marmosa velutina.*	S. America. (CI)
60	*Philander opossum.*	**Four-eyed Opossum.** Cen. and S. America. (CI/HK)
61	*Metachirus nudicaudatus.*	**Rat-tailed Opossum.** Cen. and S. America. (CI/HK)
62	*Lutreolina crassicaudata.*	**Thick-tailed Opossum.** S. America. (CI)
63	*Didelphis azarae.*	**Azara's Opossum.** S. America. (CI)
64 ►	*Didelphis marsupialis.*	**Common Opossum** (includes Virginian Opossum). N. and S. America. (CI/HK)
65	*Chironectes minimus.*	**Yapok.** Cen. and S. America. (CI/HK)

Superfamily DASYUROIDEA.

    Family DASYURIDAE.

        Subfamily PHASCOGALINAE. Marsupial "Mice".

66	*Antechinus flavipes.*	**Yellow-footed Marsupial Mouse.** Australia. (IT)
67	*Antechinus godmani.*	**Godman's Marsupial Mouse.** Australia. (IT)
68	*Antechinus bellus.*	**Fawn Marsupial Mouse.** Australia. (IT)
69	*Antechinus swainsoni.*	**Dusky Marsupial Mouse.** Tasmania and Australia. (IT)
70	*Antechinus minimus.*	**Little Tasmanian Marsupial Mouse.** Tasmania. (IT)
71	*Antechinus maculatus.*	**Pygmy Marsupial Mouse.** Australia. (IT)
72	*Antechinus bilarni.*	**Harney's Marsupial Mouse.** Australia. (T)
73	*Antechinus macdonnellensis.*	**Fat-tailed Marsupial Mouse.** Australia. (IT)
74	*Antechinus mimulus.*	**Northern Fat-tailed Marsupial Mouse.** Australia. (IT)
75	*Antechinus apicalis.*	**Speckled Marsupial Mouse.** Australia. (IT)
76	*Antechinus melanurus.*	New Guinea. (LH)
77	*Antechinus naso.*	New Guinea. (LH)
78	*Antechinus wilhelmina.*	New Guinea. (LH)
79	*Planigale ingrami.*	**Northern Planigale.** Australia. (IT)
80	*Planigale tenuirostris.*	**Southern Planigale.** Australia. (IT)
81	*Planigale subtilissima.*	**Kimberley Planigale.** Australia. (IT)
82	*Planigale novaeguineae.*	**New Guinea Planigale.** New Guinea. (LH)
83	*Phascogale tapoatafa.*	**Black-tailed Phascogale.** Australia. (IT)
84	*Phascogale calura.*	**Red-tailed Phascogale.** Australia. (IT)
85	*Dasyuroides byrnei.*	**Crest-tailed Marsupial Rat.** Australia. (IT)
86	*Dasycercus cristicauda.*	**Crest-tailed Marsupial Mouse.** Australia. (IT)
87	*Dasycercus blythi.*	**Western Crest-tailed Marsupial Mouse.** Australia. (IT)
88	*Sminthopsis rufigenis.*	**New Guinea Sminthopsis.** New Guinea. (LH)
89 ►	*Sminthopsis crassicaudata.*	**Fat-tailed Sminthopsis.** Australia. (IT)
90	*Sminthopsis granulipes.*	**Granule-footed Sminthopsis.** Australia. (IT)
91	*Sminthopsis macrura.*	**Large Grey Fat-tailed Sminthopsis.** Australia. (IT/TAI)
92	*Sminthopsis larapinta.*	**Stripe-headed Sminthopsis.** Australia. (IT/TAI)
93	*Sminthopsis murina.*	**Mouse Sminthopsis.** Australia. (IT/TAI)
94	*Sminthopsis longicaudata.*	**Long-tailed Sminthopsis.** Australia. (IT)
95	*Sminthopsis hirtipes.*	**Hairy-footed Sminthopsis.** Australia. (IT)

43

96	Sminthopsis lumholtzi.	**Lumholtz's Sminthopsis.** Australia. (IT)
97	Murexia longicaudata.	**Long-tailed New Guinea Marsupial Mouse.** New Guinea. (LH)
98	Murexia rothschildi.	**Rothschild's New Guinea Marsupial Mouse.** New Guinea. (LH)
99	Antechinomys laniger.	**Eastern Jerboa Marsupial.** Australia. (IT)
100	Antechinomys spenceri.	**Central Jerboa Marsupial.** Australia. (IT)
101	Neophascogale lorentzi.	New Guinea. (LH)
102	Phascolosorex doriae.	New Guinea. (LH)
103	Phascolosorex dorsalis.	New Guinea. (LH)
104	Myoictis melas.	New Guinea. (LH)

Subfamily DASYURINAE. Dasyures.

105	Dasyurus quoll.	**Eastern Dasyure.** Australia and Tasmania. (IT)
106	Dasyurinus geoffroii.	**Western Dasyure.** Australia. (IT)
107 ►	Satanellus hallucatus.	**Little Northern Dasyure.** Australia. (IT)
108	Satanellus albopunctatus.	**New Guinea Dasyure.** New Guinea. (LH)
109	Dasyurops maculatus.	**Spotted-tailed Dasyure.** Australia and Tasmania (IT)
110	Dasyurops gracilis.	**Little Spotted-tailed Dasyure.** Australia. (IT)
111 ►	Sarcophilus harrisi.	**Tasmanian Devil.** Tasmania. (IT)

Subfamily THYLACININAE.

| 112 ► | Thylacinus cynocephalus. | **Thylacine.** Tasmania. (IT) |

Subfamily MYRMECOBIINAE. Marsupial Anteaters.

| 113 ► | Myrmecobius fasciatus. | **Numbat.** Australia. (IT) |
| 114 | Myrmecobius rufus. | **Rusty Numbat.** Australia. (IT) |

Family NOTORYCTIDAE. Marsupial Moles.

| 115 | Notoryctes typhlops. | **Marsupial Mole.** Australia. (IT) |
| 116 | Notoryctes caurinus. | **North-western Marsupial Mole.** Australia. (IT) |

Superfamily PERAMELOIDEA.
Family PERAMELIDAE. Bandicoots.

117 ►	Perameles nasuta.	**Long-nosed Bandicoot.** Australia. (IT)
118	Parameles eremiana.	**Orange-backed Bandicoot.** Australia. (IT)
119	Perameles fasciata.	**Eastern Barred Bandicoot.** Australia. (IT)
120	Perameles gunni.	**Tasmanian Barred Bandicoot.** Tasmania. (IT)
121	Perameles bourgainvillei.	**Little Barred Bandicoot.** Australia. (IT/TA2)
122	Peroryctes raffrayanus.	**New Guinea Bandicoot.** New Guinea. (LH)
123	Peroryctes longicauda.	**Long-tailed New Guinea Bandicoot.** New Guinea. (LH)
124	Peroryctes papuensis.	**Papuan Bandicoot.** New Guinea. (LH)
125	Microperoryctes murina.	**Mouse Bandicoot.** New Guinea. (LH)
126	Echymipera clara.	New Guinea. (LH)
127	Echymipera kalubu.	New Guinea. (LH)
128	Echymipera rufescens.	Australia and New Guinea. (LH/T)

44

129	*Macrotis lagotis.*	**Rabbit Bandicoot.** Australia. (IT)
130	*Macrotis leucura.*	**White-tailed Rabbit Bandicoot.** Australia. (IT)
131	*Macrotis minor.*	**Lesser Rabbit Bandicoot.** Australia. (IT)
132	*Chaeropus ecaudatus.*	**Pig-footed Bandicoot.** Australia. (IT)
133	*Rhynchomeles prattorum.*	**Ceram Island Bandicoot.** Ceram Island (New Guinea). (LH)
134	*Thylacis obesulus.*	**Southern Short-nosed Bandicoot.** Australia and Tasmania. (IT/TA2)
135	*Thylacis barrowensis.*	**Barrow Island Bandicoot.** Barrow Island (W. Australia). (IT)
136	*Thylacis macrourus.*	**Brindled Bandicoot.** Australia and New Guinea. (LH/IT/TA2)

Superfamily CAENOLESTOIDEA.

    Family CAENOLESTIDAE.

        Subfamily CAENOLESTINAE.

137	*Caenolestes caniventer.*	S. America. (C1)
138	*Caenolestes convelatus.*	S. America. (C1)
139	*Caenolestes fuliginosus.*	S. America. (C1)
140	*Caenolestes obscurus.*	S. America. (C1)
141	*Caenolestes tatei.*	S. America. (C1)
142	*Lestoros inca.*	S. America. (C1)
143	*Rhyncholestes raphanurus.*	**Chilean Rat Opossum.** S. America. (C1)

Superfamily PHALANGEROIDEA.

    Family PHALANGERIDAE.

        Subfamily PHALANGERINAE. Phalangers.

144	*Phalanger orientalis.*	**Grey Cuscus.** Australia and New Guinea. (LH/T)
145 ►	*Phalanger maculatus.*	**Spotted Cuscus.** Australia and New Guinea. (LH/IT)
146	*Phalanger atrimaculatus.*	New Guinea. (LH)
147	*Phalanger celebensis.*	**Celebes Cuscus.** Celebes. (LH)
148	*Phalanger gymnotis.*	New Guinea. (LH)
149	*Phalanger vestitus.*	**Silky Phalanger.** New Guinea. (LH)
150	*Phalanger ursinus.*	**Bear Phalanger.** Celebes. (LH)
151 ►	*Trichosurus vulpecula.*	**Brush-tailed Phalanger.** Australia. (IT)
152	*Trichosurus fuliginosus.*	**Tasmanian Brush-tailed Phalanger.** Tasmania. (IT)
153	*Trichosurus caninus.*	**Short-eared Brush-tailed Phalanger.** Australia. (IT)
154	*Acrobates pygmaeus.*	**Pygmy Flying Phalanger.** Australia. (IT)
155	*Acrobates pulchellus.*	**New Guinea Pygmy Flying Phalanger.** New Guinea. (LH)
156	*Distoechurus pennatus.*	**Pen-tailed Phalanger.** New Guinea. (LH)
157	*Cercartetus nanus.*	**Pygmy Phalanger.** Australia and Tasmania. (IT)
158	*Cercartetus concinnus.*	**South-western Pygmy Phalanger.** Australia. (IT)
159	*Eudromicia macrura.*	**Queensland Pygmy Phalanger.** Australia. (IT)
160	*Eudromicia lepida.*	**Lesser Tasmanian Pygmy Phalanger.** Tasmania. (IT)
161	*Eudromicia caudata.*	**Dormouse Phalanger.** New Guinea. (LH)
162	*Gymnobelideus leadbeateri.*	**Leadbeater's Phalanger.** Australia. (IT)
163	*Petaurus breviceps.*	**Short-headed Flying Phalanger.** Australia and New Guinea. (IT/LH)

45

164 ►*Petaurus norfolcensis.*	**Squirrel-like Flying Phalanger.** Australia. (IT)
165 *Petaurus australis.*	**Yellow-bellied Flying Phalanger.** Australia. (IT)
166 *Dactylopsila picata.*	**Striped Phalanger.** Australia. (IT)
167 *Dactylopsila trivirgata.*	New Guinea. (LH)
168 *Dactylopsila megalura.*	New Guinea (LH)
169 *Dactylopsila tatei.*	New Guinea. (LH)
170 *Dactylonax palpator.*	**Long-fingered Striped Phalanger.** New Guinea. (LH)
171 *Wyulda squamicaudata.*	**Scaly-tailed Phalanger.** Australia. (IT)

Subfamily TARSIPEDINAE.

172 *Tarsipes spenserae.*   **Honey Phalanger.** Australia. (IT)

Subfamily PHASCOLARCTINAE.

173 ►*Phascolarctos cinereus.*	**Koala.** Australia. (IT)
174 *Pseudocheirus peregrinus.*	**Queensland Ring-tailed Phalanger.** Australia. (IT)
175 *Pseudocheirus rubidus.*	**Rufous Ring-tailed Phalanger.** Australia. (IT)
176 *Pseudocheirus laniginosus.*	**Common Ring-tailed Phalanger.** Australia. (IT)
177 *Pseudocheirus convolutor.*	**Tasmanian Ring-tailed Phalanger.** Tasmania. (IT)
178 *Pseudocheirus occidentalis.*	**Western Ring-tailed Phalanger.** Australia. (IT)
179 *Pseudocheirus herbertensis.*	**Herbert River Ring-tailed Phalanger.** Australia. (IT)
180 *Pseudocheirus caroli.*	New Guinea. (LH)
181 *Pseudocheirus forbesi.*	New Guinea. (LH)
182 *Pseudocheirus schlegeli.*	New Guinea. (LH)
183 *Pseudocheirus mayeri.*	New Guinea. (LH)
184 *Pseudocheirus canescens.*	New Guinea. (LH)
185 *Pseudocheirus albertisi.*	New Guinea. (LH)
186 *Pseudocheirus corinnae.*	New Guinea. (LH)
187 *Pseudocheirus cupreus.*	New Guinea. (LH)
188 *Pseudocheirops archeri.*	**Striped Ring-tailed Phalanger.** Australia. (IT)
189 *Hemibelideus lemuroides.*	**Brush-tipped Ring-tailed Phalanger.** Australia. (IT)
190 *Petropseudes dahli.*	**Rock-haunting Ring-tailed Phalanger.** Australia. (IT)
191 *Schoinobates volans.*	**Greater Flying Phalanger.** Australia. (IT)

Family VOMBATIDAE. Wombats.

| 192 ►*Vombatus ursinus.* | **Common Wombat.** Australia and Tasmania. (IT/TA5) |
| 193 *Lasiorhinus latifrons.* | **Hairy-nosed Wombat.** Australia. (IT/TA5) |

Family MACROPODIDAE. Wallabies and Kangaroos.
Subfamily MACROPODINAE.

194 *Lagorchestes leporides.*	**Brown Hare Wallaby.** Australia. (IT)
195 *Lagorchestes conspicillatus.*	**Spectacled Hare Wallaby.** Australia. (IT)
196 *Lagorchestes hirsutus.*	**Western Hare Wallaby.** Australia. (IT)
197 *Lagorchestes asomatus.*	**Centralian Hare Wallaby.** Australia. (T)
198 *Lagostrophus fasciatus.*	**Banded Hare Wallaby.** Australia. (IT)
199 *Petrogale penicillata.*	**Brush-tailed Rock Wallaby.** Australia. (IT/TA3)
200 *Petrogale inornata.*	**Plain Rock Wallaby.** Australia. (IT)
201 *Petrogale longmani.*	**Longman's Rock Wallaby.** Australia. (IT)

46

202	*Petrogale wilkinsi.*	**Roper River Rock Wallaby.**	Australia. (IT)
203	*Petrogale brachyotis.*	**Short-eared Rock Wallaby.**	Australia. (IT)
204	*Petrogale rothschildi.*	**Rothschild's Rock Wallaby.**	Australia. (IT)
205	*Petrogale xanthopus.*	**Ring-tailed Rock Wallaby.**	Australia. (IT)
206	*Petrogale pearsoni.*	**Pearson Island Rock Wallaby.**	Australia. (IT)
207	*Peradorcas concinna.*	**Little Rock Wallaby.**	Australia. (IT)
208	*Onychogalea unguifer.*	**Northern Nail-tail Wallaby.**	Australia. (IT)
209	*Onychogalea fraenata.*	**Bridled Nail-tail Wallaby.**	Australia. (IT)
210	*Onychogalea lunata.*	**Crescent Nail-tail Wallaby.**	Australia. (IT)
211	*Thylogale stigmatica.*	**Red-legged Pademelon.**	Australia and New Guinea. (IT/LH/TA3)
212	*Thylogale thetis.*	**Red-necked Pademelon.**	Australia. (IT)
213	*Thylogale billardierii.*	**Rufous-bellied Pademelon.**	Tasmania. (IT)
214	*Thylogale bruijni.*	**Bruijn's Pademelon.**	New Guinea. (LH)
215	*Protemnodon parma.*	**White-throated Wallaby.**	Australia. (IT/TA3)
216 ►	*Protemnodon eugenii.*	**Dama Wallaby.**	Australia. (IT/TA3)
217	*Protemnodon agilis.*	**Sandy Wallaby.**	Australia and New Guinea. (IT/LH)
218	*Protemnodon bicolor.*	**Black-tailed Wallaby.**	Australia. (IT/TA)
219 ►	*Protemnodon rufogrisea.*	**Red-necked Wallaby.**	Australia and Tasmania. (IT/TA)
220	*Protemnodon dorsalis.*	**Black-striped Wallaby.**	Australia. (IT/TA3)
221	*Protemnodon elegans.*	**Pretty-face Wallaby.**	Australia. (IT/TA3)
222	*Protemnodon irma.*	**Black-gloved Wallaby.**	Australia. (IT/TA3)
223	*Macropus robustus.*	**Wallaroo.**	Australia. (IT/TA3)
224 ►	*Macropus rufus.*	**Red Kangaroo.**	Australia. (IT/TA3)
225	*Macropus canguru.*	**Grey Kangaroo.**	Australia and Tasmania. (IT/TA3)
226	*Setonix brachyurus.*	**Quokka.**	Australia. (IT)
227	*Dendrolagus lumholtzi.*	**Lumholtz's Tree Kangaroo.**	Australia. (IT)
228	*Dendrolagus bennettianus.*	**Bennett's Tree Kangaroo.**	Australia. (IT)
229	*Dendrolagus matschiei.*	**Matschie's Tree Kangaroo.**	New Guinea. (LH)
230	*Dendrolagus goodfellowi.*	**Goodfellow's Tree Kangaroo.**	New Guinea. (LH)
231	*Dendrolagus dorianus.*	**Doria's Tree Kangaroo.**	New Guinea. (LH)
232	*Dendrolagus spadix.*		New Guinea. (LH)
233	*Dendrolagus deltae.*	**Delta Tree Kangaroo.**	New Guinea. (LH)
234	*Dendrolagus inustus.*	**Grizzled Grey Tree Kangaroo.**	New Guinea. (LH)
235 ►	*Dendrolagus ursinus.*	**Black Tree Kangaroo.**	New Guinea. (LH)
236	*Dorcopsulus macleayi.*	**New Guinea Mountain Wallaby.**	New Guinea. (LH)
237	*Dorcopsulus vanheurni.*		New Guinea. (LH)
238	*Dorcopsis mülleri.*	**Müller's New Guinea Wallaby.**	New Guinea. (LH)
239	*Dorcopsis hageni.*	**Northern New Guinea Wallaby.**	New Guinea. (LH)

Subfamily POTOROINAE.   Rat Kangaroos.

240 ►	*Bettongia penicillata.*	**Brush-tailed Rat Kangaroo.**	Australia. (IT/TA3)
241	*Bettongia lesueur.*	**Lesueur's Rat Kangaroo.**	Australia. (IT)
242	*Bettongia cuniculus.*	**Tasmanian Rat Kangaroo.**	Tasmania. (IT)
243	*Aepyprymnus rufescens.*	**Rufous Rat Kangaroo.**	Australia. (IT)
244	*Caloprymnus campestris.*	**Desert Rat Kangaroo.**	Australia. (IT)
245	*Potorous tridactylus.*	**Long-nosed Rat Kangaroo.**	Australia and Tasmania. (IT)
246	*Potorous gilberti.*	**Gilbert's Rat Kangaroo.**	Australia. (IT)
247	*Potorous platyops.*	**Broad-faced Rat Kangaroo.**	Australia. (IT)
248	*Hypsiprymnodon moschatus.*	**Musky Rat Kangaroo.**	Australia. (IT)

47

WOOLLY OPOSSUM

Caluromys lanatus

(Forests of Tropical South America)

The Woolly Opossum is found throughout much of tropical South America. It is inevitably confined to warmer climates, for like some other relatively primitive mammals it regulates its body temperature imperfectly, becoming cool and torpid in cold weather.

The dense fur to which the animal owes its name is golden-brown above, and a paler yellow-brown on the lower surface. The 20-inch tail is much longer than the head and body combined, and although it is furry at its base, it is naked for most of its length and is fully prehensile.

The eyes are large and protuberant, and are very efficient at dawn and dusk when the pupil opens fully to make use of the little light that is available; by day the vision is poor, but this is unimportant as the Woolly Opossum spends most of the daylight hours asleep in its leafy, tree-top nest.

The food consists largely of insects, but it also occasionally eats small vertebrates such as lizards and some carrion, leaves and fruit. In its tropical forest home the animal usually has little difficulty in satisfying its appetite, and often remains within a very small area for weeks on end. There are records of Woolly Opossums staying in a single tree for as long as 2 to 3 months.

The female of this species lacks a pouch. Whilst they are very young the offspring cling to the nipples, but as they grow older they ride on the mother's back in a variety of positions as the illustration shows.

48

MURINE OPOSSUM

Marmosa murina

(Central and South America)

The Murine Opossum looks very much like a golden-brown mouse with a prehensile tail. The under-surface of the body is white, whilst the naked tail and ears are pink. The large, bulging eyes are made less conspicuous by a mask of dark facial markings.

These marsupials are common at the edges of forests and in banana plantations in Central and South America. They are nocturnal and spend all their time in the trees, sleeping during the day in any suitable hole or deserted bird's nest. At night they clamber about quite rapidly. The big toe can oppose the other digits, so that the back foot readily grips the slender vines in which the Murine Opossum usually climbs. When necessary, the animal can move with some speed, scurrying noisily over the banana leaves, and jumping nimbly from frond to frond.

Although some fruit is eaten, insects, especially large crickets, form the bulk of the diet. They are grasped by the hands and nibbled by the needle-sharp teeth. The teeth are also brought into play should the opossum be threatened, when it rears up with the jaws gaping widely. It is doubtful, however, whether this defence is very effective against owls, and above all against the Coati, which is the Murine Opossum's chief enemy.

Strangely, for a marsupial, the female has no pouch. The young, of which there may be five or more, simply hang on firmly to the mother's nipples. When they are 1 month old their eyes open and they begin to eat solid food. Forty closely related species of *Marmosa* occur throughout Central and South America, from Mexico to Patagonia.

49

B 64

COMMON OPOSSUM

Didelphis marsupialis

(North, Central and South America)

Unlike many marsupials today, the Common Opossum is flourishing. It was originally confined to South America but over a period of thousands of years has successfully invaded the North American continent, where it is still spreading. It is the only marsupial to be found in North America.

There are three reasons for its success. Firstly it is extremely adaptable, and able to eat a wide variety of foods, including fruit, insects, and small vertebrates. Secondly, although it is attacked by a large number of predators, including man, it breeds rapidly and individuals that are killed are soon replaced. Thirdly, it can sometimes escape death by "playing 'possum"—death feigning—when it lies limply on its side, its tongue hanging out of its mouth and its eyes shut. In this state it allows itself to be mauled about until the killer loses interest and departs.

The gestation period is only 12 days. At birth each young one is smaller than a bee and weighs only 2 grams. As many as twenty may be born to each mother, but as she only has twelve or thirteen nipples, a number do not survive infancy. The successful ones emerge from the pouch at the end of 100 days and cling to the mother's back. In winter the Opossum sleeps a great deal, but does not truly hibernate. When nest-building, it carries bundles of leaves and stems clasped firmly in its prehensile tail.

This species is variable in both size and colour, but the North American form, often known as the Virginian Opossum (*Didelphis virginiana*), and the South American form are no more than races of a single species.

50

FAT-TAILED SMINTHOPSIS

Sminthopsis crassicaudata

(Southern Australia)

Some of the larger marsupials of Australia are well known, but it is sometimes not realized that there are also many very small species. The Fat-tailed Sminthopsis, for example, one of the Slender-footed Marsupial Mice, is distributed throughout southern Australia. It is about the size of a House Mouse and has a rather similar appearance, but the nose is more pointed and the tail is shorter and fatter. However, this species belongs to the same family as the Tasmanian Wolf and, as might be expected, is more predatory than any mouse, feeding on a wide variety of small animals. A very similar diet is eaten by the shrews in other parts of the world and Marsupial Mice do, in fact, bear an even greater resemblance to shrews than they do to mice.

Like a shrew, a Marsupial Mouse will consume more than its own weight in food in a single day. This may seem surprising until it is remembered that these small animals lead intensely energetic lives, scurrying about after tiny morsels, and that small bodies lose heat rapidly.

The Marsupial Mouse builds a nest beneath a log or a large stone. After leaving the pouch, the young, which may number as many as ten, cling to the mother's sides. The adults forage for food amongst vegetation, probably both by day and by night.

There are a number of related species, some of which superficially resemble rats, while others look more like jerboas. They are all valuable to man as predators of the various insect pests of Australia.

LITTLE NORTHERN DASYURE

Satanellus hallucatus

(Northern Australia)

The Little Northern Dasyure is, as the illustration shows, remarkably like a small carnivore in appearance. This resemblance is not due to a close relationship between the dasyures and the Carnivora, but is the result of similar feeding habits in the two cases, the dasyures being the typical small flesh-eaters of the marsupial fauna of Australia.

The Little Northern Dasyure's total length, from the pointed nose to the end of the long tail, is about 18 inches. The fur is tawny or olive-brown while the spots which mark the body and sometimes the head, but not the tail, are white. It is able to climb trees efficiently and the large eyes are adapted for a nocturnal existence.

It is a stealthy but fearless hunter, stalking rats, mice, rabbits, and even small wallabies. It also eats eggs and has been known to raid poultry runs. During the day it sleeps in a crevice with the ears folded against the body.

Although up to 24 young may be born at a time, all of this number cannot survive, because the mother has only six teats. Only when she is bearing young is the pouch of the female well developed. The gestation period, which is short as in all marsupials, is 11 days in length.

There are four other species of Australian dasyures, or "native cats", as they are sometimes called. The largest species, which comes from south-eastern Australia is, in fact, cat-sized. All are becoming rather uncommon although some are still to be found not far from Sydney. A sixth species of dasyure inhabits New Guinea.

TASMANIAN DEVIL
Sarcophilus harrisi
(Tasmania)

The Tasmanian Devil is the second largest of the Australian carnivorous marsupials, only exceeded in size by the nearly extinct Thylacine. In the past it has occurred on the Australian mainland but nowadays it has a distribution restricted to the island of Tasmania. It was particularly unpopular with early settlers, making a nuisance of itself by stealing chickens. This not unnaturally led to its persecution, but although it is now found only in the more remote and rocky parts of the island, it is not as rare as the Thylacine, and in no immediate danger of extinction.

It is a heavily-built animal with enormous jaws and rather short legs. The head and body are over 2 feet long, and the tail adds another 12 inches. It owes its name to its wheezing snarl, its black fur which is relieved only by yellowish-white patches under the throat, on the shoulders and on the rump, and to the accidentally evil expression of the face. It is also particularly aggressive and savage when cornered.

Although it is not very agile, being unable to climb vertical tree trunks, the Tasmanian Devil is a rapacious hunter, feeding on a wide variety of animals, including wallabies, rat-kangaroos, lizards, and such birds as quail and parrots. It spends a great deal of time sprawled out, basking in the sun and frequently cleans itself, washing its face laboriously with its paws.

There are about four young, and they are born in April or May after a month's gestation period. They remain in the pouch throughout the southern winter, emerging about October. Young Tasmanian Devils are very active at this time, and climb trees which would defeat the adults.

53

THYLACINE

Thylacinus cynocephalus

(Tasmania)

The Thylacine is also known as the Tasmanian Tiger because it bears on the lower part of its grey-brown back about seventeen dark stripes. It is the largest of the carnivorous marsupials, being 5 feet long overall.

It is also called the Tasmanian Wolf because it is dog-like in its basic shape, in the way that it runs on its toes, and in its tooth structure, especially the pointed canines and flesh-shearing premolars.

The Thylacine is believed to spend the day in a rocky lair in the inaccessible mountains where it lives, emerging at night to prey upon wallabies, other small marsupials, and birds. The first colonists reported that it frequently raided their sheep and poultry. It is not as fast as a dog, but is said to be able to rise on the hind limbs to hop like a kangaroo if there are difficult obstacles to be cleared. When excited it utters a hoarse guttural bark.

Although the early explorers found no Thylacines on the Australian mainland, where the dingo is thought to have caused the extinction of these predators some hundreds of years ago, they were numerous in Tasmania until much more recently. Since the arrival of white settlers they have become increasingly rare until now the species seems to be almost extinct. No living Thylacine has been seen for many years, but in August 1961 it was reported that there was evidence to suggest that an animal which entered a trap on the west coast of Tasmania was in fact a Thylacine. It managed to escape, but left behind blood and hair that could later be identified.

54

Family DASYURIDAE

NUMBAT

Myrmecobius fasciatus

(South-western Australia)

The Numbat or Marsupial Anteater exhibits a number of the adaptations associated with insectivorous habits. The teeth are numerous—there are about fifty of them—but they are degenerate and small. The claws on the fore-limbs are powerful. The tongue is 4 inches long, cylindrical, and covered with a sticky secretion. In other respects, however, the Numbat resembles a squirrel, being about the same size, and having a long bushy tail. The brown body is distinctively striped with white.

It inhabits open woodlands of south-western Australia, preferring those areas where dead eucalyptus branches litter the ground. It is solitary, each individual living in its own territory, and is active by day. Apparently it cannot climb trees or burrow very deeply, but searches busily for food on the surface, turning over the top 2 inches of soil and looking underneath fallen branches. Termites form the largest proportion of its diet, although some ants are also eaten.

From time to time it sits up looking for possible danger, such as a dog, a fox, or a Wedge-tailed Eagle, but it has a bold demeanour, and when well fed lolls in the sun with its legs outstretched and its tongue protruding. At night it retires to a grass-lined nest inside a hollow log.

There are normally four young, and they are born in the late summer or autumn. The mother has no sign of a pouch. The young simply cling to the teats, as also occurs with some of the American opossums. They remain with the mother until the following spring, and are fully-grown at a year old.

B 117   Family PERAMELIDAE

LONG-NOSED BANDICOOT

Perameles nasuta

(Eastern Australia)

In its general appearance the Long-nosed Bandicoot looks like a large shrew. It has a long pointed snout, grey-brown fur on the back which becomes lighter below, and a crouching stance. It is, however, much bigger than any shrew, being about the size of a rabbit, and it has hind feet which resemble those of a kangaroo, the second and third toes being almost completely united. There have been many arguments about the significance of this particular kind of foot structure; one fact is certain, namely that the united toes form a valuable comb that is much used in grooming the fur.

The teeth of the bandicoots are similar to those of the flesh-eating marsupials, but the animal's diet is not entirely carnivorous, as it sometimes digs up and gnaws succulent roots and sweet potatoes. Some small vertebrates such as lizards are eaten, but the bulk of the diet consists of invertebrates. Bandicoots frequently annoy gardeners by excavating conical holes in gardens and lawns in their search for insects. They are very fond of Cockchafer grubs and also like worms which they wipe clean with the fore-paws before swallowing.

They are retiring by nature but do not construct burrows, preferring to hide amongst thick vegetation where they build nests of dried leaves, coarse grass and sticks.

The Long-nosed Bandicoot is one of the largest of the twenty species alive today. It is found in eastern Australia where it is still quite common although declining in numbers. Other, very similar, forms occur elsewhere in Australia, Tasmania and New Guinea.

SPOTTED CUSCUS

Phalanger maculatus

(Northern Australia and New Guinea)

Cuscuses are the largest of the phalangers, or Australian opossums. Two species, the Grey Cuscus and the Spotted Cuscus, are found in the tropical forests of northern Australia and related races occur in Timor, New Guinea and the Solomon Islands. There are also several other rarer species on Celebes, New Guinea and near-by islands.

The sexes of the Spotted Cuscus are very distinct, the male (see below) bearing large, irregular, pale blotches, while the female is plain coloured.

The animal is about as large as a domestic cat, but more elongated. The tail is prehensile and is naked for much of its length. Cuscuses are active at night, when they climb slowly through the trees, their pace recalling that of the sloths of South America, or the Slow Loris from Asia. Moving stealthily, they manage to surprise and eat small roosting birds and some lizards. They are in fact the most carnivorous members of their family, but most of their food consists of leaves and fruit which they eat in great quantities.

Man must be included among the natural enemies of the Cuscus. In New Guinea the natives are said to climb after it through the trees, easily overtaking it and killing it for food.

The gestation period is about 13 days, and the pouches of females that have been examined have proved to contain from two to four young ones.

The Spotted Cuscus from Australia used to be thought of as a distinct species and was then referred to as *Spilocuscus nudicaudatus*. It is now considered to be no more than a race of the New Guinea *Phalanger maculatus*.

BRUSH-TAILED PHALANGER

Trichosurus vulpecula

(Australia)

The Brush-tailed Phalanger, or Possum as it is sometimes called, is the most widely distributed Australian marsupial, being found throughout the mainland of Australia and the adjacent islands. It is plentiful in most parts of this vast range despite the fact that it is extensively hunted for its fur which is sometimes sold as "Adelaide Chinchilla". It prefers wooded areas, but is sometimes found living in rabbit burrows in open country and in suburban lofts. It has been successfully introduced to New Zealand.

The Brush-tailed Phalanger is about the size of a cat, but in general appearance it is more reminiscent of a large bushbaby.

It is one of the few phalangers to have a brush of hair extending all the way to the tip of the tail. Even in this case there is a bare patch below the prehensile tip of the tail.

The food consists of a wide variety of buds, leaves and fruits, with the addition of occasional fledgling birds. Feeding takes place at night, the animal sleeping curled up in a ball during the day. The mother usually only bears one offspring each year. The young animal leaves her pouch for the first time about September, becoming independent in October or November, at the beginning of the Australian summer. By February it is fully grown.

In addition to man, the Brush-tailed Phalanger's main enemies are the Wedge-tailed Eagle, which swoops on any that venture out into the open during the day, and the Great Monitor Lizard, which is able to climb and can catch them in the trees.

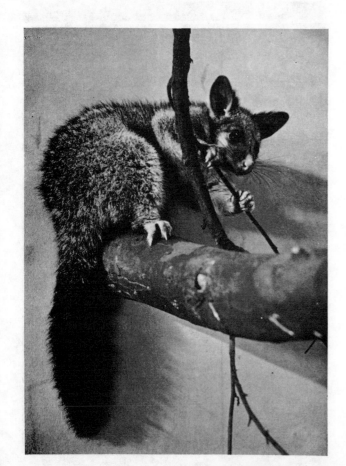

SQUIRREL-LIKE FLYING PHALANGER

Petaurus norfolcensis

(Eastern Australia)

In the year 1789 the Squirrel-like Flying Phalanger was given the Latin name of *Petaurus norfolcensis* in the mistaken belief that this species came from Norfolk Island, over 500 miles from the Australian mainland. Under the international rules controlling such names this title must stand today, as it was the first name to be published accompanied by a detailed description of the animal, even though it perpetuates an error.

This beautifully marked and noisily vocal creature is to be found in the forests of Victoria, New South Wales and southern Queensland. By day it remains inside a hollow branch, apparently living in family groups. The popular Australian name for the Flying Phalangers is "gliders". The main reason for this is that when they emerge at night they are able to take great leaps from tree to tree using a gliding membrane.

As the photograph shows, running between the fore and hind limbs is a web of loose skin. When the legs are outstretched this tightens and acts as a wing, while the fluffy tail can be used for steering. This is another striking example of convergence between marsupials and placental mammals, a similar device being used by the flying squirrels and flying lemurs. The flying phalanger hardly ever descends to the ground, finding all its food in the trees, eating buds and leaves, sucking the nectar from flowers, catching insects, and breaking open the nests of hornets for the larvae inside.

There are usually two young. They are born in July or August, and do not remain in the pouch long, but soon emerge and cling to the mother's fur.

59

B 173

KOALA
Phascolarctos cinereus
(Eastern Australia)

Koalas were once common in the eucalyptus forests of eastern Australia, but there are now few left in Victoria and New South Wales and despite protection they are not numerous in Queensland. The reason for this decline in numbers is partly that epidemic diseases killed off millions of them at the turn of the century, but mainly that they were slaughtered in large numbers for their fur. For example, 600,000 skins were exported from Queensland in 1927 alone.

The Koala is a slow-moving arboreal phalanger with a rudimentary tail and hands and feet highly specialized as climbing organs. Two of the clawed fingers oppose the other three so that the animal has in effect three fingers and two thumbs, and can take a very firm grip.

Most mammals are less specialized in their diet requirements than we imagine, but the Koala is an exception, eating only eucalyptus leaves. These leaves must be of a certain age, must come from certain species of trees only, and these must be growing in the right soil. Several acres of trees are needed to produce food for one group of Koalas. Each adult eats 2 to 3 lb. of leaves every day. These animals never drink, the name Koala meaning "no drink".

There is only one breeding season a year and usually only one young at a time. This leaves the pouch after 6 months and clings to the mother's back, staying with her until it is about a year old. As an aid to weaning the mother provides it with a special eucalyptus "soup" for a period of one month. This soup is eaten by the offspring directly from the parent's anus.

60

Family VOMBATIDAE

COMMON WOMBAT

Vombatus ursinus

(Australia and Tasmania)

Wombats bear a closer resemblance to the Koala than to any other animal, but instead of being climbers they are powerful burrowers. The common species is about 3 feet long and has a large head, a heavy body, short legs and a very short tail. Above ground, on the rough hillsides where it lives, it moves slowly. It excavates its burrows lying on its side, pushing out the loose soil with its feet. The tunnels are extensive and may be up to 100 feet long.

The teeth are very much like those of the rodents. Both upper and lower jaws have a single pair of incisors. These are chisel-like and grow continuously, being kept to a reasonable size by constant wear. Wombats eat grasses, the bark of bushes and trees, and roots, emerging from the burrows to feed in the evening. Earlier in the day they often sunbathe close to the entrance of the tunnels.

They are inoffensive animals, but until relatively recently have been widely hunted. The early settlers, who were compelled by necessity to sample many strange foods, reported that Wombat flesh was like tough mutton. More recently the fur has had some commercial importance. For this reason and because rabbits compete with them for the same food, the number of Wombats has declined.

The two species recognized today are similar in their habits and their general appearance. The rarer species, however, has a hairy nose and a softer pelt. We know from fossils that there was once a Wombat species as large as a Hippopotamus.

Like the Koala, the female Wombat has only one offspring a year.

DAMA WALLABY

Protemnodon eugenii

(Southern Australia)

This small wallaby was probably the first Australian marsupial ever encountered by a European, for it was observed and recorded by the Dutch navigator Pelsart in 1629 when he was ship-wrecked on Houtman's Abrolhos. This pre-dates Captain Cook's earliest notes on the kangaroo by a century and a half, but the Dutch records were overlooked for nearly 200 years. The species was first described scientifically in 1817 by Desmarest, from specimens taken on St. Peter's Island.

It is a coastal and insular species, a shy creature travelling silently along well-beaten pathways through dense scrubland and keeping well hidden during the day. At night it ventures on to more open grassy areas to feed. If alarmed, it gives a warning thump with its back feet, alerting its companions to possible danger. It is interesting that foot-stamping signals of this kind are given by a number of mammals in different groups, including certain rodents (acouchis), lagomorphs (rabbits) and even ungulates (chevrotains).

The Dama Wallaby can often be seen to rest in an unusual position, with its tail brought forwards between the legs. This is the characteristic posture of a female kangaroo when she is about to give birth. It helps in that case to shorten the journey to the pouch that the young animal must make, by curving the body and bringing the genital opening closer to the pouch.

Dama Wallabies have declined rapidly in numbers in the past 100 years as a result of ruthless shooting, but they are fortunately plentiful enough in certain remote (and today protected) areas to ensure their future survival.

RED-NECKED WALLABY

Protemnodon rufogrisea

(South-eastern Australia and Tasmania)

Wallabies and kangaroos are the large herbivores of Australia, replacing the deer and antelope of other continents. Those species with hind feet less than 6 inches long are usually called scrub wallabies, the slightly larger forms with feet up to 10 inches long are called brush wallabies, and the largest forms are known as kangaroos.

The Red-necked Wallaby belongs to the intermediate group. It is found in the brush country of south-eastern Australia and in Tasmania. This species usually stays close to thick cover. It can bound over rough ground with considerable speed and rarely ventures into open grassland. It feeds by browsing on the leafy shrubs.

The single young one is tiny when it is born after a gestation period of 40 days. It makes its own way to the mother's pouch, crawling through her fur by means of its strong fore-limbs, the hind limbs being only useless buds at this stage. It remains in the pouch for some weeks, firmly attached to an elongated nipple. As it grows larger it ventures out for increasingly long periods. For some months, however, until it is quite large, it dives back into the pouch at the first sign of any danger.

Red-necked Wallabies are hardy animals, breeding readily in European parks and zoos without any artificial protection from the weather. They are often referred to as Bennett's Wallabies as this was the particular race that was imported into the Northern Hemisphere in large numbers. It comes from Tasmania and is slightly greyer and smaller than the mainland form.

B 224   Family MACROPODIDAE

RED KANGAROO

Macropus rufus

(Plains of Australia)

Kangaroos are the world's largest marsupials. An old male may be over 7 feet tall and weigh over 200 lb. As the picture above shows, the hindquarters are particularly powerful. At low speeds the animal moves alternately supported by a tripod consisting of the front feet and tail, and by the hind feet. When the kangaroo is in a hurry it bounds along on the hind feet alone, with the massive tail swinging up and down as it acts as a counterweight to the body. In this way the animal can attain speeds of up to 30 m.p.h., clearing 25 or more feet with each leap, and reaching heights of up to 10 feet.

With this turn of speed it is able to escape from all its enemies except man, although dingoes and Wedge-tailed Eagles may sometimes catch a young one. If cornered, the Red Kangaroo rears up on its tail, kicking out formidably with the hind legs.

The hind feet, like those of all members of this family (and of some other marsupials such as the bandicoot) have the small second and third toes joined together for much of their length. In this form they provide a comb-like structure thought to be useful in grooming the fur. The front feet are used to grasp the branches as the kangaroo browses.

The Red Kangaroo inhabits the open plains of inland Australia, and related species are found in other areas. For example, Wallaroos are adapted to live on mountainous pastures, while in the open forests live the Grey Kangaroos.

64

BLACK TREE KANGAROO

Dendrolagus ursinus

(New Guinea)

The Black Tree Kangaroo is about the same size as a wallaby, but has a more stooping posture. Its body is dark grey to black. The fore-limbs are almost equal in size to those behind, which bear broad feet with rough pads on the soles. The tail is long, extremely muscular and has a tuft of hair at its tip. The ears are short and rounded.

These animals inhabit the dense, tropical rain-forests of New Guinea, along with six other closely related species, while in northern Australia there are two mainland representatives. During the day they sleep in the treetops in groups. They are quite at home above the ground, and have been seen jumping 20 feet from one tree to the next, but at night they spend much of their time on the forest floor. Sometimes they leap down from a considerable height, but more often they descend cautiously, tail first.

On the ground they hop actively, taking short bounds, and feed on ferns, fruit and creepers. They are always ready to seek refuge in the trees at the first sign of danger. They climb with speed and agility, grasping the stems of the creepers which festoon the large trunks.

There can be no doubt that many thousands of years ago the Black Tree Kangaroos' ancestors were normal, terrestrial members of the kangaroo family. Slowly, over countless generations, gradual changes have adapted their descendants for their present mode of life. Black Tree Kangaroos may seem rather clumsy creatures, but in the trees they find additional food and safety.

65

BRUSH-TAILED RAT-KANGAROO

Bettongia penicillata

(South-western Australia)

The Brush-tailed Rat-kangaroo was once common throughout southern Australia and was regarded by farmers as a pest because of the damage it caused to crops, but since the introduction of the European Fox it has become extinct over much of its former range.

In size it is a little larger than a rabbit, and is brown in colour except for the brush of black hairs at the end of the long tail. Rat-kangaroos differ from other members of the family in having well-developed canine teeth. Also, the largest of the cheek teeth are immediately behind these canines instead of at the back of the jaw. The ears are small and rounded. The claws of the fingers, which are extensively used for scratching and digging, are large.

Unlike some of its closest relatives, the Brush-tailed Rat-kangaroo does not construct a burrow, but spends the day in a well hidden nest of dead leaves on the surface of the ground. At night it emerges to feed on grasses, juicy stems and roots. Early settlers also reported that the Rat-kangaroos boldly approached their camp-fires at night in search of tit-bits. Under the cover of darkness these animals also collect nesting materials, making a neat bundle which is carried off under the downward-curving prehensile tail. (In this respect they are similar to the common American Opossums.)

There are eight other rather similar species of Rat-kangaroos in all but the more tropical parts of Australia. Some of these, at least, are now approaching extinction and the others are rare.

66

C. INSECTIVORES

The insectivores have a wide distribution, being found today throughout Europe, Asia (except in the extreme north), Africa, North America and Central America. There are important species in Madagascar (tenrecs) and the West Indies (solenodons). For some reason, only a small number of insectivores has penetrated into South America and the few that have done so have only just squeezed into the north-west corner. Australia, New Guinea and the Polar regions are without any indigenous representatives of this group.

There are eight distinct families, with a total of 374 species, the vast majority of which are various kinds of shrews (265 species). Over half of the members of the shrew family belong to the genus *Crocidura* (144 species). In reality this genus probably contains far fewer true species, but we simply do not have enough information at the present to be sure of this. In the meantime all we can do is to give the complete list of claimed species.

Insectivores are difficult to describe as a group because their main features are rather negative. They lack any special, advanced characters and are broadly-speaking primitive, small-bodied creatures that feed largely on invertebrates, taking a wide range from worms and molluscs to crustaceans and insects. Four of the families are shrew-like in general body shape, two are mole-like and two are hedgehog-like, the three methods of self-defence being rapid fleeing, burrowing and sharp spines respectively.

In almost all cases the eyes are poorly developed, the brain is small and the teeth are rather unspecialized. The fingers and toes are always clawed, but the first digit is never opposable to the others. In other words—insectivores are incapable of grasping anything awkward, either physically or mentally, and represent a living reminder of the sort of animals that were the ancestors of our more advanced groups.

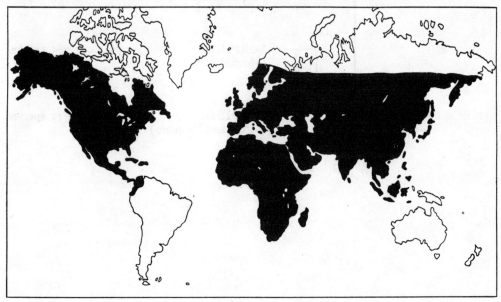

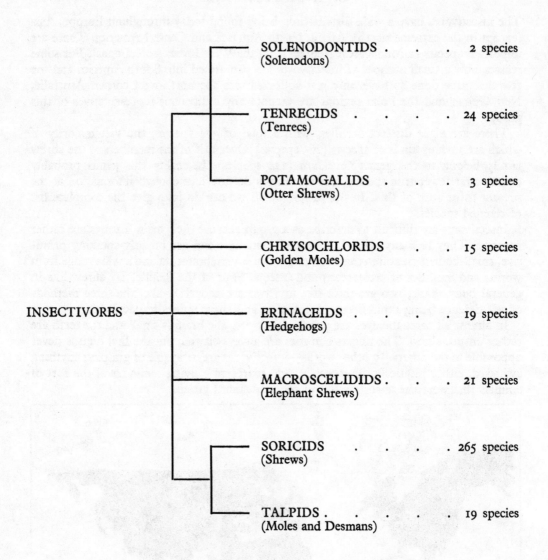

INSECTIVORES

SOLENODONTIDS . . . 2 species
(Solenodons)

TENRECIDS . . . 24 species
(Tenrecs)

POTAMOGALIDS . . . 3 species
(Otter Shrews)

CHRYSOCHLORIDS . . 15 species
(Golden Moles)

ERINACEIDS . . . 19 species
(Hedgehogs)

MACROSCELIDIDS . . . 21 species
(Elephant Shrews)

SORICIDS . . . 265 species
(Shrews)

TALPIDS . . . . 19 species
(Moles and Desmans)

C. Order INSECTIVORA.   Insectivores.

Superfamily TENRECOIDEA.

Family SOLENODONTIDAE.   Solenodons.

1 ►*Atopogale cubana.*   **Cuban Solenodon.**   Cuba. (HK)
2 *Solenodon paradoxus.*   **Haitian Solenodon.**   Haiti. (HK)

Family TENRECIDAE.   Tenrecs.

Subfamily TENRECINAE.

3 *Tenrec ecaudatus.*   **Tailless Tenrec.**   Madagascar. (A)
4 ►*Setifer setosus.*   **Hedgehog Tenrec.**   Madagascar. (A)
5 *Hemicentetes nigriceps.*   **Streaked Tenrec.**   Madagascar. (A)
6 *Hemicentetes semispinosus.*   **Streaked Tenrec.**   Madagascar. (A)
7 *Dasogale fontoynonti.*   Madagascar. (A)
8 *Echinops telfairi.*   Madagascar. (A)

Subfamily ORYZORICTINAE.

9   *Oryzorictes talpoides.*   **Rice Tenrec.**   Madagascar. (A)
10 *Oryzorictes tetradactylus.*   **Rice Tenrec.**   Madagascar. (A)
11 *Microgale brevicaudata.*   Madagascar. (A)
12 *Microgale cowani.*   Madagascar. (A)
13 *Microgale crassipes.*   Madagascar. (A)
14 *Microgale drouhardi.*   Madagascar. (A)
15 *Microgale longicaudata.*   **Long-tailed Tenrec.**   Madagascar. (A)
16 *Microgale longirostris.*   Madagascar. (A)
17 *Microgale majori.*   Madagascar. (A)
18 *Microgale parvula.*   Madagascar. (A)
19 *Microgale principula.*   Madagascar. (A)
20 *Microgale prolixacaudata.*   Madagascar. (A)
21 *Microgale pusilla.*   Madagascar. (A)
22 *Microgale sorella.*   Madagascar. (A)
23 *Microgale taiva.*   Madagascar. (A)
24 *Microgale thomasi.*   Madagascar. (A)
25 *Microgale dobsoni.*   Madagascar. (A)
26 *Microgale talazaci.*   Madagascar. (A)
27 *Microgale gracilis.*   Madagascar. (A)
28 *Microgale decaryi.*   Madagascar. (A)
29 *Microgale occidentalis.*   Madagascar. (A)
30 *Cryptogale australis.*   Madagascar. (A)
31 *Limnogale mergulus.*   Madagascar. (A)
32 *Geogale aurita.*   Madagascar. (A)

Family POTAMOGALIDAE.   Otter Shrews.

33 *Potamogale velox.*   **Otter Shrew.**   W. Africa. (EMH)
34 *Micropotamogale lamottei.*   **Lesser Otter Shrew.**   W. Africa. (HB1)
35 *Micropotamogale ruwenzorii.*   **Ruwenzori Otter Shrew.**   Cen. Africa. (GHL)

69

Superfamily CHRYSOCHLOROIDEA.

Family CHRYSOCHLORIDAE.   Golden Moles.

36	*Chrysochloris asiatica.*	**Cape Golden Mole.** S. Africa. (EMH)
37	*Chrysochloris congicus.*	Cen. Africa. (A)
38	*Chrysochloris vermiculus.*	Cen. Africa. (A)
39	*Chrysochloris stuhlmanni.*	**Stuhlmann's Golden Mole.** E. Africa. (A/EMH)
40	*Eremitalpa granti.*	**Grant's Desert Golden Mole.** S. Africa. (EMH)
41	*Cryptochloris wintoni.*	**De Winton's Golden Mole.** S. Africa. (EMH)
42	*Amblysomus hottentotus.*	**Hottentot Golden Mole.** S. Africa. (EMH)
43	*Amblysomus obtusirostris.*	**Yellow Golden Mole.** S. Africa. (EMH)
44	*Amblysomus leucorhinus.*	**Congo Golden Mole.** Cen. Africa. (EMH)
45	*Amblysomus sclateri.*	**Sclater's Golden Mole.** S. Africa. (EMH)
46	*Amblysomus gunningi.*	**Gunning's Golden Mole.** S. Africa. (EMH)
47	*Amblysomus fosteri.*	**Foster's Golden Mole.** Cen. Africa. (A)
48	*Amblysomus tropicalis.*	**Tropical Golden Mole.** Cen. Africa. (A)
49	*Chrysospalax trevelyani.*	**Giant Golden Mole.** S. Africa. (EMH)
50	*Chrysospalax villosus.*	**Rough-haired Golden Mole.** S. Africa. (EMH)

Superfamily ERINACEOIDEA.

Family ERINACEIDAE.   Hedgehogs.

Subfamily ECHINOSORICINAE.   Hairy Hedgehogs.

51 ►	*Echinosorex gymnurus.*	**Moon Rat.** S. Asia, Sumatra, Borneo. (EM)
52	*Hylomys suillus.*	**Lesser Gymnure.** S. Asia, Sumatra, Borneo. (EM)
53	*Podogymnura truei.*	**Mindanao Gymnure.** Philippines. (TAY)
54	*Neotetracus sinensis.*	**Shrew Hedgehog.** S.E. Asia. (EM)

Subfamily ERINACEINAE.   Spiny Hedgehogs.

55 ►	*Erinaceus europaeus.*	**European Hedgehog.** Europe and Asia. (EM)
56	*Erinaceus algirus.*	**Algerian Hedgehog.** N. Africa and S.W. Europe. (EM)
57	*Erinaceus frontalis.*	**Cape Hedgehog.** S. Africa. (EMH)
58	*Erinaceus sclateri.*	**Sclater's Hedgehog.** E. Africa. (A)
59	*Erinaceus albiventris.*	Africa. (A)
60	*Erinaceus pruneri.*	**Pruner's Hedgehog.** Africa. (A)
61	*Erinaceus faradjius.*	Cen. Africa. (A)
62	*Erinaceus langi.*	Cen. Africa. (A)
63	*Erinaceus spiculus.*	W. Africa. (A)
64	*Erinaceus spinifex.*	W. Africa. (A)
65	*Hemiechinus auritus.*	**Long-eared Hedgehog.** N. Africa and S.W. Asia. (EM)
66	*Hemiechinus megalotis.*	**Afghan Hedgehog.** S.W. Asia. (EM)
67	*Paraechinus aethiopicus.*	**Ethiopian Hedgehog.** N.E. Africa. (EM)
68	*Paraechinus micropus.*	**Indian Hedgehog.** S. Asia. (EM)
69	*Paraechinus hypomelas.*	**Brandt's Hedgehog.** S.W. Asia. (EM)

Superfamily MACROSCELIDOIDEA.

Family MACROSCELIDIDAE.   Elephant Shrews.

70	*Macroscelides proboscideus.*	**Short-eared Elephant Shrew.** S. Africa. (EMH)
71 ►	*Elephantulus rozeti.*	**North African Elephant Shrew.** N. and E. Africa. (EM)
72	*Elephantulus brachyrhynchus.*	**Short-snouted Elephant Shrew.** Africa. (EMH)

73	*Elephantulus intufi.*	**Bushveld Elephant Shrew.** S. Africa. (EMH)
74	*Elephantulus rupestris.*	**Rock Elephant Shrew.** S. Africa. (EMH)
75	*Elephantulus fuscipes.*	Cen. Africa. (A)
76	*Elephantulus revoilii.*	E. Africa. (A)
77	*Elephantulus somalicus.*	E. Africa. (A)
78	*Petrodromus tetradactylus.*	**Four-toed Elephant Shrew.** Africa. (EMH)
79	*Petrodromus rovumae.*	**Rovuma Four-toed Elephant Shrew.** E. Africa. (EMH)
80	*Petrodromus sultan.*	**Forest Elephant Shrew.** E. Africa. (EMH)
81	*Petrodromus matschiei.*	Cen. Africa. (A)
82	*Petrodromus robustus.*	Cen. Africa. (A)
83	*Petrodromus nigriseta.*	Cen. Africa. (A)
84	*Rhynchocyon cirnei.*	**Checkered Elephant Shrew.** Cen. Africa. (EMH)
85	*Rhynchocyon adersi.*	Zanzibar (E. Africa). (A)
86	*Rhynchocyon chrysopygus.*	E. Africa. (A)
87	*Rhynchocyon petersi.*	Cen. Africa. (A)
88	*Rhynchocyon claudi.*	Cen. Africa. (A)
89	*Rhynchocyon stuhlmanni.*	Cen. Africa. (A)
90	*Rhynchocyon swynnertoni.*	Cen. Africa. (A)

Superfamily SORICOIDEA.

Family SORICIDAE.   Shrews.

Subfamily SORICINAE.   Red-toothed Shrews.

91	*Sorex hawkeri.*	**Asiatic Pygmy Shrew.** Asia. (EM)
92	*Sorex minutus.*	**Lesser Shrew.** Europe and Asia. (EM)
93	*Sorex caecutiens.*	**Laxmann's Shrew.** Europe and Asia. (EM)
94 ►	*Sorex araneus.*	**Common Shrew.** Europe and Asia. (EM)
95	*Sorex daphaenodon.*	E. Asia. (EM)
96	*Sorex buchariensis.*	Cen. Asia. (EM)
97	*Sorex pacificus.*	**Giant Shrew.** E. Asia and W. of N. America. (EM)
98	*Sorex alpinus.*	**Alpine Shrew.** Europe. (EM)
99	*Sorex cylindricauda.*	**Stripe-backed Shrew.** S.E. Asia. (EM)
100	*Sorex cinereus.*	**Masked Shrew.** N. of N. America. (HK)
101	*Sorex lyelli.*	**Mount Lyell Shrew.** W. of N. America. (HK)
102	*Sorex preblei.*	**Malheur Shrew.** W. of N. America. (HK)
103	*Sorex milleri.*	**Carmen Mountain Shrew.** S. of N. America. (HK)
104	*Sorex fumeus.*	**Smoky Shrew.** E. of N. America. (HK)
105	*Sorex jacksoni.*	**St. Lawrence Island Shrew.** N. of N. America. (HK)
106	*Sorex arcticus.*	**Arctic Shrew.** N. of N. America. (HK)
107	*Sorex hydrodromus.*	**Unalaska Shrew.** Aleutian Islands. (HK)
108	*Sorex pribilofensis.*	**Pribilof Shrew.** Pribilof Islands. (HK)
109	*Sorex merriami.*	**Merriam Shrew.** W. of N. America. (HK)
110	*Sorex longirostris.*	**South-eastern Shrew.** S.E. of N. America. (HK)
111	*Sorex dispar.*	**Long-tailed Shrew.** E. of N. America. (HK)
112	*Sorex gaspensis.*	**Gaspé Shrew.** E. of N. America. (HK)
113	*Sorex trowbridgii.*	**Trowbridge Shrew.** W. of N. America. (HK)
114	*Sorex vagrans.*	**Vagrant Shrew.** Cen. America and W. of N. America. (HK)
115	*Sorex ornatus.*	**Ornate Shrew.** W. of N. America. (HK)
116	*Sorex juncensis.*	**Tule Shrew.** W. of N. America. (HK)
117	*Sorex trigonirostris.*	**Ashland Shrew.** W. of N. America. (HK)
118	*Sorex willetti.*	**Santa Catalina Shrew.** W. of N. America. (HK)

119	*Sorex sinuosus.*	**Suisun Shrew.** W. of N. America. (HK)
120	*Sorex tenellus.*	**Inyo Shrew.** W. of N. America. (HK)
121	*Sorex nanus.*	**Dwarf Shrew.** Cen. N. America. (HK)
122	*Sorex palustris.*	**Northern Water Shrew.** N. of N. America. (HK)
123	*Sorex alaskanus.*	**Alaska Water Shrew.** N.W. of N. America. (HK)
124	*Sorex bendirii.*	**Pacific Water Shrew.** W. of N. America. (HK)
125	*Sorex veraepacis.*	**Verapaz Shrew.** Cen. America. (HK)
126	*Sorex macrodon.*	**Large-toothed Shrew.** Cen. America. (HK)
127	*Sorex saussurei.*	**Saussure's Shrew.** Cen. America. (HK)
128	*Sorex oreopolus.*	**Mexican Long-tailed Shrew.** Cen. America. (HK)
129	*Sorex sclateri.*	**Sclater's Shrew.** Cen. America. (HK)
130	*Sorex stizodon.*	**San Cristobal Shrew.** Cen. America. (HK)
131	*Microsorex hoyi.*	**American Pygmy Shrew.** N. of N. America. (HK)
132	*Soriculus nigrescens.*	**Sikkim Large-clawed Shrew.** S. Asia. (EM)
133	*Soriculus caudatus.*	**Hodgson's Brown-toothed Shrew.** Asia. (EM)
134	*Soriculus leucops.*	**Indian Long-tailed Shrew.** Asia. (EM)
135	*Soriculus hypsibius.*	**de Winton's Shrew.** E. Asia. (EM)
136	*Soriculus salenskii.*	**Salenski's Shrew.** E. Asia. (EM)
137	*Soriculus lowei.*	**Lowe's Shrew.** S. Asia. (EM)
138 ►	*Neomys fodiens.*	**European Water Shrew.** Europe and Asia. (EM)
139	*Neomys anomalus.*	**Mediterranean Water Shrew.** S. Europe and W. Asia. (EM)
140	*Blarina brevicauda.*	**Short-tailed Shrew.** E. of N. America. (HK)
141	*Blarinella quadraticauda.*	**Short-tailed Moupin Shrew.** S. Asia. (EM)
142	*Cryptotis parva.*	**Least Shrew.** E. of N. America. (HK)
143	*Cryptotis avius.*	N. of S. America. (C1)
144	*Cryptotis montivagus.*	W. of S. America. (C1)
145	*Cryptotis squamipes.*	N. of S. America. (C1)
146	*Cryptotis surinamensis.*	**Surinam Shrew.** N. of S. America. (C1)
147	*Cryptotis thomasi.*	**Thomas' Shrew.** N. of S. America. (C1)
148	*Cryptotis pergracilis.*	**Slender Small-eared Shrew.** Cen. America. (HK)
149	*Cryptotis mexicana.*	**Mexican Small-eared Shrew.** Cen. America. (HK)
150	*Cryptotis alticola.*	**Popocatepetl Small-eared Shrew.** Cen. America. (HK)
151	*Cryptotis endersi.*	**Ender's Small-eared Shrew.** Cen. America. (HK)
152	*Cryptotis frontalis.*	**Tehuantepec Small-eared Shrew.** Cen. America. (HK)
153	*Cryptotis griseoventris.*	**San Cristobal Small-eared Shrew.** Cen. America. (HK)
154	*Cryptotis guerrerensis.*	**Guerreran Small-eared Shrew.** Cen. America. (HK)
155	*Cryptotis goodwini.*	**Goodwin's Small-eared Shrew.** Cen. America. (HK)
156	*Cryptotis gracilis.*	**Talamancan Small-eared Shrew.** Cen. America. (HK)
157	*Cryptotis jacksoni.*	**Jackson's Small-eared Shrew.** Cen. America. (HK)
158	*Cryptotis mayensis.*	**Yucatan Small-eared Shrew.** Cen. America. (HK)
159	*Cryptotis mera.*	**Mount Pirri Small-eared Shrew.** Cen. America. (HK/C1)
160	*Cryptotis nelsoni.*	**Nelson's Small-eared Shrew.** Cen. America. (HK)
161	*Cryptotis obscura.*	**Dusky Small-eared Shrew.** Cen. America. (HK)
162	*Cryptotis olivacea.*	**Olivaceous Small-eared Shrew.** Cen. America. (HK)
163	*Cryptotis zeteki.*	**Zetek's Small-eared Shrew.** Cen. America. (HK)
164	*Cryptotis fossor.*	**Zempoaltepec Small-eared Shrew.** Cen. America. (HK)
165	*Cryptotis magna.*	**Big Small-eared Shrew.** Cen. America. (HK)
166	*Cryptotis micrura.*	**Guatemalan Small-eared Shrew.** Cen. America. (HK)
167	*Cryptotis soricina.*	**Tlalpam Small-eared Shrew.** Cen. America. (HK)
168	*Cryptotis nigrescens.*	**Blackish Small-eared Shrew.** Cen. America. (HK)
169	*Cryptotis orophila.*	**Costa Rican Small-eared Shrew.** Cen. America. (HK)

170	*Cryptotis tersus.*	**Dark Small-eared Shrew.** Cen. America. (HK)
171	*Notiosorex crawfordi.*	**Crawford's Desert Shrew.** S.W. of N. America. (HK)
172	*Notiosorex gigas.*	**Merriam's Desert Shrew.** Cen. America. (HK)

Subfamily CROCIDURINAE. White-toothed Shrews.

173	*Crocidura hispida.*	**Andaman Island Spiny Shrew.** S. Asia. (EM)
174	*Crocidura floweri.*	**Flower's Shrew.** N.E. Africa. (EM)
175	*Crocidura miya.*	**Ceylon Long-tailed Shrew.** S. Asia. (EM)
176	*Crocidura religiosa.*	**Egyptian Pygmy Shrew.** N.E. Africa. (EM)
177	*Crocidura horsfieldi.*	**Horsfield's Shrew.** S. Asia. (EM)
178	*Crocidura suaveolens.*	**Lesser White-toothed Shrew.** Europe, Asia and Africa. (EM)
179	*Crocidura russula.*	**Common European White-toothed Shrew.** Europe, Asia and Africa. (EM)
180	*Crocidura leucodon.*	**Bicolor White-toothed Shrew.** Europe and Asia. (EM)
181	*Crocidura caudata.*	**Mediterranean Long-tailed Shrew.** Sicily, Corsica and Balearic Islands. (EM)
182	*Crocidura pergrisea.*	**Pale Grey Shrew.** Asia. (EM)
183	*Crocidura attenuata.*	**Grey Shrew.** Asia. (EM)
184	*Crocidura dracula.*	**Dracula Shrew.** S.E. Asia. (EM)
185	*Crocidura lasiura.*	**Ussuri Large White-toothed Shrew.** Asia. (EM)
186	*Crocidura olivieri.*	**Egyptian Giant Shrew.** N.E. Africa. (EM)
187	*Crocidura cyanea.*	**Reddish-grey Musk-Shrew.** Africa. (EMH)
188	*Crocidura hirta.*	**Zambesi Lesser Red Musk-Shrew.** Africa. (EMH)
189	*Crocidura pilosa.*	**Black Musk-Shrew.** Africa. (EMH)
190	*Crocidura smithi.*	**Desert Musk-Shrew.** Africa. (EMH)
191	*Crocidura flavescens.*	**Giant Musk-Shrew.** Africa. (EMH)
192	*Crocidura albicauda.*	Africa. (A)
193	*Crocidura allex.*	Africa. (A)
194	*Crocidura arethusa.*	Africa. (A)
195	*Crocidura aridula.*	Africa. (A)
196	*Crocidura baileyi.*	Africa. (A)
197	*Crocidura batesi.*	Africa. (A)
198	*Crocidura beta.*	Africa. (A)
199	*Crocidura bolivari.*	Africa. (A)
200	*Crocidura bottegi.*	Africa. (A)
201	*Crocidura bovei.*	Africa. (A)
202	*Crocidura boydi.*	Africa. (A)
203	*Crocidura buttikoferi.*	Africa. (A)
204	*Crocidura butleri.*	Africa. (A)
205	*Crocidura caliginea.*	Africa. (A)
206	*Crocidura cinderella.*	Africa. (A)
207	*Crocidura congobelgica.*	Africa. (A)
208	*Crocidura crossei.*	Africa. (A)
209	*Crocidura darfurea.*	Africa. (A)
210	*Crocidura dolichura.*	Africa. (A)
211	*Crocidura ferruginea.*	Africa. (A)
212	*Crocidura fischeri.*	Africa. (A)
213	*Crocidura foxi.*	Africa. (A)
214	*Crocidura fulvastra.*	Africa. (A)
215	*Crocidura fumosa.*	Africa. (A)

216	*Crocidura fuscosa.*	Africa. (A)
217	*Crocidura geoffroyi.*	Africa. (A)
218	*Crocidura giffardi.*	Africa. (A)
219	*Crocidura glebula.*	Africa. (A)
220	*Crocidura gracilipes.*	Africa. (A)
221	*Crocidura hedenborgiana.*	Africa. (A)
222	*Crocidura hildegardeae.*	Africa. (A)
223	*Crocidura hindei.*	Africa. (A)
224	*Crocidura jacksoni.*	Africa. (A)
225	*Crocidura langi.*	Africa. (A)
226	*Crocidura latona.*	Africa. (A)
227	*Crocidura littoralis.*	Africa. (A)
228	*Crocidura ludia.*	Africa. (A)
229	*Crocidura luluae.*	Africa. (A)
230	*Crocidura luna.*	Africa. (A)
231	*Crocidura lusitania.*	Africa. (A)
232	*Crocidura lutrella.*	Africa. (A)
233	*Crocidura macarthuri.*	Africa. (A)
234	*Crocidura manni.*	Africa. (A)
235	*Crocidura marita.*	Africa. (A)
236	*Crocidura martiensseni.*	Africa. (A)
237	*Crocidura maurisca.*	Africa. (A)
238	*Crocidura monax.*	Africa. (A)
239	*Crocidura muricauda.*	Africa. (A)
240	*Crocidura nigrofusca.*	Africa. (A)
241	*Crocidura niobe.*	Africa. (A)
242	*Crocidura odorata.*	Africa. (A)
243	*Crocidura oritis.*	Africa. (A)
244	*Crocidura parvipes.*	Africa. (A)
245	*Crocidura pasha.*	Africa. (A)
246	*Crocidura percivali.*	Africa. (A)
247	*Crocidura poensis.*	Africa. (A)
248	*Crocidura polia.*	Africa. (A)
249	*Crocidura raineyi.*	Africa. (A)
250	*Crocidura roosevelti.*	Africa. (A)
251	*Crocidura sansibarica*	Africa. (A)
252	*Crocidura schweitzeri.*	Africa. (A)
253	*Crocidura sericea.*	Africa. (A)
254	*Crocidura somalica.*	Africa. (A)
255	*Crocidura sururae.*	Africa. (A)
256	*Crocidura thomensis.*	Africa. (A)
257	*Crocidura ultima.*	Africa. (A)
258	*Crocidura velutina.*	Africa. (A)
259	*Crocidura viaria.*	Africa. (A)
260	*Crocidura voi.*	Africa. (A)
261	*Crocidura xantippe.*	Africa. (A)
262	*Crocidura zaphiri.*	Africa. (A)
263	*Crocidura zimmeri.*	Africa. (A)
264	*Crocidura bloyeti.*	E. Africa. (D)
265	*Crocidura nimbae.*	W. Africa. (HB3)
266	*Crocidura vulcani.*	W. Africa. (HB3)
267	*Crocidura ingoldbyi.*	W. Africa. (HB3)
268	*Crocidura eisentrauti.*	W. Africa. (HB4)

269	*Crocidura douceti.*	W. Africa. (HB5)
270	*Crocidura jouvenetae.*	W. Africa. (HB5)
271	*Crocidura wimmeri.*	W. Africa. (HBA)
272	*Crocidura monticola.*	Java, Borneo, Timor, Sumba, Flores and nearby Islands. (LH/CH)
273	*Crocidura tenuis.*	Timor. (LH)
274	*Crocidura elongata.*	Celebes. (LH)
275	*Crocidura nigripes.*	Celebes. (LH)
276	*Crocidura rhoditis.*	Celebes. (LH)
277	*Crocidura lea.*	Celebes. (LH)
278	*Crocidura levicula.*	Celebes. (LH)
279	*Crocidura parvacauda.*	Philippines. (TAY)
280	*Crocidura halconus.*	Philippines. (TAY)
281	*Crocidura beatus.*	Philippines. (TAY)
282	*Crocidura grayi.*	Philippines. (TAY)
283	*Crocidura mindorus.*	Philippines. (TAY)
284	*Crocidura grandis.*	Philippines. (TAY)
285	*Crocidura palawanensis.*	Philippines. (TAY)
286	*Crocidura edwardsiana.*	Philippines. (TAY)
287	*Crocidura negrina.*	Philippines. (SA)
288	*Crocidura orientalis.*	Java. (CH)
289	*Crocidura baluensis.*	Borneo. (CH)
290	*Crocidura villosa.*	Sumatra. (CH)
291	*Crocidura aequicauda.*	S. Asia and Sumatra. (CH)
292	*Crocidura paradoxura.*	Sumatra. (CH)
293	*Crocidura brevicauda.*	Java. (CH)
294	*Crocidura bartelsi.*	Java. (CH)
295	*Crocidura brunnea.*	Java and Sumatra. (CH)
296	*Crocidura doriae.*	Borneo. (CH)
297	*Crocidura foetida.*	Borneo. (CH)
298	*Crocidura weberi.*	Sumatra. (CH)
299	*Crocidura lepidura.*	Sumatra. (CH)
300	*Crocidura vosmaeri.*	**Banka Shrew.** Banka Islands (Sumatra). (CH)
301	*Crocidura malayana.*	S. Asia. (CH)
302	*Crocidura aagaardi.*	S. Asia. (CH)
303	*Crocidura gravida.*	**Dayang Shrew.** Dayang Bunting Islands (Straits of Malacca). (CH)
304	*Crocidura negligens.*	**Koh Shrew.** Koh Islands (off Malay coast). (CH)
305	*Crocidura klossi.*	Islands off Malay coast. (CH)
306	*Crocidura tionis.*	**Tioman Shrew.** Islands off Malay coast. (CH)
307	*Crocidura aoris.*	**Aor Shrew.** Islands off Malay coast. (CH)
308	*Crocidura maporensis.*	**Mapor Shrew.** Mapor Islands (Rhio Archipelago). (CH)
309	*Crocidura melanorhyncha.*	Java. (CH)
310	*Crocidura beccarii.*	Sumatra. (CH)
311	*Crocidura maxi.*	Java. (CH)
312	*Crocidura minuta.*	Java. (CH)
313	*Crocidura trichura.*	**Christmas Island Shrew.** Christmas Island (S. of Java). (CH)
314	*Crocidura fuliginosa.*	S. Asia and Borneo. (CH/EM)
315	*Crocidura nicobarica.*	**Nicobar Shrew.** Nicobar Islands (Indian Ocean). (EM)
316	*Crocidura andamanensis.*	**Andaman Shrew.** Andaman Islands (Bay of Bengal). (EM)
317	*Paracrocidura schoutedeni.*	Cen. W. Africa. (HB2)
318	*Praesorex goliath.*	**African Forest Shrew.** W. Africa. (A)

319	*Suncus murinus.*	**House Shrew.** Philippines, Celebes, Borneo, Sumatra, Java, S. Asia and N.E. Africa. (EM/LH/CH/TAY)
320	*Suncus occultidens.*	Philippines. (TAY)
321	*Suncus palawanensis.*	Philippines. (TAY)
322	*Suncus luzoniensis.*	Philippines. (TAY)
323	*Suncus hosei.*	Borneo. (CH)
324	*Suncus malayanus.*	S. Asia. (CH)
325	*Suncus etruscus.*	**Savi's Pygmy Shrew.** S. Europe, S. Asia and Africa. (EM)
326	*Suncus stoliczkanus.*	**Anderson's Shrew.** S. Asia. (EM)
327	*Suncus dayi.*	**Day's Shrew.** S. Asia. (EM)
328	*Suncus lixus.*	**Greater Dwarf Shrew.** E. Africa. (EMH)
329	*Suncus varius.*	**Forest Shrew.** S. Africa. (EMH)
330	*Suncus cafer.*	**Dark-footed Forest Shrew.** S. Africa. (EMH)
331	*Suncus megalura.*	**Climbing Shrew.** Africa. (EMH)
332	*Suncus blarina.*	Cen. Africa. (A)
333	*Suncus infinitesimus.*	E. Africa. (A)
334	*Suncus leucura.*	E. Africa. (A)
335	*Suncus madagascariensis.*	**Madagascar Shrew.** Madagascar. (A)
336	*Suncus granti.*	**Grant's Shrew.** E. Africa. (A)
337	*Suncus johnstoni.*	**Johnston's Shrew.** W. Africa. (A)
338	*Suncus lunaris.*	Cen. Africa. (A)
339	*Suncus morio.*	W. Africa. (A)
340	*Suncus ollula.*	W. Africa. (A)
341	*Suncus oriundus.*	Cen. Africa. (A)
342	*Suncus preussi.*	W. Africa. (A)
343	*Suncus ruandae.*	Cen. Africa. (A)
344	*Suncus suncoides.*	Cen. Africa. (A)
345	*Feroculus feroculus.*	**Kelaart's Long-clawed Shrew.** Ceylon. (EM)
346	*Solisorex pearsoni.*	**Pearson's Long-clawed Shrew.** Ceylon. (EM)
347	*Surdisorex norae.*	E. Africa. (A)
348	*Surdisorex polulus.*	E. Africa. (A)
349	*Diplomesodon pulchellum.*	**Piebald Shrew.** Cen. Asia. (EM)
350	*Anourosorex squamipes.*	**Szechuan Burrowing Shrew.** S.E. Asia. (EM)
351	*Chimmarogale platycephala.*	**Himalayan Water Shrew.** Asia. (EM)
352	*Chimmarogale phaeura.*	**Borneo Water Shrew.** Borneo and Sumatra. (CH)
353	*Nectogale elegans.*	**Szechuan Water Shrew.** Asia. (EM)

Subfamily SCUTISORICINAE. Armoured Shrews.

354	*Scutisorex congicus.*	**Congo Armoured Shrew.** Cen. Africa. (A)
355	*Scutisorex somereni.*	**Uganda Armoured Shrew.** Cen. Africa. (A)

Family TALPIDAE. Moles.
Subfamily UROPSILINAE. Shrew Mole.

356	*Uropsilus soricipes.*	**Shrew Mole.** E. Asia. (EM)

Subfamily DESMANINAE. Desmans.

357 ►	*Desmana moschata.*	**Russian Desman.** Asia. (EM)
358	*Galemys pyrenaicus.*	**Pyrenean Desman.** W. Europe. (EM)

Subfamily TALPINAE.   Old World Moles.

359 ► *Talpa europaea.* **Common Eurasian Mole.**   Europe and Asia. (EM)
360 *Talpa caeca.* **Mediterranean Mole.**   S. Europe and S.W. Asia. (EM)
361 *Talpa micrura.* **Eastern Mole.**   Asia. (EM)

Subfamily SCALOPINAE.

362 *Scaptonyx fusicaudus.* **Long-tailed Mole.**   E. Asia. (EM)
363 *Urotrichus talpoides.* **Japanese Shrew Mole.**   Japan. (EM)
364 *Urotrichus pilirostris.* **True's Shrew Mole.**   Japan. (EM)
365 *Neurotrichus gibbsi.* **American Shrew Mole.**   W. of N. America. (HK)
366 *Scapanulus oweni.* **Kansu Mole.**   E. Asia. (EM)
367 *Parascalops breweri.* **Hairy-tailed Mole.**   E. of N. America. (HK)
368 *Scapanus townsendi.* **Townsend's Mole.**   W. of N. America. (HK)
369 *Scapanus orarius.* **Coast Mole.**   W. of N. America. (HK)
370 *Scapanus latimanus.* **Broad-footed Mole.**   W. of N. America. (HK)
371 *Scalopus aquaticus.* **Eastern American Mole.**   S.E. of N. America. (HK)
372 *Scalopus inflatus.* **Tamaulipan Mole.**   S. of N. America. (HK)
373 *Scalopus montanus.* **Coahuilan Mole.**   S. of N. America. (HK)

Subfamily CONDYLURINAE.

374 *Condylura cristata.* **Star-nosed Mole.**   E. of N. America. (HK)

77

C 1

CUBAN SOLENODON

Atopogale cubana

(Cuba)

Although extinct members of this family are known from the mainland of North America the only survivors today are restricted to the West Indies. One species is found only on the island of Cuba, whilst another is confined to neighbouring Haiti. The relationship of these animals to other members of the Insectivora is not at all clear. The dentition is unusual, as one pair of upper incisors is enlarged while the premolars are reduced in number.

Solenodons are rat-sized and have long, naked tails. The five toes on each foot bear powerful claws, those on the fore-limbs being particularly large. The eyes are small, but the snout is greatly elongated, the nostrils being placed on each side of the tip. There can be little doubt that smell is the predominant sense. Scent-producing musky glands are present in the armpit and groin regions and, possibly because of this, the female's nipples are situated on her buttocks.

The Cuban Solenodon sleeps during the day, emerging from its shelter to feed on ants, other insects, small vertebrates and some fruit. In its search for food the animal sets off in a zig-zag path, rooting in the ground with its snout, and tearing open rotten logs with its claws. It has been suggested that, like some of the shrews, the Cuban Solenodon has poisonous saliva that helps it to overcome its larger prey.

Solenodons breed rather slowly, having only one to three young in each litter. For this reason they are becoming rare, being unable to maintain their numbers against such predators as dogs and mongooses which have been introduced to their islands by man.

78

HEDGEHOG TENREC

Setifer setosus

(Madagascar)

Tenrecs are found only on the island of Madagascar. Thirty species are known. Some are adapted to swimming, some have long tails and are adapted to climbing, and others live a burrowing, mole-like existence. All are modest-sized mammals with the relatively small brains typical of the Insectivora. They have sharply cusped teeth, the number of molars being reduced. The legs are short.

The hairs of the back are stiff and tend to be erected when the animal is agitated. From this beginning some species have evolved stiffer and harder hairs until sharp spines have been developed. Some of the tenrecs can even roll up into a tight ball like hedgehogs.

The illustration shows the most prickly form, the Spiny, or Hedgehog Tenrec. It is nocturnal and lives in the thick undergrowth of the forests of Madagascar. It feeds on snails, worms, insects and some fruit. The tail is short and the body is the size and shape of a small hedgehog. There are five toes on each foot, and each toe bears a strong claw. When the Hedgehog Tenrec walks, the hind feet point outwards at right-angles to the body. Like many of its relatives the animal has a strong and offensive smell.

Some tenrecs hibernate during the dry winter season but the Hedgehog Tenrec does not do so. The female gives birth to numerous progeny, a litter of twelve being far from unusual. A female Tailless, or Common Tenrec (*Tenrec ecaudatus*) is even recorded as giving birth to a litter of twenty-one.

Family ERINACEIDAE

MOON RAT

Echinosorex gymnurus

(Southern Asia, Sumatra and Borneo)

The hairy hedgehogs, or gymnures as they are sometimes called, are a little-known groups of mammals. Four distinct species exist and all are confined to South-east Asia. They have many affinities with the hedgehogs, but lack the sharp spines. Their appearance is rather rat-like, but they are true members of the Insectivora, having the sharply cusped teeth typical of this order. The legs are rather short, and terminate in flat (plantigrade) feet. The bones of the lower arm are joined near the elbow, as they are in the hedgehogs. The smallest animals in this group are only 6 inches long, but the biggest measure as much as 2 feet from nose to tail-tip.

The Moon Rat is, in fact, the largest living species of the Insectivora. Its body is about 14 to 16 inches long. In addition, there is an 8-inch long, naked, scaly, rat-like tail. The coat consists of many short, fine hairs with some longer, coarser guard hairs. It is black or very dark brown in colour, becoming almost white on the head and shoulders except for a dark patch above each eye. The ears are naked, but the long snout bears a profusion of whiskers. Anal glands secrete a musky substance that gives these animals their highly characteristic smell. This is so distinctive that it has even been made the subject of native legends.

Very little is known of the Moon Rat's habits in the wild, but it is thought to hide away in crevices amongst rocks or in hollow logs. It is said to eat fruit, cockroaches, termites and other insects.

EUROPEAN HEDGEHOG

Erinaceus europaeus

(Europe and Asia)

Like the echidnas, the porcupines and the tenrecs, hedgehogs are protected against most predators by the stiff, spiny hairs of the back. For this reason they are able to move about boldly and noisily. If alarmed they roll up into a tight prickly ball.

An adult is about 9 inches long, with a very short tail. The general outline is rounded, the sheet of muscle underlying the spines giving the animal a rolling gait when walking.

By day European Hedgehogs rest in thick hedgerows, or undergrowth, often snoring loudly. At night they patrol their territories in search of food. They are valuable pest killers, subsisting mainly on a diet of insects, worms, snails, slugs, and other small animals. They occasionally kill and eat snakes and are partially immune to viper venom. In the middle of winter, when food is scarce, they hibernate. A female may have two litters in a year, each consisting of four or five young. The gestation period is just over a month. At birth the spines of the young hedgehogs are soft, but they soon harden, the ability to roll up maturing at roughly the same rate. They are weaned after 4 weeks, but are not mature until the following year.

The animal in the above illustration is anointing its spines with its saliva. This strange pattern of behaviour, noticed for the first time only comparatively recently, is still something of a mystery. It occurs as a response to a variety of pungent substances such as cigarette smoke, perfume or black coffee.

Fifteen similar, closely related species are to be found in central and southern Asia and in Africa.

81

Family MACROSCELIDIDAE

NORTH AFRICAN ELEPHANT SHREW

Elephantulus rozeti

(North and East Africa)

Members of this family are found only in Africa where twenty-one species occur, usually in the more arid regions. They have elongated noses, prominent ears, and the largest eyes in relation to their size to be found in the Insectivora. The hind limbs are long and powerful, and on these they can bound along like miniature kangaroos. In this respect they invite comparison with the jerboas, to which they are not, however, related. Some species have five toes on the hind foot, but others have only four. A scent gland is present on the lower surface of the tail. This touches the ground each time the animal leaps, leaving a scented trail.

The East African race of the North African Elephant Shrew (shown above) is known as the Ruddy Elephant Shrew and until recently was considered to be a separate species (*Elephantulus rufescens*). The head and body are about 4 inches long and the tail is a little shorter. It is most active during the cooler parts of the day, retreating into a burrow at midday, or when disturbed whilst feeding or sun-bathing. The diet consists largely of insects.

About September the female gives birth to a litter of one or two young. At birth the offspring are quite large in relation to the mother and their backs are well covered with reddish-brown fur. Their eyes are open when they are born. They may be carried around by the mother attached to her nipples.

The largest member of the family is the Checkered Elephant Shrew (*Rhynchocyon cirnei*) from central Africa. It has an 11-inch body and a 9-inch tail.

Family SORICIDAE

COMMON SHREW

Sorex araneus

(Europe and Asia)

Common Shrews measure only 3 inches overall and weigh no more than a third of an ounce. For their size they are the fiercest of living mammals, attacking and eating not only insects, but also any other small animal they encounter. The possession of poisonous saliva aids the capture of the prey. Every 4 hours throughout the day and night the animal roams in search of food. During each 24-hour period it eats its own weight of food. This large amount is needed partly because such small mammals are rather inefficient, losing heat more rapidly than larger forms, and partly because some of the invertebrates which make up the diet are not very nourishing, consisting largely of water.

Shrews make "surface burrows" and runways through the litter of dead leaves and vegetation lying on the ground. They are solitary and, should one of them encounter another whilst hunting, they squabble shrilly. Each individual lives within a small area only tens of yards across and, should danger threaten, the whereabouts of the nearest refuge is always known. Shrews are rarely eaten by larger mammals, which are perhaps deterred by the musky scent glands, but predatory birds are their constant enemies.

Common Shrews only live for about 15 months. When she is a year old, the female bears her litter of about five in a nest of dried leaves before dying of "old age" with the coming of autumn. In certain shrew species the mother, when moving about, may be followed by a "caravan" of her young ones, each holding on to the rear end of the one in front with its teeth.

C 138   Family SORICIDAE

EUROPEAN WATER SHREW

Neomys fodiens

(Europe and Western Asia)

As its name suggests, the Water Shrew is an expert swimmer, making full use of its feet, the toes of which are fringed with hairs, and its tail, which is slightly compressed from side to side. There is also a keel of hairs along the underside of its tail. Like other aquatic mammals it has a fine set of whiskers which are sensitive to ripples caused by other swimming animals and thus assist in the location of prey. The dense velvety fur traps a layer of air, giving the swimming shrew a silvery appearance, and keeping the skin dry and warm. The fur of the back is almost black in colour, whilst that on the chest is off-white. Although larger than the Common Shrew, this species is still small, being less than 4 inches from head to tail.

Water Shrews feed on insects, fresh-water shrimps, and other invertebrates, and will even attack small fish and frogs if they get the chance. They have powerful jaws and sharply cusped teeth. As with the Common Shrew, the saliva is poisonous. Once it enters the blood stream of the prey it acts as a neurotoxin and helps to overcome resistance. Although these are truly venomous mammals, there are no reports of their bites being particularly harmful to man.

During the winter it is hard to distinguish the males from the females, but in the spring the reproductive systems undergo considerable development, and the male shrews in particular become more active, searching farther afield for mates. The young, at first blind, hairless and completely helpless, are born between April and August, after a gestation of about 3 weeks.

84

RUSSIAN DESMAN

Desmana moschata

(Asia)

The desmans belong to the mole family, but are adapted for swimming rather than burrowing. The Pyrenean species (*Galemys pyrenaicus*) inhabits certain mountain streams of the Iberian peninsula and neighbouring parts of France. The body is about 5 inches long and the tail, which is compressed from side to side towards its tip, is about the same length. The hind feet are webbed, and the fur, which is dark brown on the desman's back but lighter below, is very dense and keeps the skin dry while it is swimming.

The tubular snout is exceedingly long and mobile, and is rarely still when the animal is awake. Desmans have been seen swimming with only the nostrils on the tip of the nose showing above the surface of the water. The eyes are very small and the ears are almost invisible, being buried in the fur.

The Russian Desman is larger, but has a relatively shorter tail. It is approximately 15 inches from nose to tail-tip. The fur on its back, which is of some commercial value, is reddish-brown. This species is found in the more slowly moving rivers of western Asia. All desmans make burrows in the banks of the rivers they inhabit, but those of the Russian species open well below the surface of the water so that the animal is able to reach unfrozen water even in the depths of winter. The burrow terminates in a nest-chamber filled with dried reeds. The desman's nest is usually foul smelling, both from the musky odour of its occupant and from the discarded remains of the fish and crustaceans upon which it feeds.

C 359   Family TALPIDAE

COMMON EURASIAN MOLE

Talpa europaea

(Europe and Asia)

Moles are so highly adapted for a burrowing existence that on the surface of the ground they find it difficult to walk, clumsily rowing themselves along with their great feet. Below ground, on the other hand, they have been known to construct a burrow 22 yards long in a single day, using the broad fore-paws to loosen the soil and kicking back the excavated earth with the hind feet. The muscles of the fore-limbs are powerful and the paws form efficient shovels, having an extra bone which looks almost like a sixth finger.

Living almost entirely in dark burrows the mole's eyes are of little importance. Some species are blind, but Common Eurasian Moles have tiny eyes 1 millimetre in diameter. No external ears protrude from the dark, velvety fur, but there are ear openings at the back of the head and moles have quite a keen sense of hearing.

Their food consists largely of earthworms, although other invertebrates are also eaten. They are voracious feeders, consuming many worms daily. Should they find more than they require, the surplus worms are bitten at the front end and immobilized. They are then stored away in special "larders", to be eaten later. Fresh tunnels are dug each day in the search for food. These radiate from the permanent galleries which in turn surround the nest. The nest is situated under a mound known as the mole's "fortress". In the nest of the female the young, usually about four of them, are born in May after a gestation period of 4 weeks. They are weaned after only 3 weeks.

86

D. FLYING LEMURS

The Flying Lemurs are confined to southern Asia, Sumatra, Java, Borneo and the Philippines. There are only two species and these are not strikingly different.

The name Dermoptera means "skin-winged" and refers to the extensive fold of skin between the legs that is stretched out tight when the animals leap and glide (not fly) from tree to tree. The limbs have become so specialized in connection with the gliding locomotion that the Flying Lemur can no longer stand up when on the ground, but must crawl along rather like a bat.

They are nocturnal creatures, sleeping in holes in the trees during the daytime and emerging at dusk to feed. The female bears a single offspring once a year. The young animal is hung up in the tree, by itself, when the mother is away foraging.

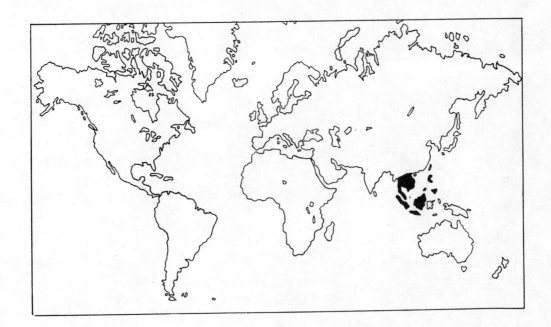

D. Order DERMOPTERA. Flying Lemurs.
   Family CYNOCEPHALIDAE.

1 *Cynocephalus variegatus.* **Malayan Flying Lemur.** S. Asia, Sumatra, Java, Borneo.
                                                                                                  (EM)
2 ►*Cynocephalus volans.* **Philippines Flying Lemur.** Philippines. (TAY)

PHILIPPINES FLYING LEMUR

Cynocephalus volans

(Philippines)

The Flying Lemurs, or Colugos, have always presented zoologists with something of a problem, for these two closely related species, one from the Philippines (shown below) and the other from Indo-China, Burma, Malaya, Sumatra, Borneo and Java have no other close relatives. Their name suggests an affinity with the primates, but they must be placed in an order of their own.

The face does rather resemble that of a lemur, but the teeth are more like those of the insectivores. The body is about 2 feet long. The "wings" are largely formed of skin, as in the bats, but Flying Lemurs do not have greatly elongated fingers. Their "wings" are more like exaggerated versions of the gliding membranes of the flying squirrels, the skin being stretched between the fore- and hind limbs and the tail. With limbs and tail outspread, a Flying Lemur is able to launch itself from a tree and glide for as much as 70 yards before coming to rest, usually in another tree, where it runs nimbly up the trunk to regain height. Only rarely does one descend to the ground, but should it do so it makes for the nearest tree at a gallop.

The food consists of young leaves, buds and fruits. Whilst feeding, the animal hangs upside down, pulling the food towards its mouth with its fore-limbs. Most of its time is spent in this inverted position. The dorsal surface of the body looks like part of a lichen-covered tree-trunk, and the sleep-ing animal is well concealed.

89

E. BATS

These are the only mammals that truly fly. There are 981 species alive today, making this order second only in size to the rodents. The distribution is virtually world-wide, only the polar regions being completely batless. Even New Zealand has two species of native bats. (Apart from the Maori Rat, these are the only indigenous mammals present there.)

Bats have evolved in two main directions—fruit-eating and insect-eating. Fruit bats are generally large, have good vision and fly in weak light. The insectivorous bats are usually smaller, have poor eyes, but an excellent echo-sounding system, and can fly in pitch darkness. They send out beams of supersonic squeaks and listen to the returning echoes as they bounce off obstacles or their insect prey. In this way they can navigate blind and track down their food with ease.

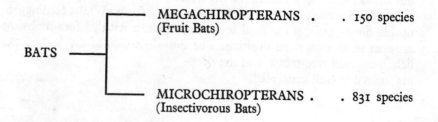

BATS

MEGACHIROPTERANS . . 150 species
(Fruit Bats)

MICROCHIROPTERANS . . 831 species
(Insectivorous Bats)

Classification Note

Owing to the huge number of species, it has only been possible to list the genera of bats. In each case, however, the number of living species is given and, where there is only a single species in a genus, its full name is included. All the reference works consulted when arriving at a decision concerning the number of valid species in a genus have been listed by their symbols in every instance.

E. Order CHIROPTERA. Bats.

Suborder MEGACHIROPTERA. Fruit-eating Bats.

Family PTEROPIDAE.

Subfamily PTEROPINAE.

1	*Cynopterus* (5 species).	**Short-nosed Fruit Bats.** S. Asia, Philippines, Java, Sumatra, Borneo and near-by islands. (EM/CH/LH/TAY)
2	*Thoopterus nigrescens.*	**Short-nosed Fruit Bat.** Celebes, Philippines. (LH/TAY)
3	*Aethalops alecto.*	S. Asia, Sumatra, Borneo. (CH/JEH)
4	*Chironax melanocephalus.*	**Black-capped Fruit Bat.** S. Asia, Sumatra, Java. (CH/JEH)
5	*Dyacopterus* (2 species).	S. Asia, Borneo, Sumatra. (CH/JEH)
6	*Penthetor lucasi.*	**Dusky Fruit Bat.** S. Asia. (CH)
7	*Sphaerias blanfordi.*	**Blanford's Bat.** S. Asia. (EM)
8	*Ptenochirus jagori.*	Philippines. (TAY)
9	*Megaerops* (2 species).	**Tailless Fruit Bats.** S. Asia, Sumatra, Borneo, Philippines. (EM/CH/TAY)
10	*Balionycteris maculata.*	**Spotted-winged Fruit Bat.** S. Asia and Borneo. (CH)
11	*Rousettus* (13 species).	**Rousette Bats.** Africa, Madagascar, S. Asia, Java, Sumatra, Borneo, Celebes, Philippines, New Guinea and nearby islands. (EM/EMH/A/CH/LH/TAY)
12	*Myonycteris* (4 species).	**Little Collared Fruit Bats.** Africa. (EMH/A)
13	*Haplonycteris fischeri.*	Philippines. (L)
14 ►*Pteropus* (51 species).		**Flying Foxes.** Madagascar, Seychelles, Pemba, S. Asia, Java, Sumatra, Borneo, Australia and Pacific Islands. (EM/A/CH/LH/TAY/IT)
15	*Neopteryx frosti.*	Celebes. (LH)
16	*Acerodon* (5 species).	Philippines, Celebes and near-by islands. (LH/TAY)
17	*Pteralopex atrata.*	Solomon Islands. (LH)
18	*Boneia bidens.*	Celebes. (LH)
19	*Styloctenium wallacei.*	Celebes. (LH)
20	*Dobsonia* (9 species).	**Bare-backed Fruit Bats.** Philippines, New Guinea, Celebes and near-by islands. (LH/TAY)
21	*Epomophorus* (7 species).	**Epauletted Bats.** Africa. (EMH/A)
22	*Nanonycteris veldkampi.*	W. Africa. (A)
23	*Scotonycteris* (2 species).	W. Africa. (A/P)
24 ►*Epomops* (3 species).		**Epauletted Bats.** Africa. (EMH/A)
25	*Hypsignathus monstrosus.*	**Hammer-headed Bat.** Africa. (EMH/A)
26	*Plerotes anchietai.*	**Anchieta's Fruit Bat.** Africa. (EMH/A)
27	*Micropteropus* (2 species).	**Dwarf Epauletted Fruit Bats.** Africa. (EMH/A)
28	*Casinycteris argynnis.*	Cen. W. Africa. (A)
29 ►*Eidolon* (3 species).		**Straw-coloured Fruit Bats.** Africa, Madagascar, S.W. Asia. (EM/EMH/A)

Subfamily MACROGLOSSINAE. Long-tongued Fruit Bats.

30	*Eonycteris* (5 species).	**Long-tongued Fruit Bats.** S. Asia, Java, Sumatra, Borneo, Philippines, Celebes. (EM/CH/LH/TAY)
31	*Macroglossus* (4 species).	**Long-tongued Fruit Bats.** S. Asia, Java, Sumatra, Borneo, Philippines. (EM/CH/LH/TAY)
32	*Syconycteris* (3 species).	**Blossom Bats.** Australia, New Guinea and near-by islands. (IT/LH)

91

33	*Megaloglossus woermanni.*	**African Long-tongued Fruit Bat.** Cen. Africa. (A)
34	*Melonycteris melanops.*	New Guinea and near-by islands. (LH)
35	*Nesonycteris woodfordi.*	**Solomons Long-tongued Fruit Bat.** Solomon Islands. (LH)
36	*Notopteris* (2 species).	**Long-tailed Fruit Bats.** Islands of W. Polynesia. (AN)

Subfamily NYCTIMENINAE.   Tube-nosed Fruit Bats.

| 37 | *Nyctimene* (7 species). | **Tube-nosed Bats.** Australia, New Guinea, Celebes, Timor and near-by islands. (IT/LH) |
| 38 | *Paranyctimene raptor.* | **Lesser Tube-nosed Bat.** New Guinea. (LH) |

Subfamily HARPYIONYCTERINAE.

| 39 | *Harpyionycteris whiteheadi.* | **Harpy Fruit Bat.** Celebes and Philippines. (LH/TAY) |

Suborder MICROCHIROPTERA.   Insect-eating Bats.
Superfamily EMBALLONUROIDEA.
Family RHINOPOMATIDAE.

| 40 ► | *Rhinopoma* (4 species). | **Mouse-tailed Bats.** N. Africa, S. Asia, Sumatra. (EM/CH) |

Family EMBALLONURIDAE.   Sac-winged Bats.
Subfamily EMBALLONURINAE.

41	*Emballonura* (7 species).	**Sheath-tailed Bats.** Madagascar, S. Asia, Java, Sumatra, Borneo, New Guinea, Philippines, Celebes, Pacific Islands. (A/EM/LH/CH/TAY)
42	*Coleura* (4 species).	**Sheath-tailed Bats.** Africa and Seychelles. (EM/EMH/A)
43	*Rhynchonycteris naso.*	**Proboscis Bat.** Cen. and S. America. (C1/HK)
44	*Saccopteryx* (6 species).	**White-lined Bats.** Cen. and S. America. (C1/HK)
45	*Cormura brevirostris.*	**Wagner's Sac-winged Bat.** Cen. and S. America. (C1/HK)
46	*Peropteryx* (3 species).	**Dog-like Bats.** Cen. and S. America. (C1/HK)
47	*Centronycteris maximiliani.*	**Thomas' Bat.** Cen. and S. America. (C1/HK)
48	*Balantiopteryx* (3 species).	Cen. and S. America. (C1/HK)
49	*Depanycteris isabella.*	S. America. (C1)
50	*Taphozous* (21 species).	**Tomb Bats.** Africa, Madagascar, S. Asia, Java, Sumatra, Borneo, New Guinea, Philippines, Australia and Pacific islands. (EMH/A/EM/LH/CH/TAY/IT)

Subfamily DICLIDURINAE.

| 51 | *Diclidurus* (3 species). | **Ghost Bats.** Cen. and S. America. (C1/HK) |
| 52 | *Cyttarops alecto.* | S. America. (C1) |

Family NOCTILIONIDAE.

| 53 | *Noctilio* (2 species). | **Bulldog Bats.** Cen. and S. America. (C1/HK) |

92

Superfamily RHINOLOPHOIDEA.
Family NYCTERIDAE.

54 *Nycteris* (20 species). **Slit-faced Bats.** Africa, Madagascar, S. Asia, Java, Borneo. (EM/EMH/A/CH)

Family MEGADERMATIDAE. False Vampires.

55 *Megaderma* (2 species). **False Vampires.** S. Asia, Sumatra, Borneo, Java, Celebes, Philippines. (EM/CH/TAY/LH)
56 *Macroderma gigas.* **Australian False Vampire.** Australia. (IT)
57 *Lavia frons.* **Yellow-winged Bat.** E. Africa. (A/EMH)
58 *Cardioderma cor.* E. Africa. (A)

Family RHINOLOPHIDAE. Horseshoe Bats.

59 ►*Rhinolophus* (74 species). **Horseshoe Bats.** Africa, Europe, Asia, Java, Sumatra, Borneo, New Guinea, Philippines, Celebes, Australia and Pacific islands. (EM/EMH/A/CH/LH/TAY/IT)
60 *Rhinomegalophus paradox-olophus.* S. Asia. (B)

Family HIPPOSIDERIDAE. Leaf-nosed Bats.

61 *Hipposideros* (49 species). **Leaf-nosed Bats.** Africa, Madagascar, S. Asia, Java, Sumatra, Borneo, New Guinea, Celebes, Philippines, Australia and Pacific islands. (EMH/A/EM/LH/CH/TAY/IT)
62 *Anthops ornatus.* **Flower-faced Bat.** Solomon Islands. (LH)
63 *Asellia* (2 species). **North African Trident Bats.** N. Africa, S.W. Asia. (EM/A)
64 *Aselliscus* (4 species). **Tate's Trident Bats.** S. Asia, New Guinea and Pacific islands. (EM/LH/CH)
65 *Coelops* (3 species). **Tailless Leaf-nosed Bats.** S. Asia, Java, Philippines. (EM/CH/TAY)
66 *Paracoelops megalotis.* S. Asia. (DO)
67 *Cloeotis percivali.* **East African Trident Bat.** E. and S. Africa. (A/EMH)
68 *Rhinonicteris aurantius.* **Orange Leaf-nosed Bat.** Australia. (IT)
69 *Triaenops* (5 species). S.W. Asia, E. Africa, Madagascar. (EM/A)

Superfamily PHYLLOSTOMATOIDEA.
Family PHYLLOSTOMATIDAE.
Subfamily CHILONYCTERIINAE.

70 *Chilonycteris* (7 species). **Moustached Bats.** W. Indies, Cen. and S. America. (CI/HK)
71 *Pteronotus* (2 species). **Naked-backed Bats.** Cen. and S. America. (CI/HK)
72 *Mormoops* (2 species). **Leaf-chinned Bats.** Cen. America and W. Indies. (HK)

Subfamily PHYLLOSTOMATINAE.

73 *Micronycteris* (10 species). **Large-eared Bats.** Cen. and S. America. (CI/HK)
74 *Macrotus* (3 species). **American Leaf-nosed Bats.** S. of N. America, Cen. America, W. Indies. (HK)

93

75	*Lonchorhina aurita.*	**Tome's Long-eared Bat.** Cen. and S. America, W. Indies. (CI/HK)
76	*Macrophyllum macrophyllum.*	**Long-legged Bat.** Cen. and S. America. (CI/HK)
77	*Tonatia* (7 species).	**Round-eared Bats.** Cen. and S. America. (CI/HK)
78	*Mimon* (6 species).	**Spear-nosed Bats.** Cen. and S. America. (CI/HK)
79	*Phyllostomus* (4 species).	**Spear-nosed Bats.** Cen. and S. America. (CI/HK)
80	*Phylloderma* (2 species).	**Spear-nosed Bats.** Cen. and S. America. (CI/HK)
81	*Trachops cirrhosa.*	**Fringe-lipped Bat.** Cen. and S. America. (CI/HK)
82	*Chrotopterus auritus.*	**Peter's False Vampire.** Cen. and S. America. (CI/HK)
83	*Vampyrus spectrum.*	**Linnaeus' False Vampire.** Cen. and S. America. (CI/HK)

Subfamily GLOSSOPHAGINAE.

84	*Glossophaga* (2 species).	**Long-tongued Bats.** Cen. and S. America, W. Indies. (CI/HK)
85	*Lonchophylla* (5 species).	**Long-tongued Bats.** Cen. and S. America. (CI/HK)
86	*Monophyllus* (7 species).	**Long-tongued Bats.** W. Indies. (HK)
87	*Anoura* (2 species).	**Tailless Bats.** Cen. and S. America. (CI/HK)
88	*Platalina genovensium.*	S. America. (CI)
89	*Scleronycteris ega.*	S. America. (CI)
90	*Lionycteris spurrelli.*	S. America. (CI)
91	*Choeroniscus* (4 species).	**Long-tongued Bats.** Cen. and S. America. (CI/HK)
92	*Choeronycteris mexicana.*	**Mexican Long-tongued Bat.** Cen. America. (HK)
93	*Hylonycteris underwoodi.*	**Underwood's Long-tongued Bat.** Cen. America. (HK)
94	*Leptonycteris nivalis.*	**Long-nosed Bat.** S. of N. America and Cen. America. (HK)
95	*Lichonycteris* (2 species).	**Long-nosed Bats.** Cen. and S. America. (CI/HK)
96	*Musonycteris harrisoni.*	**Banana Bat.** Cen. America. (SM)

Subfamily CAROLLIINAE.

97	*Carollia* (3 species).	**Short-tailed Bats.** Cen. and S. America. (CI/HK)
98	*Rhinophylla pumilio.*	S. America. (CI)

Subfamily STURNIRINAE.

99	*Corvira bidens.*	S. America. (CI)
100	*Sturnira* (3 species).	**Yellow-shouldered Bats.** Cen. and S. America, W. Indies. (CI/HK/GG)
101	*Sturnirops mordax.*	**Hairy-footed Bat.** Cen. America. (HK)

Subfamily STENODERMINAE.

102	*Brachyphylla* (4 species).	**West Indian Fruit-eating Bats.** W. Indies. (HK)
103	*Uroderma bilobatum.*	**Tent-making Bat.** Cen. and S. America. (CI/HK)
104	*Vampyrops* (9 species).	**Broad-nosed Bats.** Cen. and S. America. (CI/HK)
105	*Vampyrodes* (2 species).	**Great Stripe-faced Bats.** Cen. and S. America. (CI/HK)
106	*Vampyriscus bidens.*	S. America. (CI)
107	*Vampyressa* (5 species).	**Yellow-eared Bats.** Cen. and S. America. (CI/HK)
108	*Chiroderma* (6 species).	**White-lined Bats.** Cen. and S. America and W. Indies. (CI/HK/GG)
109	*Mesophylla macconelli.*	S. America. (CI)

110	*Ectophylla alba.*	**Honduran White Bat.** Cen. America. (HK)
111	*Artibeus* (7 species).	**American Fruit-eating Bats.** Cen. and S. America and W. Indies. (CI/HK)
112	*Enchisthenes harti.*	**Little Fruit-eating Bat.** Cen. and S. America. (CI/HK)
113	*Ardops* (4 species).	**Antillean Tree Bats.** Lesser Antillean Islands. (HK)
114	*Phyllops* (2 species).	**Fig-eating Bats.** W. Indies. (HK)
115	*Ariteus flavescens.*	**Jamaican Fig-eating Bat.** Jamaica. (HK)
116	*Stenoderma rufum.*	**Red Fig-eating Bat.** Cen. America. (HK)
117	*Pygoderma bilabiatum.*	**Ipanema Bat.** Cen. and S. America. (CI/HK)
118	*Centurio senex.*	**Wrinkle-faced Bat.** Cen. America. (HK)
119	*Sphaeronycteris toxophyllum.*	S. America. (CI)
120	*Ametrida* (2 species).	S. America. (CI)

Subfamily PHYLLONYCTERINAE. Flower Bats.

| 121 | *Phyllonycteris* (4 species). | **Flower Bats.** W. Indies. (HK) |
| 122 | *Erophylla* (2 species). | **Flower Bats.** W. Indies. (HK) |

Family DESMODONTIDAE. True Vampires.

123 ►	*Desmodus rotundus.*	**Vampire Bat.** Cen. and S. America. (CI/HK)
124	*Diaemus youngi.*	**White-winged Vampire Bat.** S. America. (CI)
125	*Diphylla ecaudata.*	**Hairy-legged Vampire Bat.** Cen. and S. America. (CI/HK)

Superfamily VESPERTILIONOIDEA.
Family NATALIDAE.

| 126 | *Natalus* (11 species). | **Funnel-eared Bats.** Cen. and S. America and W. Indies. (CI/HK) |

Family FURIPTERIDAE.

| 127 | *Furipterus horrens.* | **Smoky Bat.** S. America. (CI) |
| 128 | *Amorphochilus schnablii.* | S. America. (CI) |

Family THYROPTERIDAE.

| 129 | *Thyroptera* (2 species). | **Disc-winged Bats.** Cen. and S. America. (CI/HK) |

Family MYZOPODIDAE.

| 130 | *Myzopoda aurita.* | **Golden Bat.** Madagascar. (A) |

Family VESPERTILIONIDAE.
Subfamily VESPERTILIONINAE.

131	*Myotis* (71 species).	**Common Bats.** World-wide. (EM/EMH/A/CH/LH/TAY/ HK/CI)
132	*Pizonyx vivesi.*	**American Fish-eating Bat.** W. of N. America. (HK)
133	*Lasionycteris noctivagans.*	**Silver-haired Bat.** N. America. (HK)

95

| 134 | *Pipistrellus* (50 species). | **Pipistrelles.** N. and Cen. America, Europe, Africa, Asia, Australia, New Guinea, Celebes, Java, Borneo, Sumatra, Philippines and near-by Islands. (HK/EM/EMH/A/CH/TAY/LH/IT) |

134   *Pipistrellus* (50 species).   **Pipistrelles.** N. and Cen. America, Europe, Africa, Asia, Australia, New Guinea, Celebes, Java, Borneo, Sumatra, Philippines and near-by Islands. (HK/EM/EMH/A/CH/TAY/LH/IT)

135   *Glischropus* (3 species).   **Thick-thumbed Pipistrelles.** S. Asia, Java, Sumatra, Borneo, Philippines, Australia, Tasmania. (EM/LH/IT/CH/TAY)

136   *Nyctalus* (6 species).   **Noctules.** Africa, Europe, Asia, Sumatra, Borneo, Philippines. (EM/EMH/CH/TAY)

137   *Eudiscopus denticulus.*   **Disc-footed Bat.** S. Asia and Philippines. (EM/CON)

138   *Eptesicus* (47 species).   **Big Brown Bats.** N. and S. America, W. Indies, Europe, Asia, Africa, Madagascar. (EM/EMH/A/CH/HK/CI)

139   *Hesperoptenus* (4 species).   **False Serotines.** S. Asia, Borneo. (EM/CH)

140   *Tylonycteris* (3 species).   **Club-footed Bats.** S. Asia, Sumatra, Java, Borneo, Philippines, Celebes. (EM/CH/LH/TAY)

141   *Mimetillus moloneyi.*   **Moloney's Flat-headed Bat.** Africa. (EMH/A)

142   *Philetor rohui.*   New Guinea. (LH)

143   *Histiotus* (4 species).   **Big-eared Brown Bats.** S. America. (CI)

144   *Laephotis wintoni.*   **De Winton's Long-eared Bat.** E. Africa. (EMH/A)

145   *Vespertilio* (2 species).   **Particoloured Bats.** Europe and Asia. (EM)

146   *Otonycteris hemprichi.*   **Hemprich's Long-eared Bat.** S.W. Asia and N. Africa. (EM)

147   *Nycticeius* (15 species).   **Evening Bats.** S.E. of N. America, W. Indies, S. Asia, New Guinea, Australia, Africa. (HK/EM/EMH/A/LH/IT)

148   *Scotomanes ornatus.*   **Harlequin Bat** S. Asia. (EM)

149   *Rhogeëssa* (4 species).   **Little Yellow Bats.** Cen. and S. America. (HK/CI/GG)

150   *Baeodon alleni.*   **Allen's Baeodon.** Cen. America. (HK)

151   *Scotophilus* (10 species).   **Old World Yellow Bats.** Africa, Madagascar, S. Asia, Java, Borneo, Philippines, Celebes. (EM/EMH/A/LH/CH/TAY)

152   *Chalinolobus* (5 species).   **Lobe-lipped Bats.** New Guinea, Australia, New Zealand. (LH/IT/HU)

153   *Glauconycteris* (7 species).   **Butterfly Bats.** Africa. (EMH/A)

154   *Lasiurus* (7 species).   **Hairy-tailed Bats.** N. and S. America, W. Indies, Galapagos. (HK/CI)

155   *Dasypterus* (4 species).   **New World Yellow Bats.** N. and S. America, W. Indies. (HK/CI)

156   *Barbastella* (2 species).   **Barbastelles.** Europe, Asia, N.E. Africa. (EM/A)

157   *Plecotus auritus.*   **Long-eared Bat.** Europe, Asia, N. Africa. (EM/A)

158   *Corynorhinus* (2 species).   **Big-eared Bats.** N. America. (HK)

159   *Idionycteris phyllotis.*   **Allen's Big-eared Bat.** S.E. of N. America. (HK)

160   *Euderma maculata.*   **Spotted Bat.** W. of N. America. (HK)

Subfamily MINIOPTERINAE.

161   *Miniopterus* (18 species).   **Long-winged Bats.** Africa, Madagascar, S. Europe, S. Asia, Sumatra, Java, Borneo, Philippines, Celebes, New Guinea, Australia. (EM/EMH/A/CH/LH/TAY/SA/IT)

Subfamily MURININAE.

162   *Murina* (9 species).   **Tube-nosed Bats.** Asia, Philippines, Borneo, Java, Sumatra and near-by islands. (EM/LH/TAY/CH)

163   *Harpiocephalus harpia.*   **Hairy-winged Bat.** S. Asia, Java, Sumatra. (EM/LH/CH)

96

Subfamily KERIVOULINAE.

164   *Kerivoula* (26 species).   **Painted Bats.** S. Asia, Sumatra, Java, Borneo, Philippines, Celebes, New Guinea, Africa. (EM/LH/CH/TAY/EMH/A)

165   *Anamygdon solomonis.*   Solomons. (LH)

Subfamily NYCTOPHILINAE.

166   *Antrozous* (2 species).   **Pale Bats.** W. of N. America. (HK)
167   *Nyctophilus* (7 species).   **Australasian Big-eared Bats.** Australia, New Guinea, Tasmania. (LH/IT)

168   *Pharotis imogene.*   **Papuan Big-eared Bat.** New Guinea. (LH)

Subfamily TOMOPEATINAE.

169   *Tomopeas ravus.*   S. America. (CI)

Family MYSTACINIDAE.

170   *Mystacina tuberculata.*   **New Zealand Short-tailed Bat.** New Zealand. (HU)

Family MOLOSSIDAE.

171   *Eomops* (3 species).   Cen. Africa. (A)
172   *Molossops* (7 species).   **Dog-faced Bats.** Cen. and S. America. (CI/HK/GG)
173 ►*Cheiromeles* (2 species).   **Hairless Bats.** S. Asia, Sumatra, Java, Borneo, Philippines, Celebes. (LH/CH/TAY)

174   *Xiphonycteris spurrelli.*   **Spurrell's Free-tailed Bat.** W. Africa. (A)
175   *Tadarida* (74 species).   **Free-tailed Bats.** World-wide, excluding polar regions. (HK/CI/EM/EMH/A/CH/LH/TAY/IT)

176   *Platymops* (3 species).   **Flat-headed Free-tailed Bats.** Africa. (EMH/A/DLH)
177   *Otomops* (5 species).   **Big-eared Free-tailed Bats.** Africa, S. Asia, Java, New Guinea, Celebes. (EMH/A/EM/LH/CH)

178   *Molossus* (11 species).   **Velvety Free-tailed Bats.** Cen. and S. America, W. Indies. (HK/CI/GG)

179   *Promops* (5 species).   **Dome-palate Mastiff Bats.** Cen. and S. America. (HK/CI)

180   *Eumops* (8 species).   **Mastiff Bats.** N. and S. America, W. Indies. (HK/CI)

97

GREATER INDIAN FRUIT BAT

Pteropus giganteus

(Southern Asia)

The Fruit Bats, or members of the suborder Megachiroptera, differ from the Insect-ivorous Bats in being far less specialized for nocturnal life in the air. Most species possess a free claw extending from the second finger in addition to the claw usually present on the thumb. There are other striking differences. Fruit Bats have smooth ears like those of non-flying mammals and do not develop the nasal processes found in many insect-eating bats. Their tails are very small, or absent.

As their name implies, most of these bats are fruit-eaters. Their molar teeth have become flattened in connection with this habit and all are resident in the tropical regions where fruit is always abundant. They roost either in caves or in colonies in any suitably large tree. The eyes of these bats are large and functional, and most are completely helpless if blindfolded. Only the "tomb bats" belonging to the genus *Rousettus* are capable of flying in the complete dark; they produce an audible clicking sound when doing so.

The largest bats of this group are the Flying Foxes of the Pacific region which may have a wing-span of up to 5 feet in length. One-third of all the Fruit Bat species belong to the genus *Pteropus*. Bare-backed Fruit Bats of the genus *Dobsonia* are also resident in the Pacific area. These are peculiar in that the wing membranes are joined right across the back and attached to the back bone by an upright flange. The most odd-looking member of the group is the Hammer-headed Bat, *Hypsignathus*, of the African Tropics which has an almost horse-like head.

The bat illustrated is the largest living species in the world. The photograph shows a female with a young bat clinging tightly to her body.

Family PTEROPIDAE
BUTTIKOFER'S EPAULETTED FRUIT BAT
Epomops buttikoferi
(Tropical West Africa)

The photograph above shows very clearly the arrangement of the bones of the fore-limbs of bats. Pointing downward, and free of the wing membrane for much of their length, are the sharply hooked thumbs. Next to these, the four elongated fingers radiate, supporting the naked skin of the flying membrane. The first finger points slightly downward, the second finger runs the full length to the wing-tip, and the third and fourth fingers point upward, ending on the trailing edge of the wings. The feet have five short, clawed toes of approximately equal length. This is the basic limb design that is common to all bats, although there is, of course, a considerable amount of variation with regard to the smaller details.

The Epauletted Bats, like many of the fruit bats, have no tails. They have long noses and powerful, muscular lips that are useful when squeezing the juices from the soft fruits on which they feed. The epaulets themselves are strange tufts of yellowish-white hairs that protrude from pouches on the sides of the neck. They are only present in the males. Their function is unknown, although it is reasonable to suppose that they are connected in some way with either courtship or aggressive behaviour. In both sexes there are conspicuous tufts of white hairs at the corners of the ears. One of these is visible in the above photograph.

Buttikofer's Epauletted Fruit Bat is found in Liberia and Sierra Leone. There are two other species in this genus: Franquet's Fruit Bat (*E. franqueti*) from Angola, Rhodesia, Tanganyika and westward to Nigeria; and Dobson's Fruit Bat (*E. dobsoni*) from Angola and the Congo.

STRAW-COLOURED FRUIT BAT

Eidolon helvum

(Africa)

The Straw-coloured Fruit Bat is found over a large part of the African continent. A seasonally nomadic species, it moves about in vast flocks of as many as 1,000 individuals, searching for suitable feeding sites. When it finds an area where soft, ripe fruits are plentiful it descends and gorges itself, clambering through the branches and noisily gulping huge mouthfuls. Much of the fleshy pulp of the fruit is rejected after it has been squeezed dry. The juices are swallowed and then the pips, seeds and pulp are dropped from the mouth in the form of a small pellet. Wild figs, guavas and bananas are the favourite foods of this species, but it also takes ripe dates and many other fruits. It sometimes gnaws into the stems of soft wood, apparently in search of sap to supplement the diet.

During feeding and roosting there is a great deal of shrieking and squabbling, with

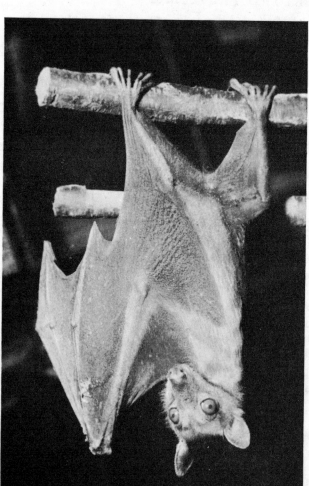

individual bats flying off from a dense group every so often and then returning to find a new hanging position. The roosts are sometimes temporary, but in the less nomadic situations, where food is plentiful all the year round, there may be permanent dormitory sites, rather like starling roosts. At one place in the Cameroons an *Eidolon* dormitory that has been used for generations now has a population of 10,000 bats.

Fruit bats are sometimes seen for sale as food in the African markets, but they are not popular.

There are three species of *Eidolon*, the common one shown here and two rarer ones from southern Arabia (*E. sabaeum*) and Madagascar (*E. dupreanum*).

LARGER RAT-TAILED BAT

Rhinopoma microphyllum

(North-east Africa and South-west Asia)

This species, also known as the Long-tailed or Mouse-tailed Bat, is found in Egypt, Arabia and Persia. There are three other species of *Rhinopoma*: *R. kinneari*, the Larger Indian Rat-tailed Bat; *R. hardwickei*, the Lesser Rat-tailed Bat from Egypt and the Sudan, through Arabia to south-east Asia; and *R. sumatrae*, the Sumatran Rat-tailed Bat. These are the only four species in the family. They differ from all other insectivorous bats in that they have retained two joints in the index finger in the wing; also in that they have a long, rodent-like tail, the length of which is accentuated by the brevity of the membrane between the hind legs.

The face is almost hairless. The nostrils are unusual, appearing as transverse slits. On the body, the fur is extremely short and the posterior region of the back is naked and finely wrinkled. They are reputed to build up a store of fat in the rump area, as a reserve to be used in periods of starvation.

Rat-tailed Bats inhabit caves, rock crevices and buildings, where they usually cling by all four limbs, instead of hanging by their hind feet. They are particularly fond of deserted ruins and tombs, and prefer desert or semi-desert conditions. They live, for example, in many of the crevices and recesses of the Great Pyramids. In fact, the earliest reference we have to this species of bat appears in the works of the French naturalist Pierre Belon who, in 1547, journeyed to Egypt where, in the tombs, he found and recorded "a bat with a tail like a mouse".

E 59

GREATER HORSESHOE BAT

Rhinolophus ferrumequinum

(Europe, Asia and North Africa)

The Greater Horseshoe Bat is so named because of the peculiar fleshy outgrowth surrounding the nostrils. This structure is a sort of megaphone which functions in concentrating the supersonic sounds that are emitted through the nostrils when navigating by "echo-location". Other species which lack this nose-leaf emit sounds through their mouths. Like nearly all bats belonging to the suborder Microchiroptera, the Greater Horseshoe species has large ears. These collect the echoes of the emitted high-frequency sounds as they bounce back from objects in the vicinity.

The Greater Horseshoe Bat has a wing span of 14 inches. It sleeps in colonies in caves, hollow trees and old buildings. When feeding, it often takes its prey from the ground, swooping along only inches above the surface. It is fond of beetles and sometimes takes the larger species back to the roost and eats them there. Hibernation takes place in caves from October until March. Mating occurs during the summer, but fertilization is delayed until the following spring, the sperm being stored by the female throughout the winter. The young cling to their mother's fur and she carries them out on her hunting flights every evening until they are too heavy to support.

As the photograph shows, the legend about bats becoming entangled in women's hair is not confirmed by experiment with an adult Greater Horseshoe Bat. It has, however, been suggested that a very young bat, losing its grip on its mother's body and falling from the rafters of an old cottage, might well attempt to re-attach itself to a warm, hairy object such as a human head. This could lead to entanglement in long hair.

102

VAMPIRE BAT

Desmodus rotundus

(South and Central America)

The Vampires are the most specialized of the microchiropteran bats. There are only three living species, all confined to the tropical areas of South and Central America. All three species are unable to eat anything but blood which they obtain by biting larger mammals and perhaps large birds, such as pelicans.

The Vampire does not hover to take its food, but alights gently on or near the sleeping animal and stalks to the feeding position using a quadrupedal gait with the body well elevated from the surface. The incisors of the Vampire are specially adapted for lancing and inducing a flow of blood which is not sucked, but is lapped up by the long, narrow tongue. Coagulation of blood in the wound is prevented by a special chemical in the bat's saliva.

The bite of the Vampire is said to be so carefully inflicted as not to wake a sleeping man. One bat cannot take enough blood from an animal the size of a goat to do it any harm from loss of blood alone, but the most serious danger is from diseases such as horse-fever and rabies which the Vampire is known to transmit.

Most bats are difficult to keep in captivity, but the Vampire is easy to feed and has even been known to breed in the laboratory. The average life span is probably about 10 years.

Vampires emit several audible cries of fairly long duration, but their high-frequency sounds, if any exist, have proved almost impossible to record.

103

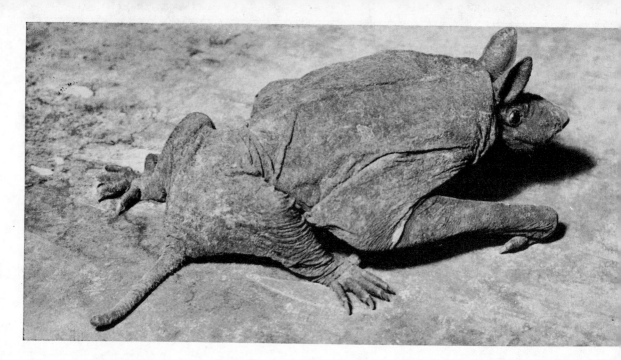

E 173   Family MOLOSSIDAE

NAKED BAT

Cheiromeles torquatus

(Malaya, Sumatra, Java, Borneo and the Philippines)

The Naked Bat, also known as the Hairless Bat or the Naked Bulldog Bat, is one of the weirdest looking mammals alive today. It is insectivorous and usually makes its roosts in hollow trees. There are two species—the one shown above and the Celebes Naked Bat (*C. parvidens*).

Its odour is as striking as its appearance, resembling an intense version of unwashed humanity. If the animal is held firmly in the hand and its strange glandular neck-pouch is pulled open with the fingers, the stench becomes almost overpowering. The exact function of this pouch in the natural life of the bat remains unknown at the present time, but it is interesting that its structure differs in the male and the female. In the former the neck glands discharge their oily secretions into it via a series of small pores collected into two circular, elevated patches. In the female the glands discharge through a single, large orifice.

There are two further pouches, one on each flank, between the wing and the side of the body. At the front end of these side pouches, in the female, the nipples are situated. It has been claimed that these are nursing pouches, and that in them the young bats are safely carried when the parent is in flight. In this way the Naked Bat could compensate for the absence of a furry coat to which the young can cling, but it is strange that the male also possesses these side pouches. A more likely explanation is that they are simply cavities to receive the adult's own wing extremities when it is not in flight.

104

F. PRIMATES

There are 193 species of living primates, of which 70 are found in the tropical regions of South and Central America and 123 in Africa and southern Asia.

Primates evolved from ancient insectivore stock, the basic trend being towards a more active, diurnal, arboreal existence, with the emphasis on sight rather than smell, on grasping hands and feet with flat nails rather than claws, and on an omnivorous, fruit-rich diet rather than an exclusively insectivorous one. The tree-shrews surviving today are interesting intermediate forms, bridging the gap between the insectivores and the primates. They have characters that relate them to both and have often been placed with the insectivores. At present, however, it is customary to consider them as primates, this decision being based on certain brain and skeletal similarities.

The less advanced primates include the lemurs of Madagascar, the bushbabies of Africa and the lorises and tarsiers of southern Asia. These, along with the tree-shrews, are referred to collectively as the prosimians. They comprise 53 species.

The more advanced primates are referred to as the anthropoids and include 70 species of New World monkeys, 58 species of Old World monkeys, 11 species of great apes, and man himself, a total of 140 species. The anthropoids have flatter, more expressive faces and better brains than the prosimians. They are almost entirely day-active animals, the only real exception being the South American Douroucouli (*Aotus*). Amongst the prosimians, on the other hand, a number of the lemurs, as well as the lorisids and tarsiers are primarily nocturnal.

The New World monkeys (cebids) are all forest-dwelling creatures, as are most of the Old World monkeys (cercopithecids). Some of the latter, however, such as certain macaques and the baboons, have partially or largely abandoned the trees and have become modified for life on the grassy plains, or amongst the rocks. Like man, they have lost many of their arboreal specializations and have developed new, secondary, ground-living adaptations.

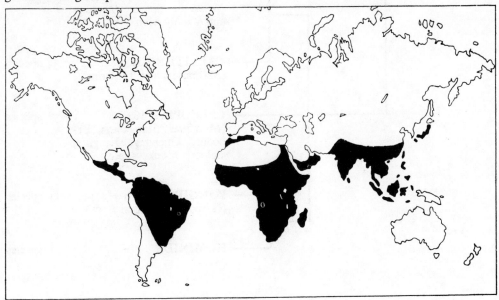

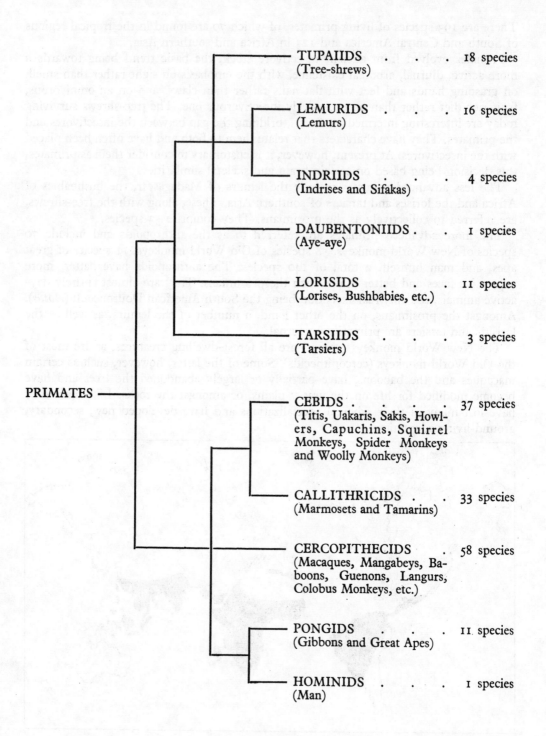

TUPAIIDS . . . 18 species
(Tree-shrews)

LEMURIDS . . 16 species
(Lemurs)

INDRIIDS . . . 4 species
(Indrises and Sifakas)

DAUBENTONIIDS . . . 1 species
(Aye-aye)

LORISIDS . . 11 species
(Lorises, Bushbabies, etc.)

TARSIIDS . . . 3 species
(Tarsiers)

PRIMATES

CEBIDS . . . 37 species
(Titis, Uakaris, Sakis, Howlers, Capuchins, Squirrel
Monkeys, Spider Monkeys
and Woolly Monkeys)

CALLITHRICIDS . . 33 species
(Marmosets and Tamarins)

CERCOPITHECIDS . . 58 species
(Macaques, Mangabeys, Ba-
boons, Guenons, Langurs,
Colobus Monkeys, etc.)

PONGIDS . . . 11. species
(Gibbons and Great Apes)

HOMINIDS . . . 1 species
(Man)

F. Order PRIMATES.

    Suborder PROSIMII. Prosimians.

        Infraorder LEMURIFORMES.

            Superfamily TUPAIOIDEA.

                Family TUPAIIDAE. Tree-shrews.

                    Subfamily TUPAIINAE.

1 ►	*Tupaia glis.*	**Common Tree-shrew.**	S. Asia, Sumatra, Java, Borneo. (EM)
2	*Tupaia splendidula.*	**Red-tailed Tree-shrew.**	Borneo. (CH)
3	*Tupaia carimatae.*	**Karimata Tree-shrew.**	Borneo. (CH)
4	*Tupaia mulleri.*	**Müller's Tree-shrew.**	Borneo. (CH)
5	*Tupaia montana.*	**Mountain Tree-shrew.**	Borneo. (CH)
6	*Tupaia javanica.*	**Small Tree-shrew.**	Java and Sumatra. (CH)
7	*Tupaia nicobarica.*	**Nicobar Tree-shrew.**	Nicobar Islands (Indian Ocean). (EM)
8	*Tupaia minor.*	**Günther's Tree-shrew.**	S. Asia, Borneo, Sumatra. (EM)
9	*Tupaia gracilis.*	**Slender Tree-shrew.**	Borneo. (CH)
10	*Tupaia picta.*	**Painted Tree-shrew.**	Borneo. (CH)
11	*Tupaia dorsalis.*	**Striped Tree-shrew.**	Borneo. (CH)
12	*Tupaia tana.*	**Large Tree-shrew.**	Sumatra and Borneo. (CH)
13	*Tupaia palawanensis.*	**Palawan Tree-shrew.**	Philippines. (TAY)
14	*Anathana ellioti.*	**Madras Tree-shrew.**	S. Asia. (EM)
15	*Dendrogale melanura.*	**Southern Smooth-tailed Tree-shrew.**	Borneo. (CH)
16	*Dendrogale murina.*	**Northern Smooth-tailed Tree-shrew.**	S. Asia. (EM)
17	*Urogale everetti.*	**Philippines Tree-shrew.**	Philippines. (TAY)

                    Subfamily PTILOCERCINAE.

18	*Ptilocercus lowi.*	**Pen-tailed Tree-shrew.**	S. Asia, Borneo, Sumatra. (CH)

            Superfamily LEMUROIDEA.

                Family LEMURIDAE. Lemurs.

                    Subfamily LEMURINAE.

19	*Hapalemur griseus.*	**Grey Gentle Lemur.**	Madagascar. (OI)
20	*Hapalemur simus.*	**Broad-nosed Gentle Lemur.**	Madagascar. (OI)
21 ►	*Lemur catta.*	**Ring-tailed Lemur.**	Madagascar. (OI)
22 ►	*Lemur variegatus.*	**Ruffed Lemur.**	Madagascar. (OI)
23	*Lemur macaco.*	**Black Lemur.**	Madagascar. (OI)
24 ►	*Lemur fulvus.*	**Brown Lemur.**	Madagascar. (OI)
25	*Lemur mongoz.*	**Mongoose Lemur.**	Madagascar. (OI)
26	*Lemur rubriventer.*	**Red-bellied Lemur.**	Madagascar. (OI)
27	*Lepilemur mustelinus.*	**Weasel Lemur.**	Madagascar. (OI)
28	*Lepilemur ruficaudatus.*	**Sportive Lemur.**	Madagascar. (OI)

                    Subfamily CHEIROGALEINAE. Dwarf Lemurs.

29	*Cheirogaleus trichotis.*	**Hairy-eared Dwarf Lemur.**	Madagascar. (OI)
30	*Cheirogaleus major.*	**Greater Dwarf Lemur.**	Madagascar. (OI)
31	*Cheirogaleus medius.*	**Fat-tailed Lemur.**	Madagascar. (OI)

107

32 ►*Microcebus murinus.*	**Lesser Mouse Lemur.** Madagascar. (O1)
33 *Microcebus coquereli.*	**Coquerel's Mouse Lemur.** Madagascar. (O1)
34 *Phaner furcifer.*	**Fork-marked Mouse Lemur.** Madagascar. (O1)

Family INDRIIDAE.

35 *Avahi laniger.*	**Woolly Indris.** Madagascar. (O1)
36 *Propithecus diadema.*	**Diademed Sifaka.** Madagascar. (O1)
37 ►*Propithecus verreauxi.*	**Verreaux's Sifaka.** Madagascar. (O1)
38 ►*Indri indri.*	**Indris.** Madagascar. (O1)

Superfamily DAUBENTONIOIDEA.
Family DAUBENTONIIDAE.

39 ►*Daubentonia madagascariensis.* **Aye-aye.** Madagascar. (O1)

Infraorder LORISIFORMES.
Family LORISIDAE.
Subfamily LORISINAE.

40 ►*Loris tardigradus.*	**Slender Loris.** S. Asia. (EM)
41 ►*Nycticebus coucang.*	**Slow Loris.** S. Asia, Sumatra, Java, Borneo. (EM)
42 *Nycticebus pygmaeus.*	**Lesser Slow Loris.** S. Asia. (EM)
43 ►*Arctocebus calabarensis.*	**Angwantibo.** Cen. W. Africa. (O1)
44 ►*Perodicticus potto.*	**Potto.** Cen. Africa. (O1)

Subfamily GALAGINAE. Bushbabies.

45 ►*Galago crassicaudatus.*	**Thick-tailed Bushbaby.** Africa. (EMH)
46 *Galago senegalensis.*	**Senegal Bushbaby.** Africa. (EMH)
47 *Galago alleni.*	**Allen's Bushbaby.** Cen. W. Africa. (O1)
48 *Galago demidovi.*	**Demidoff's Bushbaby.** Cen. Africa. (EMH)
49 *Euoticus elegantulus.*	**Needle-clawed Bushbaby.** Cen. W. Africa. (O1)
50 *Euoticus inustus.*	**Eastern Needle-clawed Bushbaby** Cen. Africa. (O1)

Infraorder TARSIIFORMES. Tarsiers.
Family TARSIIDAE.

51 ►*Tarsius syrichta.*	**Philippine Tarsier.** Philippines. (O2)
52 *Tarsius bancanus.*	**Western Tarsier.** Sumatra and Borneo. (O2)
53 *Tarsius spectrum.*	**Eastern Tarsier.** Celebes. (LH)

Suborder ANTHROPOIDEA.
Superfamily CEBOIDEA.
Family CEBIDAE. New World Monkeys.
Subfamily AOTINAE.

54 ►*Aotus trivirgatus.*	**Douroucouli.** Cen. and S. America. (O4/HK/C1)
55 *Callicebus torquatus.*	**Collared Titi.** S. America. (O4)
56 ►*Callicebus cupreus.*	**Red Titi.** S. America. (O4)

57	*Callicebus brunneus.*	**Brown Titi.** S. America. (O4/C1)
58	*Callicebus moloch.*	**Orabussu Titi.** S. America. (O4)
59	*Callicebus cinerascens.*	**Ashy Titi.** S. America. (O4)
60	*Callicebus melanochir.*	**Grey Titi.** S. America. (O4/C1)
61	*Callicebus personatus.*	**Masked Titi.** S. America. (O4/C1)
62	*Callicebus nigrifrons.*	**Black-fronted Titi.** S. America. (O4/C1)

Subfamily PITHECIINAE.

63	*Cacajao calvus.*	**Bald Uakari.** S. America. (O4)
64 ►	*Cacajao rubicundus.*	**Red Uakari.** S. America. (O4)
65	*Cacajao melanocephalus.*	**Black-headed Uakari.** S. America. (O4)
66 ►	*Pithecia monachus.*	**Hairy Saki.** S. America. (O4)
67	*Pithecia pithecia.*	**Pale-headed Saki.** S. America. (O4)
68	*Chiropotes satanas.*	**Black Saki.** S. America. (O4/C1)
69	*Chiropotes albinasus.*	**White-nosed Saki.** S. America. (O4/C1)

Subfamily ALOUATTINAE.   Howler Monkeys.

70	*Alouatta villosa.*	**Guatemalan Howler** Cen. America. (O5/HK)
71	*Alouatta palliata.*	**Mantled Howler.** Cen. and S. America. (O5)
72 ►	*Alouatta seniculus.*	**Red Howler.** S. America. (O5)
73	*Alouatta guariba.*	**Brown Howler.** S. America. (O5)
74	*Alouatta belzebul.*	**Rufous-handed Howler.** S. America. (O5)
75	*Alouatta caraya.*	**Black Howler.** S. America. (O5)

Subfamily CEBINAE.

76	*Cebus capucinus.*	**White-throated Capuchin.** Cen. and S. America. (O4/HK)
77	*Cebus nigrivittatus.*	**Weeper Capuchin.** S. America. (O4/C1)
78	*Cebus albifrons.*	**White-fronted Capuchin.** S. America. (O4)
79 ►	*Cebus apella.*	**Brown Capuchin.** S. America. (O4)
80	*Saimiri oerstedi.*	**Red-backed Squirrel Monkey.** Cen. America. (HK)
81 ►	*Saimiri sciureus.*	**Common Squirrel Monkey.** S. America. (O4/C1)

Subfamily ATELINAE.

82 ►	*Ateles geoffroyi.*	**Central American Spider Monkey.** Cen. and N. of S. America. (HK/C1)
83	*Ateles paniscus.*	**Black Spider Monkey.** S. America. (O5)
84	*Ateles belzebuth.*	**Long-haired Spider Monkey.** S. America. (O5)
85	*Ateles fusciceps.*	**Brown-headed Spider Monkey.** Cen. and S. America. (O5/HK)
86	*Brachyteles arachnoides.*	**Woolly Spider Monkey.** S. America. (O5)
87	*Lagothrix lagothricha.*	**Humboldt's Woolly Monkey.** S. America. (O5)
88 ►	*Lagothrix cana.*	**Smoky Woolly Monkey.** S. America. (O5)
89	*Lagothrix hendeei.*	**Hendee's Woolly Monkey.** S. America. (O5)

Subfamily CALLIMICONINAE.

| 90 | *Callimico goeldii.* | **Goeldi's Monkey.** S. America. (O3) |

Family CALLITHRICIDAE. Marmosets and Tamarins.

91	*Callithrix jacchus.*	**Common Marmoset.** S. America. (O3/C1)
92	*Callithrix flaviceps.*	**Buff-headed Marmoset.** S. America. (O3/C1)
93	*Callithrix chrysoleuca.*	**Yellow-legged Silky Marmoset.** S. America. (O3/C1)
94	*Callithrix santaremensis.*	**Santarem Marmoset.** S. America. (O3/C1)
95	►*Callithrix penicillata.*	**Black-pencilled Marmoset.** S. America. (O3/C1)
96	*Callithrix aurita.*	**White-eared Marmoset.** S. America. (O3/C1)
97	*Callithrix geoffroyi.*	**White-fronted Marmoset.** S. America. (O3/C1)
98	►*Callithrix argentata.*	**Silvery Marmoset.** S. America. (O3/C1)
99	►*Cebuella pygmaea.*	**Pygmy Marmoset.** S. America. (O3)
100	►*Leontideus rosalia.*	**Golden Lion Marmoset.** S. America. (O3/C1)
101	*Leontideus chrysomelas.*	**Golden-headed Tamarin.** S. America. (O3/C1)
102	*Leontideus chrysopygus.*	**Golden-rumped Tamarin.** S. America. (O3/C1)
103	*Leontocebus oedipus.*	**Cotton-headed Tamarin.** S. America. (O3/C1)
104	*Leontocebus geoffroyi.*	**Geoffroy's Tamarin.** Cen. and S. America. (O3/C1/HK)
105	*Leontocebus bicolor.*	**Pied Tamarin.** S. America. (O3/C1)
106	*Leontocebus martinsi.*	**Martin's Tamarin.** S. America. (O3/C1)
107	*Leontocebus tamarin.*	**Negro Tamarin.** S. America. (O3/C1)
108	*Leontocebus midas.*	**Red-handed Tamarin.** S. America. (O3/C1)
109	*Leontocebus nigricollis.*	**Black-and-red Tamarin.** S. America. (O3/C1)
110	*Leontocebus weddelli.*	**Weddell's Tamarin.** S. America. (O3/C1)
111	*Leontocebus devillei.*	**Deville's Tamarin.** S. America. (C1)
112	*Leontocebus fuscicollis.*	**Brown-headed Tamarin.** S. America. (O3/C1)
113	*Leontocebus fuscus.*	**Brown Tamarin.** S. America. (C1)
114	*Leontocebus illigeri.*	**Red-mantled Tamarin.** S. America. (O3/C1)
115	*Leontocebus lagonotus.*	**Golden-mantled Tamarin.** S. America. (O3/C1)
116	*Leontocebus mystax.*	**Moustached Tamarin.** S. America. (O3/C1)
117	*Leontocebus pluto.*	**Lönnberg's Tamarin.** S. America. (O3/C1)
118	*Leontocebus graellsi.*	**Rio Napo Tamarin.** S. America. (O3/C1)
119	*Leontocebus pileatus.*	**Red-capped Tamarin.** S. America. (O3/C1)
120	*Leontocebus labiatus.*	**Red-bellied White-lipped Tamarin.** S. America. (O3/C1)
121	*Leontocebus imperator.*	**Emperor Tamarin.** S. America. (O3/C1)
122	*Leontocebus melanoleucus.*	**White Tamarin.** S. America. (O3/C1)
123	*Leontocebus leucopus.*	**White-footed Tamarin.** S. America. (O3/C1)

Superfamily CERCOPITHECOIDEA. Old World Monkeys.
Family CERCOPITHECIDAE.
Subfamily CERCOPITHECINAE.

124	*Macaca sinica.*	**Toque Monkey.** Ceylon. (EM)
125	*Macaca radiata.*	**Bonnet Monkey.** S. Asia. (EM)
126	►*Macaca silenus.*	**Lion-tailed Macaque.** S. Asia. (EM)
127	*Macaca nemestrina.*	**Pig-tailed Macaque.** S. Asia, Sumatra, Borneo. (EM)
128	*Macaca irus.*	**Crab-eating Macaque.** S. Asia, Sumatra, Java, Borneo, Philippines. (EM)
129	►*Macaca mulatta.*	**Rhesus Macaque.** S. Asia. (EM)
130	*Macaca assamensis.*	**Assamese Macaque.** S. Asia. (EM)
131	*Macaca cyclopis.*	**Formosan Macaque.** Formosa. (EM)
132	►*Macaca speciosa.*	**Stump-tailed Macaque.** S. Asia. (EM)
133	*Macaca fuscata.*	**Japanese Macaque.** Japan. (EM)
134	►*Macaca sylvana.*	**Barbary Ape.** N. Africa. (EM)

135	*Macaca maurus.*	**Moor Macaque.** Celebes. (LH)
136 ►	*Cynopithecus niger.*	**Black Ape.** Celebes. (LH)
137	*Cercocebus albigena.*	**Grey-cheeked Mangabey.** Cen. Africa. (A)
138	*Cercocebus aterrimus.*	**Black Mangabey.** Cen. Africa. (A)
139	*Cercocebus galeritus.*	**Agile Mangabey.** Cen. Africa. (A)
140 ►	*Cercocebus torquatus.*	**Sooty Mangabey.** Cen. W. Africa. (A)
141 ►	*Papio hamadryas.*	**Hamadryas Baboon.** N.E. Africa and S.W. Asia. (EM)
142	*Papio cynocephalus.*	**Yellow Baboon.** E. Africa. (EMH)
143	*Papio ursinus.*	**Chacma Baboon.** S. Africa. (EMH)
144	*Papio doguera.*	**Anubis Baboon.** Cen. Africa. (A)
145	*Papio papio.*	**Guinea Baboon.** W. Africa. (A)
146 ►	*Mandrillus sphinx.*	**Mandrill.** W. Africa. (A)
147 ►	*Mandrillus leucophaeus.*	**Drill.** W. Africa. (A)
148 ►	*Theropithecus gelada.*	**Gelada Baboon.** N.E. Africa. (A)
149 ►	*Cercopithecus aethiops.*	**Grass Monkey** (includes Vervet, Grivet and Green Monkey.) Africa. (EMH)
150	*Cercopithecus cephus.*	**Moustached Monkey.** Cen. W. Africa. (A)
151	*Cercopithecus diana.*	**Diana Monkey.** Cen. W. Africa. (A)
152	*Cercopithecus hamlyni.*	**Owl-faced Monkey.** Cen. Africa. (A)
153	*Cercopithecus l'hoesti.*	**L'hoest's Monkey.** Cen. Africa. (A)
154	*Cercopithecus mitis.*	**Diadem Monkey.** Africa. (EMH)
155 ►	*Cercopithecus mona.*	**Mona Monkey.** Cen. W. Africa. (A)
156 ►	*Cercopithecus neglectus.*	**De Brazza's Monkey.** Cen. Africa. (A)
157	*Cercopithecus nictitans.*	**White-nosed Monkey.** Africa. (EMH)
158 ►	*Cercopithecus talapoin.*	**Talapoin Monkey.** Cen. W. Africa. (EMH)
159	*Allenopithecus nigroviridis.*	**Allen's Monkey.** Cen. Africa. (A)
160 ►	*Erythrocebus patas.*	**Patas Monkey.** Africa. (A)

Subfamily COLOBINAE.

161	*Presbytis entellus.*	**Entellus Langur.** S. Asia. (EM)
162	*Presbytis senex.*	**Purple-faced Langur.** Ceylon. (EM)
163	*Presbytis johni.*	**John's Langur.** S. Asia. (EM)
164	*Presbytis melalophos.*	**Banded Leaf Monkey.** S. Asia, Sumatra, Borneo. (EM)
165	*Presbytis cristatus.*	**Silvered Leaf Monkey.** S. Asia, Sumatra, Java, Borneo. (EM)
166	*Presbytis pileatus.*	**Capped Langur.** S. Asia. (EM)
167	*Presbytis obscurus.*	**Dusky Leaf Monkey.** S. Asia. (EM)
168	*Presbytis phayrei.*	**Phayre's Leaf Monkey.** S. Asia. (EM)
169	*Presbytis francoisi.*	**François' Monkey.** S. Asia. (EM)
170	*Presbytis potenziani.*	**Mentawi Leaf Monkey.** Mentawi Islands (Sumatra). (CH)
171	*Presbytis aygula.*	**Sunda Island Leaf Monkey.** Java, Borneo, Sumatra. (CH)
172	*Presbytis rubicundus.*	**Maroon Leaf Monkey.** Borneo. (CH)
173	*Presbytis frontatus.*	**White-fronted Leaf Monkey.** Borneo. (CH)
174 ►	*Pygathrix nemaeus.*	**Douc Langur.** S. Asia. (EM)
175	*Rhinopithecus roxellanae.*	**Snub-nosed Monkey.** Asia. (EM)
176	*Rhinopithecus avunculus.*	**Tonkin Snub-nosed Monkey.** S. Asia. (EM)
177	*Simias concolor.*	**Pig-tailed Langur.** Mentawi Islands (Sumatra). (CH)
178 ►	*Nasalis larvatus.*	**Proboscis Monkey.** Borneo. (CH)
179 ►	*Colobus polykomos.*	**Black-and-white Colobus.** Africa. (A)
180	*Colobus badius.*	**Red Colobus.** Africa. (A)
181	*Colobus verus.*	**Green Colobus.** W. Africa. (OH)

III

Superfamily HOMINOIDEA.

Family PONGIDAE. Apes.

Subfamily HYLOBATINAE. Gibbons.

182 ►*Hylobates lar.*	**White-handed Gibbon.**	S. Asia and Sumatra. (EM)
183 *Hylobates agilis.*	**Dark-handed Gibbon.**	S. Asia and Sumatra. (CH)
184 *Hylobates hoolock.*	**Hoolock Gibbon.**	S. Asia. (EM)
185 *Hylobates concolor.*	**Black Gibbon.**	S. Asia. (EM)
186 *Hylobates moloch.*	**Grey Gibbon.**	Java and Borneo. (CH)
187 *Hylobates klossi.*	**Dwarf Gibbon.**	Mentawi Islands (Sumatra). (CH)
188 ►*Hylobates syndactylus.*	**Siamang.**	S. Asia and Sumatra. (EM)

Subfamily PONGINAE. Great Apes.

189 ►*Pongo pygmaeus.*	**Orang-Utan.**	Sumatra and Borneo. (CH)
190 ►*Pan troglodytes.*	**Chimpanzee.**	Cen. W. Africa. (A)
191 *Pan paniscus.*	**Pygmy Chimpanzee.**	Cen. W. Africa. (A)
192 ►*Gorilla gorilla.*	**Gorilla.**	Cen. W. Africa. (A)

Family HOMINIDAE. Men.

193 *Homo sapiens.*	**Man.**	World-wide. (A)

Family TUPAIIDAE

COMMON TREE-SHREW

Tupaia glis

(Southern Asia, Sumatra, Java, Borneo)

The Tree-Shrew is well named, for it is arboreal in habit, being a skilful climber, and yet in other ways it shows strong similarities to the shrews. The teeth, for example, bear the sharp cusps typical of the Insectivora. Nevertheless we now classify the animal in a different order, regarding it as one of the most primitive living primates. A Tree-Shrew probably looks very much like the primate ancestors which diverged from the insectivore stock many millions of years ago.

The total length of the animal is about 14 inches. It bears a superficial resemblance to a squirrel and has even evolved similar flicking and jerking movements of its long, bushy tail. It also sits up to eat like a squirrel, holding the food up in its front paws. Good vision is important in climbing and it has large eyes, whilst the thumbs and big toes are slightly opposable to the other digits so that a firm grip can be taken on small branches. It moves with great rapidity, not only when fleeing, but also during almost all other activities, giving the appearance of being in a constant state of agitation.

Each animal occupies a territory which it frequently defends against its own kind, squabbling shrilly. The Tree-Shrew is omnivorous, eating a wide variety of animal and plant foods. Little is known of the breeding habits, but one related species has a gestation period of 56 days. The female usually bears two young at a time.

Various sub-species of the Common Tree-Shrew are found in Thailand, Malaya, Java, Sumatra and Borneo, and seventeen related species occur from Assam to Indonesia.

RING-TAILED LEMUR

Lemur catta

(Madagascar)

The Ring-tailed Lemur is perhaps the best known of the ten species of typical lemurs. All these animals have foxy faces and long tails. They are gregarious, vocal and moderately intelligent. As day-active, tree-dwelling primates of a comparatively large size, they take the place of typical monkeys on the island of Madagascar.

The Ring-tailed Lemur is a quick-moving species with grey fur and a striking black and white tail. Unlike most lemurs it is not strictly arboreal, but lives amongst the rocks in the south of Madagascar. A great deal of social grooming takes place, the animals licking and cleaning each other's fur. The lower front teeth form a kind of comb which is employed during this activity. Although the lemurs have nails like other primates, the second toe is equipped with a claw used for scratching.

The Ring-tailed Lemur feeds largely on fruit, but it also eats insects and some birds' eggs.

The young (usually two but sometimes only one) are born in March and April. They cling tightly to the underside of the mother for the first 3 weeks and after this ride on her back. They are reared in communal nurseries, often being cared for by females other than their mothers.

When agitated, this species crouches in a posture similar to the one shown and runs its tail repeatedly through its arms. As it does this, it presses its wrists against the tail-fur. The wrists bear black scent-glands and this action spreads their secretions on to the tail. The latter then acts as a scent flag, signalling its owner's mood. There are further scent glands in the shoulder region.

114

RUFFED LEMUR

Lemur variegatus

(Madagascar)

The Ruffed Lemur is the largest of all the true lemurs of Madagascar. When fully grown it measures 4 feet from the tip of its nose to the end of its tail. As the illustration shows, the body is boldly marked with a black and white pattern, while the dark tail sometimes shows traces of the rings which are so much more prominent in the closely related Ring-tailed Lemur.

The Ruffed Lemur is becoming increasingly rare and is found only in the tall trees of the forests which fringe the northern coasts of the island. Once, considerable bands of these sociable, graceful mammals were to be found, but they are now in danger of extinction. When moving through the trees they rely, like other lemurs, on their elongated hind legs, progressing in a series of bounding leaps. The tail flows out behind, giving stability and assisting balance on landing.

There is some doubt concerning the function of the black and white markings. They may serve to break up the outline of the body, making it less conspicuous when the animal is motionless in the leafy shade, or as it sunbathes in the early morning and evening. At one time the natives of Madagascar believed the Ruffed Lemur to be sacred, saying that it prayed to the sun every morning.

The patterns on the fur vary considerably from one animal to another. In some specimens the lighter areas are bright reddish-brown instead of white. Individual variations of this sort are common in a number of the lemur species, but their significance is not yet understood.

BROWN LEMUR

Lemur fulvus

(Madagascar and the Comoro Islands)

Not all of the lemurs are as beautifully marked as the Ring-tailed and Ruffed species. The Brown Lemur, as its name suggests, has fur which is almost uniformly brown all over the body except for the face, which is almost black. This species was at one time quite commonly seen in zoological gardens, but the strict protection that it and the other lemurs are now given by the Malagasy authorities means that today it is seen in captivity much less frequently.

Surprisingly, very little is known of the habits of the Brown Lemur in the wild. It is exceedingly difficult to distinguish from some related species. The Mongoose Lemur, from the Comoro Islands and central Madagascar, is very similar, but lacks the black cheeks, while the Red-bellied Lemur, which is found all over Madagascar, is also brown, but with varying areas of a lighter hue. Dark specimens of the Brown Lemur can also be confused with yet another species, the Black Lemur, which despite its name is not always completely black.

All of the *Lemur* species are social and to a great extent diurnal. Their diet is composed largely of fruits and small animals. The lemurs that are dull in colour appear to make more use of vocalizations in communicating with each other than do their more distinctively marked relatives. Brown Lemurs, for example, can frequently be heard grunting rather like pigs.

Despite protection, lemurs of all types are becoming progressively rarer. At one time they were hunted for food—their flesh is said to taste something like rabbit—but nowadays the increasingly efficient agriculture of Madagascar is their greatest enemy.

LESSER MOUSE LEMUR

Microcebus murinus

(Madagascar)

The Lesser Mouse Lemur is the smallest living primate, being little bigger than a large mouse.

It is rather squirrel-like in its behaviour, jumping and climbing nimbly in the branches of trees or amongst lakeside reeds. There are folds of skin on either side of the body stretching between the elbows and knees, and through these run air sacs which also extend over the back and head. It is thought that these spaces may be inflated when the animal is leaping in the finer branches of the trees, so that it can glide.

The eyes are big and set close together and the membranous ears are large compared with those of most lemurs. This is characteristic of an animal which is both nocturnal and insectivorous. It also occasionally eats leaves and fruits.

Mouse Lemurs are extraordinary as primates in that they spend the dry season in a torpid state. This is known as aestivation and is analogous to the hibernation of animals living in cold climates. The animal rolls itself into a ball and sleeps in a nest of leaves and grass, or in a hollow tree. During the wet season, when food is plentiful, it stores fat in the body, particularly in the tail. Animals captured at this time are so much sturdier that they were once thought to belong to a different species. A special nest is made for the young. This is not unlike a bird's nest; two or three young are born in it at the beginning of the wet season.

The Mouse Lemurs are aggressive animals, uttering shrill whistling cries when they fight.

VERREAUX'S SIFAKA

Propithecus verreauxi

(Madagascar)

The Sifaka is a large, long-haired lemur which is found in the coastal forest belt of Madagascar. This animal is rather rare, but when it is seen is easily recognized by its striking black and white patterning and its long white tail.

The Sifakas and the Indrises are grouped together as Indrisoid Lemurs. They cling to the upright branches of trees, and jump from one upright to the next, gripping with their pincer-like back feet. When they are descending they climb down tail first and once on the ground they move by hopping, keeping the body upright and holding the arms out in front.

The Sifaka has a patagial membrane between the front and hind limbs on either side of the body and this enables the animal to make enormous gliding leaps between the trees.

It is diurnal and sociable, living in small groups of from six to eight. They are strictly herbivorous and eat mostly leaves and bark.

These animals will often rest during the day sitting propped in the crook of a branch with their tails curled between their legs and their hands on their knees in a very human attitude, or with the palms of their hands held out to the sun; this posture has given rise to the legend that they are sun-worshippers.

One young is produced at a time and is carried by the mother. At first it clings to her ventral fur, but later it clutches on to her back as she moves about in the trees.

The animal shown in the illustration was photographed in its natural habitat in south-west Madagascar.

118

INDRIS

Indri indri

(Eastern Madagascar)

The Indris is even more difficult to locate in the wild than the Sifaka. It lives in the high tree-tops of the mountain forests of eastern Madagascar in isolated localities.

It is a large lemur standing 3 feet high with long back legs and virtually no tail. These characteristics give it a rather humanoid appearance. Its face, however, is more like that of a dog and, as its voice is also dog-like, its native name is "dog of the forest".

The name Indris has a different origin, however, deriving from the Malagasy *Indri izy* meaning "There it is!", which the discoverer mistook for the local name.

The Indris is diurnal and lives singly or in small groups of up to five. One young is produced at a time. Like the Sifaka it is primarily a leaf eater.

The Indris has a very loud, far-carrying cry, due to the presence of a laryngeal air-sac. This cry, in addition to being considered dog-like, has also been likened to a human voice. Like the Sifaka, the Indris also sun-bathes, holding its arms up towards the sun, and is believed by the natives to be a sun-worshipper.

The animal is surrounded by legend. It was considered sacred by some tribes. No natives would hunt it as it was said to catch any spears directed at it, hurling them back with unerring aim. There is also a legend that the natives have caught and trained Indrises like dogs for hunting.

The unique photograph of an Indris shown below was taken in the animal's natural habitat by David Attenborough during a recent expedition.

AYE-AYE

Daubentonia madagascariensis

(Eastern Madagascar)

The Aye-aye is a rare, aberrant lemuroid. It has claw-like nails and teeth which are more like those of a rodent. There are two pairs of chisel-like incisors and no canines. When first captured it was thought to be some kind of squirrel, but its opposable thumbs and the presence of a nail on the big toe, as well as some details of the skull, proved it to be a primate.

The peculiar dentition is connected with the diet of the Aye-aye and the manner in which it obtains its food. It feeds on the pith of bamboo and sugar-cane and also certain insects, particularly on the larvae of wood-boring beetles. A very acute sense of hearing enables it to discover these larvae, both by listening for their movements and by tapping the wood with its long fingers and listening for the different timbre. Once located, the larvae are dug out with the very long skeleton-like middle finger, or gnawed out by the sharp incisors.

The Aye-aye is arboreal and nocturnal. It lives singly or in pairs in dense forests or bamboo thickets, sleeping by day in a hollow tree, or in a temporary, globular nest, with its tail wrapped round its body. The female produces one young in February or March in a special breeding nest which she constructs herself.

The large eyes, the bony fingers and the shaggy black hair give it an eerie appearance. This, and the fact that it is quite fearless of man and strikes out with its hands if annoyed, make it feared by the natives. To touch it is said to cause death.

SLENDER LORIS

Loris tardigradus

(South India and Ceylon)

The Slender Loris is smaller and much lighter in build than its close relative the Slow Loris. Its spindly legs, its clinging hands and feet and its stealthy gait are all reminiscent of a chameleon rather than a primate. If disturbed it sways from side to side growling and chattering.

The animal's large brilliant eyes give it a peculiar beauty and have been used at certain times to make love potions.

The female usually only has one young at a time. This she carries about, almost invisibly, on her body. There are two breeding seasons each year, in April–May and November–December. The gestation period is lengthy: 174 days.

In the wild the Slender Loris feeds almost entirely on insects, small birds and lizards, although in captivity it will eat large quantities of fruit. The prey is caught with the hands and killed by a series of rapid bites.

It is nocturnal, sleeping by day curled into a ball in the high branches of the trees. In this position, with its head tucked down between its thighs, it is difficult to see, looking like part of the branch it is gripping.

At sundown the Slender Loris wakes and like the other lorises and the lemuroids goes through a complicated toilet, scraping and combing the fur with the lower incisor teeth and scratching itself with the special "cleaning claw" on its hind foot.

The lorises and the galagos have the unusual habit of urinating regularly on their hands and feet. It would appear that this either improves their grip when climbing, or provides a territorial scent trail, or both.

SLOW LORIS

Nycticebus coucang

(Southern Asia, Sumatra, Java, Borneo)

The lorises, unlike the lemuroids, are slow, deliberate climbers. They progress through the tops of the forest trees by a stealthy hand-over-hand movement, often climbing along the underside of the branch. As the loris walks, its spine undulates slightly from side to side. This movement and the rather forlorn, quizzical expression produced by the wide-open eyes and the face-markings gave rise to its name, which comes from the Dutch, *loeris*, meaning a clown.

The Slow Loris sleeps by day in the crotch of a branch, with its head tucked well down and its hands and feet gripping the branch. Its extremely strong grasp is made possible by the well-developed thumb and big toe and by the development of specialized muscle fibres in the limbs. An improved blood supply to this region enables the grip to be held for a long time without the muscles tiring. The grasp is so sure that the animal can hang by one leg and can even feed in this position. In becoming pincer-like, the hands have almost lost the index fingers.

The Slow Loris feeds on small birds, insects and geckos, stalking them slowly and silently through the branches. It also eats certain fruits and berries.

One young is born and is carried about clinging tightly to the ventral fur of the mother.

It has often been recorded that this species has a shorter gestation period than the much smaller Slender Loris. Typically, the bigger an animal is, the longer its gestation; the exception in this case is puzzling, and may well be based on inaccurate records.

122

ANGWANTIBO

Arctocebus calabarensis

(Forest belt of Western Africa)

The Angwantibo is a small golden-coloured primate with thick woolly hair, about the size of a half-grown kitten. It is very like the Potto, but is smaller and can be identified by the lack of defensive spines on the neck vertebrae, the more pointed face, the absence of a tail and the extreme specialization of its hands. The first and second fingers of the hands are reduced in size, the first finger having almost disappeared, being represented only by a nailless bump. This reduction in the number of fingers enables the Angwantibo to use its hands like a pair of pincers, with the thumb on one side of the branch and the fourth and fifth fingers on the other. This gives it an extremely powerful grip.

The Angwantibo sleeps clinging to a horizontal branch, its arms between its legs and its head bent forward. When it is soundly asleep the limbs apparently become numb, for they can be pinched without the animal being disturbed, although it can be roused easily in other ways. During sleeping periods the limbs are colder than the rest of the body and quite rigid.

They are slow but excellent climbers, living in the high branches of deciduous forest. They often climb along the underside of branches and can even turn somersaults there by walking back between their hind legs.

They are thought to be omnivorous. In captivity they feed on fruit and insects and are particularly fond of small birds. This species is extremely rare. It occurs only in the Cameroons area and even there is seldom seen.

123

Family LORISIDAE

POTTO

Perodicticus potto

(Forest belt of West, Central and East Africa)

Unlike the Angwantibo, the Potto has a wide distribution and is quite common in the forest areas it inhabits. There are five different races of this species, extending over the tropical forest belt of Africa. It lives in the lower branches of tall trees, or in the top branches of the smaller trees of the deciduous forest.

It is rather like the Slow Loris in appearance but lacks the face markings of that animal and also has an inch-long tail. The index finger is reduced, as in the Angwantibo, but not to such an extent, and the third and fifth fingers are joined to the fourth by a web.

The most outstanding physical characteristic of this animal is the row of horny tubercles which cover the elongated spines of the last cervical and first two thoracic vertebrae. These spikes protrude through the skin of the back of the neck and are used in self-defence, the Potto curling itself up and flinging this region at its attacker's face. The animal seems to have special control of the hair tracts on either side of these tubercles, the fur being actively parted to lay them bare. Its chief enemy is the Two-spotted Palm Civet.

Like the lorises and Angwantibo, the Potto is nocturnal, sleeping curled up with its head between its legs during the day. It is omnivorous, feeding on insects, fruits, berries and small birds.

The Potto has specialized sex organs surrounded by reticulated skin which is some kind of glandular device. Copulation is said to take place from the ventral side, in contrast with most mammals, although this requires some verification.

THICK-TAILED BUSHBABY

Galago crassicaudatus

(Southern and Eastern Africa)

The galagos, or bushbabies, are the long-legged acrobats of the loris family. Unlike the non-jumping lorises and pottos they are very fast-moving, making the most spectacular leaps from branch to branch, the greatest jumps of all having been recorded for the Needle-Clawed Bushbaby. When moving on the ground, the bushbaby hops like a small kangaroo with its body upright and its tail stretched out behind.

In addition to the large Thick-tailed Bushbaby seen below, there are four medium-sized and one very small species, *Galago demidovi*, the last fitting easily in a man's hand. Senegal Bushbabies (the species most familiar as pets) live in small groups and spend a great deal of time in grooming themselves and each other with the comb-like lower incisor teeth. The Thick-tailed species, on the other hand, appears to be a more solitary creature and is more aggressive.

Like the lorises, the bushbabies urinate regularly on their hands and feet. They are nocturnal and mainly insectivorous in their diet, the enormous eyes and large membranous ears being of great value during their hunting expeditions at dawn and dusk.

The bushbaby has a gestation period of 120 days, producing litters of one or two young. These are not carried about by the female for any length of time, but are left in the nest, as the weight of a baby would obviously impede the mother when leaping. On the occasions when they are carried, they either cling to her underside or she takes them by the scruff of the neck like a cat with her kittens. The offspring are weaned when aged between 3 and 4 months and are mature at 20 months.

PHILIPPINE TARSIER

Tarsius syrichta

(Philippines)

The Tarsier is one of the strangest of all living primates. It has a globular skull with enormous staring eyes set close together in a flat face. The ears are large, naked and bat-like. The small (6 ounce) body is covered in soft, silky fur. It is 6 inches long, with a 10-inch tail that is naked and rat-like, except for a tuft of hairs at the tip. The fingers and toes are long and end in a special "adhesive" pad that enables the Tarsier to cling with ease to a comparatively smooth vertical surface. The hind legs are much longer than the front legs, the ankles in particular being unusually elongated (hence the name Tarsier).

With this body structure, the animal is well equipped for its nocturnal searches for small vertebrates and insect prey. It leaps acrobatically through the trees, jumping in a frog-like manner as far as 6 feet at a time. As it takes off, the tail is held out horizontally behind and the limbs are bent. As it lands, the tail flies up over its back and the limbs are extended, absorbing the shock. It catches prey by springing at them and grabbing them with both hands at once, shutting its eyes as it does so.

Tarsiers breed all through the year. There is a single offspring, born with its eyes open. Little is known about the social life of the species, but four have been found living together in the wild and a male has been taken from the same tree as a pregnant female.

DOUROUCOULI

Aotus trivirgatus

(Central and South America)

The Douroucouli, also known as the Night Ape or Owl Monkey, is the only true monkey that is nocturnal. It is, like an owl, quite noiseless in movement and this no doubt assists it when hunting certain kinds of prey. It is omnivorous, living on small birds, bats, insects, fruit and leaves. The insects are often caught on the wing. Being nocturnal it suffers very little water loss and rarely needs to drink, getting the water it needs from the dew and by eating young tree shoots. As a result, it may sometimes be found far from fresh water, on the banks of brackish rivers.

Douroucoulis sleep by day hunched up in hollow trees. They are easily roused and peer out to investigate when anyone passes, and this often leads to their capture. They run on all fours and leap between branches using the non-prehensile tail as a balancing organ. The voice is very loud due to a dilatable trachea and the presence of air-sacs in the throat. The volume of sound is increased by using the lips as a funnel to make a booming noise. Their vocalizations have been variously described as sounding like cats, dogs and Jaguars.

This species does not have a restricted breeding season. The single offspring clings tightly to its mother's fur. If it strays on to its father's body, the male will carry it around, thus sharing the parental duties. In captivity they become tame and confiding, though they are easily frightened by strangers or by loud noises.

Several species have been named, but it is now believed that they are merely races of a single Douroucouli species.

127

RED TITI

Callicebus cupreus

(Amazonian forests)

The eight species of titi monkeys live in the Amazon region where they are found climbing in the finer branches of the high forest trees. They are small monkeys often with long and beautifully coloured fur and with non-prehensile tails. Their resting position is characteristic; the body is hunched, the four feet hold the branch close together and the tail hangs straight down.

Titis are slower moving than most New World monkeys. They have a very characteristic odour said to be reminiscent of tinned orange juice. In captivity they keep to the highest perches of their cages and are very reluctant to descend to the floor. It seems likely that they rarely leave their tree-tops in the wild. This is one reason why comparatively little is known of their reproductive habits. It is probable that there is no fixed breeding season. A single offspring is produced.

Titi monkeys are omnivorous and feed on fruit, insects, birds' eggs and small birds. They live in family parties of about five or six individuals and are very noisy when together in the wild. Their voices are loud and carry for great distances. Their early morning concerts are one of the most characteristic noises of the forests of the Amazon and Orinoco rivers.

Various races of the Red Titi, shown here, are found in central and western Brazil, in Peru east of the Andes, in northern Ecuador and in parts of Bolivia. Other species of titis are found in this same region and some extend into Colombia, Venezuela and Paraguay.

RED UAKARI

Cacajao rubicundus

(Eastern Peru and Western Brazil)

There are three species of uakari. They are comparatively rare and restricted in range. They live on the banks of the Amazon and its tributaries, where the rivers form natural barriers preventing the mixing or spreading of the populations.

The Red Uakari has richly coloured chestnut hair. Its bare face and head are bright scarlet. The tail is short, unlike those of other New World monkeys, and is of little use in balancing. It is difficult to see what possible function it could serve, unless it is employed as a signalling device of some sort.

They live in small bands in the tops of high trees and seldom if ever descend to the ground. They move about normally on all fours, but it is said that occasionally they walk on their back legs holding their arms above them; this gives them a very strange appearance, with their seemingly emaciated bodies and their long sparse hair flowing behind them in the wind.

Uakaris are shy and timid creatures and do not seem to thrive in captivity. They are gentle and rather clumsy in their movements. When disturbed or agitated they indicate their mood by a deep blushing of the naked head region. The male is said to attack anyone who interferes with his mate or his young. When aggressive, Uakaris vigorously shake the branches they are sitting on. When approached closely they may respond with a slow, rhythmic smacking of the lips.

Their diet consists of fruit, nuts and leaves and in feeding they may use their fore-arms as a sort of tray, the food being eaten off the upturned palms and the insides of the wrists.

HAIRY SAKI

Pithecia monachus

(Guianas and Amazon Basin)

Looking rather as though it belongs to a shrunken human head, the face of the Hairy Saki has a wide nose, due to swollen nasal bones, and a broad, turned-down mouth, giving it a permanently melancholy expression. The cape of long hair which covers its shoulders and forehead looks like a monk's habit and gives the animal its other name of Monk Saki. There are three other species of saki, one of which, the Pale-headed Saki, shows sexual dimorphism, the male's curious-looking face being covered in short yellow or white hair.

These monkeys live in bands of up to ten along the river banks, or on the edge of the forest bordering the savannahs, where there are berry-bearing creepers and vines. They feed mainly on these berries but also eat leaves, flowers, small birds, bats and mice. They are strictly arboreal and rarely seem to drink. They are extremely feeble at walking on the ground, but can move very quickly in the trees, usually running on all fours, but sometimes making enormous leaps. They have been seen running bipedally in file along branches, their hands held above their heads.

One young is born in the spring and clings to its mother's belly, or is carried by the scruff of the neck in her hand.

Sakis do not thrive in captivity, rarely surviving for long. They are easily frightened and have been known to die from shock simply because their cage or cage companion has been changed. They sometimes exhibit uncontrolled panic, rushing round their cages and battering their heads until they become unconscious, a reaction also seen occasionally in acouchis and agoutis.

RED HOWLER

Alouatta seniculus

(Amazonian forests)

Like song-birds, Red Howler Monkeys defend a territory vocally. Sometimes only the largest male in the troop howls, but on other occasions the cry is taken up by the whole group, in which case the ringing calls can be heard for several miles. Neighbouring troops are stimulated to reply, and once such a choral contest starts it may continue for hours. The volume of noise produced by the vocal chords of each monkey is amplified by a bony box consisting of the modified hyoid apparatus, which in most mammals forms the skeleton of the tongue. To accommodate this organ Howler Monkeys have enlarged lower jaws and throats, which are only partly concealed by the "beard" formed from the luxuriant fur of this region. Apart from the howl itself, they perform at least eight other distinct vocalizations.

Red Howlers come from the northern region of South America. They have deep orange-brown fur. Related species, differing mainly in colour, inhabit other parts of Central and tropical South America. It is necessary to be careful when identifying Howler species, however, for according to some reports the colour can be washed from the fur. Apparently an animal which has a dark coat before being soaked in water may be a yellowish shade afterwards.

Howlers have prehensile tails and are good climbers. They rarely leap, but usually run steadily through the trees. In diet they are largely restricted to young shoots, fruits and leaves, sometimes letting go of the branches with all four limbs simultaneously and swinging by their tails alone in order to reach a particularly tempting morsel.

BROWN CAPUCHIN

Cebus apella

(South America)

The four species of capuchin have a very wide range, being found from Honduras in the north to Argentina in the south. They live in thick forest in troops of up to thirty animals. Extraordinary acrobats, they have been seen to leap as much as 50 feet downward from one tree-top to another. It is reported that they often move in single file and make tracks through the trees from their more or less permanent sleeping-quarters to their feeding grounds. They eat leaves, fruit (sometimes holding it in their prehensile tails), insects, small birds, and grubs and spiders which they prise out from under the bark of trees. They often raid plantations to steal fruit and maize. Hard food objects are rhythmically hammered open. This action appears to be instinctive.

They are very noisy, making a continuous weeping sound that keeps the troop together. If approached in the wild they have been observed to break off twigs and branches and throw them at the enemy.

They are intelligent animals and very dexterous with their hands, concentrating on a task for far longer than an Old World monkey. They will use simple tools when trying to secure a difficult food object. If the hammering of a nut will not open it, they pick up a stone and strike it with that. In captivity they have made drawings and even paintings, to date being the only sub-ape to perform this activity.

In states of excitement capuchins will cover themselves in ants, an activity more commonly associated with certain birds. Self-anointing with saliva (cf. European Hedgehog) has also been seen and, like some lorisids, they sometimes urinate on their hands.

132

Family CEBIDAE

COMMON SQUIRREL MONKEY

Saimiri sciureus

(Northern South America)

This species is perhaps the most common primate in the whole of the Americas. It occurs in large troops of up to 100 individuals and these groups are very numerous throughout Amazonia. They live in the few hundred yards of forest bordering the many river banks. They are dependent on the riverside creepers for food, living chiefly on their flowers and fruits, though they also eat insects (caught on the wing) and possibly frogs, snails and small birds. Like the uakaris and the capuchins they sometimes use their forearms as a tray when feeding.

They are inquisitive, noisy and quarrelsome, squabbling for central positions in the troop at night, when they sleep with their tails wrapped round them for warmth. It has recently been discovered that the males establish their dominance by threatening one another with an erect penis. Their voices are usually flute-like, but when angry or frightened they shriek loudly and a whole troop is said to sound like surf breaking on a shore. The Common Squirrel Monkey has an olive-green back, yellowish-white underparts and orange feet and limbs. The tufted ears and the rings around the eyes are white, while the muzzle and the tip of the tail are black. The body is small, being little more than a foot in length. The tail is not prehensile.

One young is born and at first is carried on the mother's underside, but later rides on her back. A curious dimorphism is supposed to exist in Squirrel Monkey troops, for as well as young monkeys and normal-sized adults there are said to be giant specimens with 2-foot long bodies. There is, however, no solid evidence to support this claim.

133

CENTRAL AMERICAN SPIDER MONKEY

Ateles geoffroyi

(Forests of Central America)

Four species of spider monkeys occur in the New World forests, from southern Mexico to south-eastern Brazil. Together with the squirrel monkeys and the capuchins they are the most common of the American monkeys.

Spider monkeys are more perfectly adapted to an arboreal life than any other member of their family. They have slender bodies, while their limbs are elongated and muscular. In climbing they tend to swing underneath the branches, using their hands as hooks. This form of climbing is unusual in a monkey, being more typical of an ape such as a gibbon or chimpanzee. With this method of progression, opposable thumbs are of little use, and those of the spider monkeys are reduced or absent. The muscular tail is strongly prehensile, easily capable of supporting the entire weight of the animal. Beneath the lower surface of its tip is a naked pad, the skin of which is slightly ridged, giving a sensitive and firm grip.

The Central American, or Geoffroy's Spider Monkey, has fine reddish-brown hair which is lighter on the chest and the undersides of the limbs. This species has a range extending from Mexico south to the northernmost point of South America. It inhabits the thickest of the forest regions. Each family group keeps to its own territory, which it patrols during the day, feeding chiefly on unripe seeds and leaves, and some insects. A single young one is born after a gestation period of 20 weeks.

The rare Woolly Spider Monkey (*Brachyteles*) comes from south-eastern Brazil. It is in some ways transitional between the spider monkeys and the woolly monkeys, but little is known of its habits.

134

Family CEBIDAE

SMOKY WOOLLY MONKEY

Lagothrix cana

(Amazonian forests)

Closely related to the acrobatic Spider Monkeys are the densely furred Woolly Monkeys found in the forest regions of western Brazil, eastern Ecuador, eastern Peru and parts of Colombia. Although capable of intricate manoeuvres in the tree-tops, they are generally more sedate and silent.

Superficially their coat is reminiscent of that of the Gorilla. It is thick and woolly and gives the animals a "crew-cut" appearance.

Three species are generally accepted at the present time. The most common one is the Smoky Woolly Monkey seen below. It has brown, grey or black body fur, typically with a much darker head region, although some of the pale grey ones also have a pale-grey head Humboldt's Woolly Monkey (*L. lagothricha*) is brown all over, with a uniform brown head that is not darker than the body. The very rare Hendee's Woolly Monkey (*L. hendeei*), found only in one region of north Peru, is a deep mahogany colour, with a buff-coloured nasal patch on its brown face and with a yellow streak on the underside of its tail.

The adults, especially the males, are stocky, heavily built animals and may measure as much as 4 feet from the nose to the tip of the tail. They have large teeth and powerful jaws and although often extremely friendly in captivity, have been known to make sudden, unpredictable and rather serious attacks on their owners.

In the wild they live in small family troops feeding on fruits, leaves and unripe nuts. When food is plentiful, they gorge themselves and become strikingly pot-bellied. This tendency is so well known that in Brazil they are called *barrigudos* (big-bellies).

135

BLACK-PENCILLED MARMOSET

Callithrix penicillata

(South-eastern Brazil)

There are thirty-three species of marmosets and tamarins, all located in the Amazonian region. They are dwarf monkeys with characteristically shrill, twittering voices. The sounds they produce are often so high-pitched that they begin in the supersonic range before descending into the audible higher sonic range.

Marmosets feed on insects, small birds, fruits, shoots and other plant foods. They are highly strung and move quickly and jerkily with a crouching, scurrying gait. Their hands and feet are long and narrow and the digits are equipped with claws. The big toe is an exception to this rule, bearing a flat nail. It is believed that the possession of claws in these species is not a primitive feature, but is instead a more recent specialization to their rather squirrel-like bark-climbing activities.

Marmosets not only move like squirrels but also often lie like them, with their bellies resting on a branch and their limbs hanging down on either side. They live in small family groups and give birth to two or sometimes three young at a time. The gestation period of 144 days is as long as that for the much larger Spider and Woolly Monkeys.

All of the marmosets and tamarins have long, hairy, non-prehensile tails. Many of them have head adornments such as crown-tufts, ear-plumes, beards and even long moustaches. In general the tamarins are larger animals than the marmosets but this rule does not apply in every case. Three similar species of marmosets have often been confused as the "Common" species—the White-eared (with white ear-plumes), the Black-pencilled (with black ear-plumes) and the true Common Marmoset (with white ear-tufts).

136

SILVERY MARMOSET

Callithrix argentata

(Amazonian forests)

The majority of mammals have rather poor eyesight, and make comparatively little use of visual signals in communicating with each other. The higher primates, on the other hand, are adapted for a diurnal, arboreal existence in which sharp vision is at a premium, and they have evolved efficient eyes that can see in detail, in colour, and in depth. Alongside this development, visual signalling has improved and the markings and colours of these animals have become more elaborate and exaggerated. This trend is very obvious in the marmosets.

The Silvery Marmoset has long, soft fur which is almost white on the body, but black on the tail. In many situations this sharp contrast between the tail and the head makes the animal appear to be tailless (see photograph below). The large, naked ears and the face are pink, and the latter shows a variety of darker red markings. The voice, like that of all marmosets, is shrill and bird-like. A troop consisting of some dozens of these creatures is therefore conspicuous, relying for safety on swift flight through the tree-tops rather than concealment. By contrast, the Pygmy Marmoset is the best camouflaged and also the most furtive member of the family.

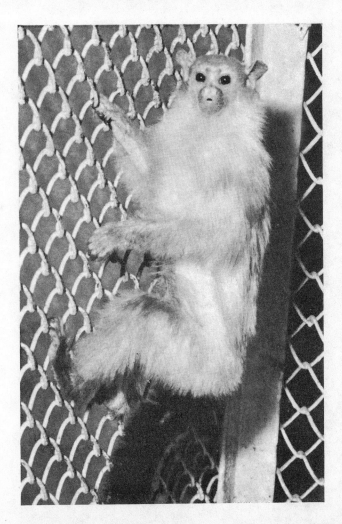

Silvery Marmosets come from the dense forests to the south of the Amazon river. Like other marmosets, but unlike any other higher primates, they usually give birth to more than one offspring at a time, two or three being the rule. The gestation period is about 20 weeks. Young animals at first lack the detailed markings typical of adults, acquiring these only with age.

PYGMY MARMOSET

Cebuella pygmaea

(Amazonian forests)

The smallest of all living monkeys, the Pygmy Marmoset has an adult body length of only 4 inches, with a hairy tail of a similar length. Unlike its larger, more brightly marked relatives, its fur is a plain, dull mousy colour. For many years it was thought to be a juvenile form of some other Marmoset species. When it was definitely established as a distinct form, the situation became reversed, with unscrupulous dealers offering young Common Marmosets as specimens of the rare Pygmy species.

There has also been some confusion about its geographical range. Originally it was recorded only from Ecuador and Peru, east of the Andes, but it was later found thousands of miles away in south-eastern Brazil. It is rather mystifying that there are no records of it occurring anywhere in between these two regions. Recently the specimen shown below was caught in southern Colombia, somewhere along the Putumayo River, adding yet another area to the range of the species. It seems likely now that this secretive,

inconspicuous little creature may be more common than was once thought and more careful collecting may reveal that its distribution is much greater than has hitherto been believed.

The Pygmy Marmoset has small naked ears that are completely hidden by its thick mane. It is constantly shifting its head from side to side when scrutinizing the environment and at signs of danger will disappear around the far side of the branch, rather like a tree squirrel.

The litter of two is said to be carried about mainly by the father, one on each thigh, and it is claimed that they are returned to the mother only at feeding time.

138

Family CALLITHRICIDAE   F 100

GOLDEN LION MARMOSET

Leontideus rosalia

(South-eastern Brazil)

This is, without doubt, the most brightly coloured of all living mammals, being an intense, shimmering golden yellow. The function of this coat colour is not understood. There are virtually no markings and even the naked face is of a similar tone and offers no contrast. The first living specimen seen in Europe was apparently owned by Madame Pompadour.

The male is said to assist at the birth of the young and to wash them as they are born. He is then supposed to transfer them to his body where they cling inconspicuously to his fur, wrapping their tails tightly around his flanks. He carries them about for 6 to 7 weeks, transferring them to the female only for feeding. Later, when they are being weaned, he is said to pre-chew food for them. The diet, as with most members of this family, is extremely varied, including insects, small vertebrates, fruits, seeds and shoots. Like all marmosets, they are diurnal and extremely active.

The Golden Lion Marmoset and its two close relatives the Golden-headed Tamarin and the Golden-rumped Tamarin are all found in the coastal forests of south-eastern Brazil and together form a separate genus, in some ways intermediate between the typical marmosets (*Callithrix*) and the typical tamarins (*Leontocebus*). Some authorities consider them to be true tamarins because they share the typical dental features of that group (typical marmosets are "short-tusked", the lower incisors being as long as the canines; typical tamarins are "long-tusked", the incisors being shorter than the canines, which therefore appear as tusks), but in other respects they are sufficiently unique to be maintained as a separate genus.

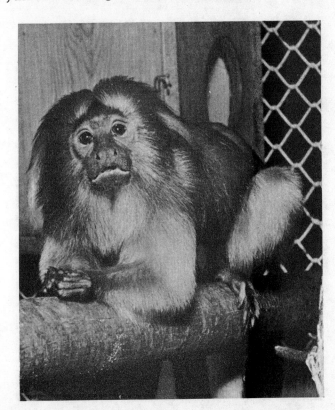

139

LION-TAILED MACAQUE

Macaca silenus

(Southern India)

There are twelve species of macaques alive today. They are distributed across the Old World from North Africa to Celebes, but the majority are concentrated in the southern Asiatic region. They are intelligent monkeys with elaborate social communication systems involving a wide variety of calls, facial expressions, postures and movements. Unlike South American monkeys, they possess naked areas of hardened skin on the rump, known as the ischial callosities.

The Lion-tailed Macaque is the least typical and perhaps the least known of the group. It inhabits dense forest regions of the mountains near the west coast of southern India and is said to be shy and retiring, unlike many of its close relatives. It is easily identified by the stiff, broad ruff of hair around its face and by the leonine tuft of hair at the tip of its tail (missing in the specimen shown below). The hair is rather silky in texture and black or very dark brown in colour, except for the face ruff which is a paler grey-brown. The ruff is more exaggerated in the males than in the females. The body of this species is 2 feet long and the tail approximately 10 inches.

The Lion-tailed Macaque is often known by the name of Wanderoo. This is a misnomer, however, as it was originally intended for certain langurs in Ceylon. It is not clear how it came to be adopted for the macaque species. Misuse of animal names is not uncommon, the word macaque itself being used originally for an African monkey, until it was misapplied to the Asiatic group by Buffon.

RHESUS MACAQUE

Macaca mulatta

(Southern Asia)

The best known of all the monkeys, the Rhesus Macaque is the typical member of its group with a wide distribution from Afghanistan in the west to China in the east. Vast numbers of this species are exported from India and other countries in South-east Asia every year for use in medical research in Europe and America. They have not only provided us with a great deal of medical knowledge, but have also travelled into outer space.

The adult Rhesus is a large, stockily built creature with a dull yellowish-brown coat. Like most macaques it has a shortish tail and rather short limbs, the hind legs being about the same length as the fore-legs. As with all Old World monkeys and apes, a single offspring is the rule. This is born after a gestation period of 164 days and feeds from the mother for a period of up to a year. It is sexually mature at 4 years, fully grown at 5, and may live to be 20.

The Rhesus lives in large colonies in forest regions or on open, rocky hillsides. In some parts of India it is regarded as a sacred species and is protected and fed. In other regions it is looked upon as a pest. It can become a serious nuisance in gardens and orchards where it steals fruits and other foods, cramming as much as possible into its large cheek pouches and then retreating to near-by trees or rocks to eat in safety.

There are two closely related species, the heavily-furred Assamese Macaque (*M. assamensis*) and the shorter-tailed Formosan Macaque (*M. cyclopis*).

F 132

STUMP-TAILED MACAQUE

Macaca speciosa

(South-east Asia)

The Stump-tailed Macaque is a heavily built, very hairy species that is found from Assam to south-east China, often at high altitudes and in regions where the animals are forced to endure periods of considerable cold. In some areas they have been seen digging for food in the snow.

Because of their brightly-coloured naked faces and their stocky bodies they are sometimes known as Red-faced Monkeys or Bear Monkeys. They have a close relative in Japan, the Japanese Macaque (*M. fuscata*), often known as the Japanese Ape because, like the Stump-tailed, it is almost tailless, possessing only a brief, insignificant, 2-inch long tail. It has an even longer, thicker coat.

The Stump-tailed Macaque is an opportunist, omnivorous feeder. It can be seen digging for succulent roots, turning over stones and logs for insects and other creatures, beach-combing for crustaceans, or raiding plantations in search of fruits and leaves. It lives in large colonies that may be settled in one area, if food is reasonably plentiful, or may move about as the food supplies change. Little is known about the details of its social organization in the wild, but detailed studies are now being made of its Japanese relative. In particular we now learn that traditional patterns of behaviour can develop in one colony of these animals and may be performed by all the individuals of that group, while they are completely missing from the behaviour repertoire of a near-by colony. For example, one colony has learnt to wash certain food objects in the sea before eating them, but another has not.

142

BARBARY APE

Macaca sylvana

(North Africa)

The only species of macaque to be found outside Asia is the well-known Barbary Ape, or Magot. It inhabits the rocky forests of north-west Africa, in Morocco and Algeria. It is generally accepted that this is a relic African population and that intermediate populations once existed right across to south-west Asia, but have since vanished leaving this one surviving pocket in the west. It has also been suggested that man may have been responsible and that thousands of years ago Arab tribes brought the monkey with them as they travelled west. If they did, then they must also have exterminated the more easterly ancestral population from which the animal supposedly originated.

Barbary Apes are large, tailless, ground-dwelling macaques with dense coats and are capable, like the Stump-tailed species in the East, of withstanding conditions of considerable cold. They are reported to roam through the forests in large bands feeding on leaves, fruit and pine-cones and supplementing this diet with insects, scorpions and any small creatures they can find. In some areas they are notorious for raiding farm lands. The gestation period is longer than that of the Rhesus Macaque, being 210 days.

A small colony of Barbary Apes has been maintained on the Rock of Gibraltar for many years. They live wild, but were almost certainly introduced by man in this case, despite the persistent legend that the vast network of caves inside the Rock leads to an under-sea tunnel to Ceuta in North Africa and through which the animals pass, and despite the more serious belief that they represent a relic European population.

143

BLACK APE

Cynopithecus niger

(Celebes)

The Black Ape, like the Barbary Ape, is a monkey with the tail so considerably reduced that it does not show on the outside of the body. Rather surprisingly for a tailless species, it spends most of its time climbing in the forests and mangrove swamps of its native island of Celebes. It is of average monkey size, being about 2 feet long, and has long black hair which, as the illustration shows, stands up to form a remarkable crest on the top of the head.

It is presumed that the Black Ape is related to the macaques, but although it is not a ground-dwelling species it appears to have some affinities with the baboons of Africa. It is sometimes regarded as being intermediate between these two types, although in its general behaviour it seems to be closer to the macaques. It is interesting, however, that in some parts of Celebes it is popularly called a "baboon".

In the northern part of the island they are quite common and the local inhabitants regard them as sacred, considering them to be the ancestors of their own tribe. Black Apes live in small groups, or sometimes even in pairs, and on the whole cause little trouble, although they do sometimes raid plantations. At low tide they sometimes work along the seashore in search of animal additions to their diet.

Also found in Celebes is a rather similar species called the Moor Macaque (*Macaca maurus*). These animals are about the same size as the Black Ape but lack the crest and have a very short tail. They are true macaques, are very dark brown in colour, and live in large troops.

144

Family CERCOPITHECIDAE

SOOTY MANGABEY

(*Cercocebus torquatus*)

(Forests of Central West Africa)

Mangabeys are long-tailed monkeys of rather more than average size, and are found in the thick closed-canopy forests of Central Africa. Their arms and legs are long and they have powerful, well-muscled bodies. They are wonderful climbers and seldom descend to the ground. In temperament they are fierce, yet shy, and they are much more silent by nature than are the related baboons and macaques, although male mangabeys sometimes utter a loud, chattering cry.

Mangabeys make great use of grimaces in communicating with each other. The upper eyelids are almost white in colour, and add emphasis to the facial expressions. For example, threat, which involves a fixed stare with raised eyebrows, exposes the prominent upper lids fully.

Mangabeys live in troops and eat a diet consisting mainly of fruit. Four species are recognized. The illustration shows a male Sooty Mangabey from the forests that fringe the Atlantic coast of central and west Africa. The fur is grey, and is especially long on the sides of the head, while the skin of the face is pink with grey-brown freckles. The distinctive White-collared or Red-capped Mangabey is a race of the Sooty species with white markings around the neck and striking reddish-brown fur on top of the head. To the east, from the Cameroons to Uganda, is found the Grey-cheeked Mangabey (*C. albigena*) which is dark grey and bears a spreading crest on the head. Agile Mangabeys (*C. galeritus*) are brown, and occur in the Congo and an isolated pocket in Kenya, while from the south of the Congo comes the Peaked or Black Mangabey (*C. aterrimus*).

145

HAMADRYAS BABOON

Papio hamadryas

(Hillsides of North-east Africa and Arabia)

The Sacred, or Hamadryas Baboon inhabits the rocky hillsides of eastern Sudan, Abyssinia and south-western Arabia. Formerly it was also found in the Nile Valley, where it was one of the animals regarded as sacred by the ancient Egyptians.

This baboon, like its close relatives, has an enormously enlarged and elongated muzzle housing huge teeth. The silvery-brown hair of the head, shoulders and chest is long and flowing, particularly in the male. The tail is over a foot long, but is rather thick and is carried in the peculiar drooping manner which is characteristic of all true baboons.

Four other species of baboons are recognized, and all inhabit grassland or bush. All are very much alike in appearance, differing only slightly in size and colour. These other species have less distinctive capes than the Hamadryas Baboon. The brown Guinea Baboon (*P. papio*) comes from West Africa, while the Olive or Anubis Baboon (*P. doguera*) inhabits the vast area between the forests and the Sahara Desert from Lake Chad in the west to Abyssinia in the east. Farther south in East Africa occurs the lanky Yellow Baboon (*P. cynocephalus*), and in Southern Rhodesia and South Africa the black-faced, dark-furred Chacma Baboon (*P. ursinus*), is found.

Baboons live in large troops, numbering up to 100, and feed on juicy stems and roots, insects and honey. They pay little attention to the presence of most other animals and often live near to human settlements. In parts of South Africa quite close to large cities Chacma Baboons remain numerous.

MANDRILL

Mandrillus sphinx

(Forests of Central West Africa)

The Mandrill is in some ways the strangest of all monkeys in appearance. It is related to the baboons and like them has a long dog-like muzzle with huge teeth. The body is rather heavy, and the limbs are thick and straight. Although it comes from the forests of the southern Cameroons and might be expected to spend much of its time in the trees, it does, in fact, confine its activities largely to the forest floor. As with certain other ground-dwelling primates, the tail has become considerably shortened and is little more than a conical stump.

The fur is mostly brown, although that on the muzzle and the underparts is yellowish-white and there are long yellow tufts on the sides of the head. The exposed parts of the skin are the most highly coloured to be seen in any mammal. The long nose is an intense red, while the strikingly ridged skin of the cheeks is bright blue. The hind-quarters are also vivid, being suffused with red and blue which in places blend to give a delicate shade of mauve. These hues are to be seen at their best in the adult males which are considerably larger and more brightly coloured than the females.

Mandrills live in small family groups and spend much of their time in forest clearings and rocky outcrops. In addition to plant food they are fond of insects which they find beneath dead bark and under stones. The young, which are born after a gestation period of about 245 days, at first look very much like any other young short-tailed monkey.

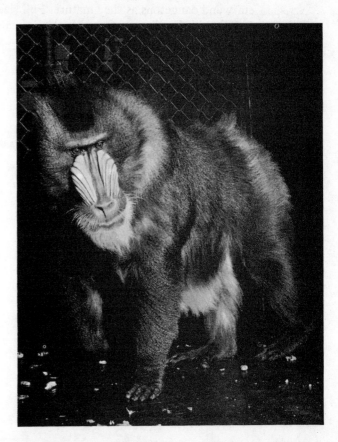

147

DRILL

Mandrillus leucophaeus

(Forests of Central West Africa)

Drills are very similar to Mandrills in shape, but are smaller and much less brightly coloured. They have dark brown fur and the skin of the face is jet black. Their range does not overlap that of their larger relative as they are found only in the forests of the northern Cameroons. The Sanaga River marks the boundary between the two species.

Drills move about, most often on the ground, in small bands. They eat a wide variety of foods, including leaves, fruit, roots, fungi, worms, insects and small vertebrates. Much of their time is spent grubbing amongst the dead leaves on the forest floor and turning over stones in search of delicacies. In this search they are aided by a keen sense of smell. The hands are remarkably human in appearance and are well suited for the dexterous manipulation of each find.

Although they do not normally hunt or feed on large animals, Drills are aggressive and well able to defend themselves if attacked. Usually this activity is performed by the largest males in the troop, which are reputed to hurl sticks and stones at the attacker, or may dash forward with their large fangs bared. In the face of such a defence even a Leopard may retire.

Like other monkeys Drills make engaging pets whilst they are young, but become surly and dangerous as they mature. Full size is not reached by a male until he is about 9 years old, but long before this the animal is able to breed and has the courage and temper of an adult.

GELADA BABOON

Theropithecus gelada

(Hillsides of North-east Africa)

The Gelada Baboon is a little larger than the Hamadryas Baboon, which it resembles in having a cape of long hair on the shoulders. The hair is, however, dark brown in colour, and the muzzle bears ridges above the hollow cheeks which are reminiscent of those of the Drill. These ridges, combined with the strangely shortened nose and the prominent brow ridges, give the Gelada a most unusual appearance. This is enhanced by the way in which the animal holds its head high and by the wide range of facial expressions which sometimes involve turning the upper lip inside-out.

The skin on the chest is bare and red, and in the female these red patches are surrounded by chains of bead-like swellings which vary in size according to the stage of the reproductive cycle which the animal has reached. It has been suggested that these chest markings are mimics of the rump markings of the species, enabling the animal to perform displays whilst sitting down. The reason for this is not known.

Like all higher primates the female Gelada normally bears one young one at a time. The two nipples are set very close together and, when the mother is suckling, the offspring usually feeds from both at the same time, a tendency which is rare amongst monkeys. If the red chest-patches are mimics of the red rump patches, then the nipples, in their odd position, are almost certainly mimics of the female genitals.

Geladas live in large troops on the hillsides of Abyssinia at heights of up to 8,000 feet above sea-level, where their range overlaps that of the Hamadryas Baboon.

149

GRASS MONKEY

Cercopithecus aethiops

(African Grasslands)

The Grass Monkey is one of the most common of all African primates. It has a wide distribution, from Sierra Leone in the west to the Red Sea in the east and down to the Cape. It is a graceful, cat-sized monkey with a slender body and very long limbs and tail. The fur is yellowish-brown, often with a blue-green tinge. The face is dark and is surrounded by a fringe of whitish hairs.

This species is typically found in Savannah districts, where it divides its time between the trees and the grass. It is intermediate in this respect between its close relative, the Patas Monkey, which is almost exclusively ground-living, and the other, more typical, forest-dwelling, tree-climbing guenons. Grass Monkeys travel about in large troops sometimes covering considerable distances. Their food consists not only of plant matter, but also insects, centipedes and lizards.

Many races of this species have been named. The most important are: the West African form, known as the Green Monkey, with a very dark face and a stronger greenish tinge in its fur; the East African form, known as the Grivet Monkey, with long white tufts on either side of the face; and the South African form, known as either the Vervet Monkey or Blue Monkey, with dark hair on the hands and feet and reddish hair beneath the tail. At one time these three races were erroneously thought to be distinct species. The form shown in the photograph is the Vervet Monkey.

MONA MONKEY

Cercopithecus mona

(Forests of West Africa)

Mona Monkeys are conspicuously marked guenons found throughout much of the forested region of equatorial Africa. The fur on their undersides and the insides of their legs is white or yellow and contrasts vividly with the darker markings of the rest of the body. In the race seen above there are also conspicuous white patches on the rump on either side of the base of the tail. On the face there are yellowish cheek tufts and a yellow brow-stripe. A striking sub-species in the Congo region, called the Wolf Monkey, has orange-brown fur on its limbs. There are many other minor variations in coat colours in different races.

These monkeys are good climbers and spend much of their time in the leafy canopy 100 feet above the ground. As is shown in the illustration, they climb in the manner typical of the majority of tree-dwelling monkeys, walking above the branch on all fours, taking a grip by means of their long fingers and toes, and adjusting their balance by movements of the tail. They have keen eyesight, and make good use of it in judging distances as they leap from one tree to the next.

Monas feed upon leaves, shoots and fruit. They are particularly fond of unripe nuts. In addition they eat large numbers of insects and spend much time searching for tree-dwelling snails. They live in big troops, and their activities are often boisterous and noisy. The young are born at all times of the year, after just under 7 months' gestation. At first they grow rapidly, but they do not reach maturity until they are about 5 years old.

DE BRAZZA'S MONKEY

Cercopithecus neglectus

(Forests of Central Africa)

This is one of the largest and the most dramatically marked of the ten species of guenons. The illustration below shows a young specimen, but already the characteristic white beard is conspicuous. As the animal grows older, more elaborate head markings develop, including a white-edged, orange brow-patch topped by a broad black band of fur across the front of the crown. The insides of the limbs are white, the outsides and the hands and feet black. The body of the adult, especially the male, is sturdy and powerful.

This species represents a peak in guenon evolution, where the trend is to elaborate body markings and colours, but relatively little facial expression. It is true that guenons have simple threatening and frightened gestures, but they lack the complicated range

of detailed grimacing typical of macaques and baboons. This emphasis on markings rather than gestures in social communication seems to be connected with their more strictly arboreal, forest-bound mode of existence, where bright colour patches and coat-contrasts are more effective as signalling systems.

De Brazza's Monkeys live in the most central regions of equatorial Africa, in the forests of the Congo and in parts of Uganda. They occur in both open and closed forests in certain regions, but prefer the gallery forests.

Like most monkeys they feed on a wide variety of plant foods and also take animal material such as large insects. They are particularly partial to big grasshoppers and locusts. Although primarily climbers and jumpers, they can gallop at high speeds whenever they descend to the ground in search of extra food.

152

TALAPOIN MONKEY

Cercopithecus talapoin

(Central West Africa)

The Talapoin Monkey is the smallest of the guenons and, indeed, the smallest of all the true monkeys in the Old World. Its body length is only 12 to 13 inches, little more than half that of a typical guenon such as the Grass Monkey.

With its sexual swellings and its rather plain olive-green coat, it is rather un-guenon-like in appearance. It has unusual hands, with short, slightly webbed fingers and has sometimes been placed in a separate genus of its own (*Miopithecus*), and referred to as the Pygmy Guenon. Another feature that distinguishes it from the typical *Cercopithecus* species is the reduction in size of the face in relation to the large cranium. However, despite all these special features, the little Talapoin remains, for the time being at any rate, as a member of the ordinary guenon genus. Perhaps, when we know more about its behaviour and its way of life in the wild, we shall be able to justify its separation as a unique form, but for the present we can only reserve our judgement.

It inhabits the swampy forests near the mouth of the Congo River, and is also found on Mt. Ruwenzori nearly 2,000 miles away. Another unusual swamp-living species from the western Congo is Allen's Monkey (*Allenopithecus nigroviridis*) which, unlike the Talapoin, has been more generally accepted as a distinct genus. It has a face that is sharply divided into two colour regions—blackish above the lips and yellowish-white below. Some authorities consider it to be closely related to the Talapoin, but it has been studied so little that no definite conclusions can be drawn at the present time. Clearly, both these small swamp monkeys would amply repay more detailed investigations.

F 160   Family CERCOPITHECIDAE

PATAS MONKEY

Erythrocebus patas

(Grasslands of Western and Central Africa)

To the north of the tropical rain forests of Africa and to the south of the Sahara Desert, a great belt of dry grassland and semi-desert stretches from the Atlantic Ocean to the Nile Valley and East Africa, and this is the area inhabited by the Patas Monkey.

This monkey, like many animals from dry regions, is rather pale in colour, having orange fur which becomes lighter on the extremities of the body and on the sides of the head. Although the jaw protrudes rather in the same way as that of a mangabey or a macaque, the Patas Monkey is more like the guenons in bodily form.

It is a long-tailed species and can easily climb the rocks and ΄isolated trees which are found in its habitat, but normally spends most of its time on the ground. The limbs are long and the short toes have callosities on their under-surfaces. Patas Monkeys are therefore well adapted for running. When excited, they have the strange habit of skipping up and down on the spot. The origin of this behaviour pattern is not clear, but it seems possible that the movement originated with curious monkeys jumping repeatedly up and down when trying to obtain a better view over tall grass.

Members of this species live in small, silent troops. Quite often the group moves in some semblance of order and it is to this, as much as to the hint of red in their coats, that Patas Monkeys owe their alternative names of Hussar or Military Monkeys. The eastern race, sometimes known as the Nisnas Monkey, has a white nose, in contrast to the black-nosed western forms.

154

DOUC LANGUR

Pygathrix nemaeus

(Forests of South-east Asia)

The Douc is a representative of a group of eighteen species of monkeys known collectively as the langurs. These all come from tropical Asia and, like the colobus monkeys to which they are closely related, are leaf-eaters. Langurs are rarely seen in captivity, where they seldom thrive, but are numerous in the wild. The group includes some of the most highly coloured of all primates.

Doucs inhabit the forests of Viet-Nam. Much of the dense fur covering the body is grey, but the hands and feet are black, the forearms and wrists white, and the shins brown. The tail and hindquarters are also white. The most striking markings of all, however, are found on the head. A yellow and black collar encircles the neck, and there are reddish-brown tufts on the cheeks. In the typical race, the naked skin of the face is yellow. A second race is very similar except that the skin of the face is black. The animal has an overall length of about 40 inches, rather less than half of this being the tail.

A number of species of typical langurs from the sub-continent of India are rather larger, with longer tails and fur. These langurs have beetling brows and powerful protruding jaws. This gives them an aggressive appearance which they do not belie. Although regarded as sacred and accorded almost complete protection, they apparently engage in battles with rival troops of their own kind, as well as with Rhesus Monkeys.

As with a number of mammals that have specialized in difficult diets, the leaf-eating monkeys have developed a highly modified digestive system, with a complex, sacculate stomach.

F 178   Family CERCOPITHECIDAE

PROBOSCIS MONKEY

Nasalis larvatus

(Forests of Borneo)

Proboscis Monkeys are found only in Borneo. They are powerfully built and measure up to 5 feet, half of this length being the tail. A big male may weigh over 50 lb. Their fur is yellow-brown. The development of the nose is truly remarkable and is unequalled by any other primate. In a large male this bulbous organ may be 3 inches long. The function of this exaggerated structure is by no means clear.

These animals live in large groups, and although they can defend themselves when necessary they are generally of a placid disposition. They spend a part of each day sitting motionless in the tree-tops as they sun-bathe. At other times they swim expertly, and odd specimens have even been found swimming out to sea. They feed upon young palm leaves, and two or more troops sometimes share the same feeding place, apparently without friction.

Several related species have notable upturned noses. One, the Pig-tailed Langur, inhabits islands off the coast of Sumatra. Its tail is similar to that of the Pig-tailed Macaque. Two similar, but long-tailed, Snub-nosed Monkeys are found on the mainland of southern Asia. The larger one is found as far north as Tibet and may measure 30 inches, excluding the tail. It has long golden fur and a blue face. It usually lives on the ground in mountain evergreen forests and bamboo thickets.

Very few live specimens of Proboscis or Snub-nosed Monkeys have ever been seen in captivity. The young pair of *Nasalis* shown above are rare exceptions. They were 3 years old when photographed and the male's proboscis was not yet fully developed.

156

Family CERCOPITHECIDAE   F 179

BLACK-AND-WHITE COLOBUS

Colobus polykomos

(Forests of Tropical Africa)

The Colobus Monkeys or Guerezas of Africa, and the Langurs of Asia are placed together in a distinct subfamily, the Colobinae, comprising the leaf-eating monkeys of the Old World. The cheek pouches, typical of other members of the family, are absent or reduced and this gives them a strange, hollow-cheeked appearance. Additionally they have complicated stomachs specially adapted to digest the tough leaves upon which they largely subsist. In all species the thumbs are very much reduced in size or are completely absent.

Colobus Monkeys are widely distributed in the African forests. A number of forms have been described, but today only three are accepted as valid species. Green Colobus are found in West Africa, and Red Colobus in both West Africa and the Congo forests, while Black-and-White Colobus come from a broad area right across equatorial Africa, from the Cameroons in the west to Abyssinia in the east. There is a great deal of variation in the arrangement and extent of the white markings in the various races of the Black-and-White species.

The fur is handsomely marked and is very long and silky. For this reason these large monkeys have been hunted for hundreds of years. During the last decades of the nineteenth century hundreds of thousands were slaughtered to satisfy the demands of fashion.

In addition to leaves they eat some lichens and possibly fruits. Only rarely do they descend to the ground, where other foods such as ripening seed pods are to be found. Apart from man they have few enemies except for the Leopard and the Crowned Hawk Eagle, both of which prey on all forest-dwelling monkeys.

157

WHITE-HANDED GIBBON

Hylobates lar

(Forests of Sumatra and Southern Asia)

The anthropoid apes differ from the true monkeys in that they are tailless and have elongated arms. Also, their brains are more highly developed and their level of intelligence is greater than that of any other animal except man. The seven species of gibbons are the smallest of the anthropoid apes. Unlike their larger relatives, the Great Apes, they have rough patches of skin, the ischial callosities, on the hindquarters.

White-handed or Lar Gibbons live in family groups, normally consisting of an adult male and female and their young. Each group occupies a territory of up to 100 acres, and defends this area against rival families both vocally and by combat if necessary. They are expert climbers, hooking their long fingers over branches and swinging along hand over hand. This mode of progression, called brachiation, which is characteristic of the anthropoid apes, is seen at its best in the gibbons. Being lightly built they can travel at great speed and can swing across gaps 20 feet wide. Very young ones cling to the mother's waist as she moves about and seem to make little difference to her progress as she searches for fruit and green nuts.

On the ground gibbons walk on their hind legs with the arms held up rather awkwardly. When running fast they move on all fours. In drinking, they usually dip their hands into water and then lick them, although it is not unknown for them to put their heads down and lap up water in the more usual way.

Young gibbons are born after a gestation period of 7 months, and are fully grown at 6 years.

SIAMANG

Hylobates syndactylus

(Forests of Malaya and Sumatra)

The Siamang is the largest member of the gibbon group. It may stand up to 3 feet tall and have an arm span of 5 feet. The general body shape is similar to that of the more typical gibbons, but the feet are unusual, the second and third toes being united by a web of skin as far as the last joint.

The strangest feature of the Siamang, however, is its huge, naked, reddish-brown vocal sac. This is present on the throat of both male and female and is inflated (as shown below) just prior to calling. Like all members of the subfamily, the Siamang gives vent to loud, whooping cries with tremendous carrying power, and the sac undoubtedly assists in exaggerating these vocalizations. As the cries are repeated the sac deflates and is then re-inflated for a new bout of calling. When the animal is silent the pouch is inconspicuous in the shaggy black fur.

Siamangs live in family groups and vocalize together at dawn and dusk. They live in the uppermost branches of the trees and rarely come down to the ground. On the Mentawi Islands, to the south-west of Sumatra, there lives a pygmy version of the Siamang—*Hylobates klossi*, the Dwarf Gibbon. Like its larger relative it has vocal pouches in both sexes and webbing between the second and third toes. This webbing is, however, much less extensive. The only other member of the family possessing a vocal sac is the Black Gibbon, *Hylobates concolor*, from the mainland of southern Asia, but in this case it is present only in the males.

159

F 189

ORANG-UTAN

Pongo pygmaeus

(Forests of Borneo and Sumatra)

The only Great Apes to be found outside Africa are the Orang-utans, which inhabit the low-lying forests of Borneo and Sumatra. No doubt similar apes occurred on the mainland of Asia not many hundreds of years ago, but now even the island form is on the decline and it is estimated that less than 5,000 remain alive today. If the present rate of destruction continues, the species will soon become completely extinct.

If an adult male was to stand erect, it would be over 4 feet tall. The arms are much longer than the legs and have a total span of well over 7 feet. The body is covered with long, shaggy, reddish-brown hair. The features of young Orang-utans sometimes appear remarkably human, but the mature male has a large pouch which hangs below the chin and fleshy blinkers growing from the sides of the face.

Although Orangs can travel quickly when they choose, they usually move lethargically through the forest in small groups in search of food, especially the fruit of the durian, of which they are particularly fond. At nightfall each animal makes a platform of branches in the fork of a tree.

The gestation period is just under 8 months. When an Orang-utan was born at the London Zoo recently the mother, which had not previously seen a young one of her own kind, nevertheless aided the delivery with her own hands and gently breathed into her offspring's mouth. Orangs can breed when they are 8 years old, but do not become fully mature until several years later.

CHIMPANZEE

Pan troglodytes

(Forests of Central West Africa)

Judged by our own standards, the Chimpanzee is undoubtedly the most intelligent of all infra-human primates. It has a high level of curiosity, sensitive manipulatory abilities, and an active brain capable of simple reasoning. It has even been shown to possess a crude aesthetic sense and to be able to draw and paint organized abstract patterns. These and other exploratory activities are frequently performed for their own sake, but the animal has one great short-coming; namely, that it is unable to concentrate on any one of these tasks for any length of time.

In the wild these apes live a quiet, fruit-gathering life, moving about in mixed groups from one feeding site to another, or to a suitable sleeping place where, like the Orang-utan and the Gorilla, they construct individual beds of twigs and leaves. These are often built in the trees, but sometimes on the ground. Chimpanzees do, in fact, spend most of their time at ground level, ascending only when on a specific quest. They eat nuts, berries and fruits of various kinds and one group has recently been seen to devour a monkey and a small wild pig. Termites are also swallowed. These are obtained by probing with a stick or stem into a hole in a termite hill.

Chimpanzees communicate with a variety of loud calls and with facial expressions. The shape of the mouth is extremely variable and highly significant.

The common Chimpanzee is found north of the Congo river. South of it is a second species, the Pygmy Chimpanzee, or Bonobo (*Pan paniscus*). This is black-faced, slender, and much smaller. It is also said to have a different vocabulary of calls.

GORILLA

Gorilla gorilla

(Forests of Central West Africa)

The Gorilla is the largest of the living primates. An adult male stands 5½ feet high, with an arm spread of 8 feet. When mature, the body weight exceeds 400 lb. and in some cases has even reached the surprising figure of 600 lb. (43 stone).

Gorillas live in the dense forests of tropical Africa, in inaccessible regions. As a result, many of the details of their life in the wild remain something of a mystery. We know, however, that they spend most of their time down on the ground, roaming about in family groups during the day and sleeping in specially prepared beds or "nests" at night. These beds, some of which are made on the ground and others up in the trees, are formed of twigs and leaves. They are abandoned and new ones made when the family moves on.

Despite their great canine teeth, Gorillas are primarily vegetarians, like their close relatives the Chimpanzee, the Pygmy Chimpanzee and the Orang-utan. Together, these four primates are known as the Great Apes.

Gorillas have no natural enemies except for the leopard, which may attempt to carry off a young one if it strays too far from the group.

There are two forms of Gorilla. The Lowland Gorilla (seen below) still occurs in fair numbers, but the shaggy-coated Mountain Gorilla, which was only discovered in 1901 living high up in the forest-covered mountain ranges on the borders of the Congo, is comparatively rare. It is difficult to obtain figures of the exact populations, but it has recently been estimated that there are more than 5,000, but fewer than 15,000 Mountain Gorillas alive today.

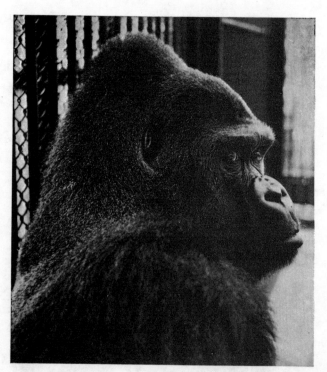

G. EDENTATES

The edentates are an exclusively New World order and, except for one species, are confined to the tropical regions of South and Central America. (The exception, the Nine-banded Armadillo, extends up into the southern States of the United States.) There are thirty-two species and they fall into three strikingly different groups—the anteaters, the sloths and the armadillos.

The name edentate means literally "without teeth", but it is misleading, for only the anteaters are completely toothless. Indeed some of the armadillos have more teeth than any other kind of land mammal. However, in both the sloths and the armadillos the incisors and canine teeth are missing and the cheek teeth are relatively simple. They are without enamel and grow throughout life as they are worn down. In the sloths there are sixteen to twenty, but in the armadillos there may be as many as 100.

The brain of edentates is small and primitive, and they are in general rather unintelligent, almost reptilian personalities. In most species the claws are massive and some are larger than any found in other orders of mammals.

The three groups that have survived are highly specialized forms that have managed to hold their own in competition with more advanced and intelligent mammals. Two groups of edentates that lost the battle and became extinct are the extraordinary glyptodonts and the gigantic ground-sloths. The former were relatives of the modern armadillos and some of them reached a length of 6 feet, with a rigid, 5-foot long shell and a heavily armoured head and tail. The ground-sloths were huge leaf-eaters the size of smallish elephants and must have weighed several tons. They became extinct comparatively recently and it is now known that they were still alive when early man first arrived in South America. Patches of their skin and hair have even been preserved intact to the present day.

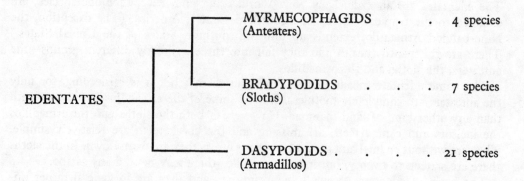

G. Order EDENTATA.   Edentates.

Suborder XENARTHRA.

Infraorder PILOSA.

Superfamily MYRMECOPHAGOIDEA.

Family MYRMECOPHAGIDAE.   Anteaters.

1 ►*Myrmecophaga tridactyla.*   **Giant Anteater.** Cen. and S. America. (CI/HK)
2   *Tamandua longicaudata.*   **Long-tailed Tamandua.** S. America. (CI)
3 ►*Tamandua tetradactyla.*   **Tamandua.** Cen. and S. America. (CI/HK)
4 ►*Cyclopes didactylus.*   **Dwarf Anteater.** Cen. and S. America. (CI/HK)

Superfamily BRADYPODOIDEA.

Family BRADYPODIDAE.   Sloths.

5   *Bradypus boliviensis.*   **Bolivian Three-toed Sloth.** S. America. (CI)
6   *Bradypus infuscatus.*   Cen. and S. America. (CI)
7   *Bradypus griseus.*   **Grey Three-toed Sloth.** Cen. America. (HK)
8   *Bradypus tridactylus.*   **Three-toed Sloth.** S. America. (CI)
9   *Bradypus torquatus.*   S. America. (CI)
10   *Choloepus didactylus.*   **Two-toed Sloth.** S. America. (CI)
11 ►*Choloepus hoffmanni.*   **Hoffmann's Sloth.** Cen. and S. America. (CI/HK)

Infraorder CINGULATA.

Superfamily DASYPODOIDEA.

Family DASYPODIDAE.   Armadillos.

Subfamily DASYPODINAE.

Tribe EUPHRACTINI.

12   *Chaetophractus nationi.*   S. America. (CI)
13   *Chaetophractus vellerosus.*   **Long-haired Armadillo.** S. America. (CI)
14   *Chaetophractus villosus.*   **Hairy Armadillo.** S. America. (CI)
15   *Euphractus sexcinctus.*   **Six-banded Armadillo.** S. America. (CI)
16   *Zaedyus pichiy.*   **Little Armadillo.** S. America. (CI)

Tribe PRIODONTINI.

17 ►*Priodontes giganteus.*   **Giant Armadillo.** S. America. (CI)
18   *Cabassous hispidus.*   S. America. (CI)
19   *Cabassous loricatus.*   S. America. (CI)
20   *Cabassous tatouay.*   S. America. (CI)
21   *Cabassous unicinctus.*   **Broad-banded Armadillo.** S. America. (CI)
22   *Cabassous centralis.*   **Central American Five-toed Armadillo.** Cen. America. (HK)

Tribe TOLYPEUTINI.

23   *Tolypeutes matacus.*   **La Plata Three-banded Armadillo.** S. America. (CI)
24   *Tolypeutes tricinctus.*   **Brazilian Three-banded Armadillo.** S. America. (CI)

Tribe DASYPODINI.

25	*Dasypus hybridus.*	**Mulita Armadillo.**	S. America. (C1)
26	*Dasypus kappleri.*	**Kappler's Armadillo.**	S. America. (C1)
27	*Dasypus mazzai.*		S. America. (C1)
28 ►	*Dasypus novemcinctus.*	**Nine-banded Armadillo.**	N. and S. America. (C1/HK)
29	*Dasypus pilosus.*		S. America. (C1)
30	*Dasypus septemcinctus.*	**Seven-banded Armadillo.**	S. America. (C1)

Subfamily CHLAMYPHORINAE. Fairy Armadillos.

31 ►	*Chlamyphorus truncatus.*	**Lesser Pichiciego.**	S. America. (C1)
32	*Burmeisteria retusa.*	**Greater Pichiciego.**	S. America. (C1)

GIANT ANTEATER

Myrmecophaga tridactyla

(Central and South America)

The Giant Anteater is one of the most remarkable of all mammals in appearance. It is 6 feet long from the tip of the extraordinary, tapering, tubular snout to the end of the long, bushy tail. (The tails of the captive specimens shown above are abnormally hairless.) Most of the body is grey-brown, the hindquarters being darker in tone than the rest of the body, while the bold wedge-shaped pattern on the throat and shoulders is black, outlined with white. These markings have the effect of disrupting the general body shape.

It is a creature of the grasslands and more open forests, although it may occasionally venture into the thicker regions, and is found from Guatemala to northern Argentina. As might be expected from its appearance this is not an opportunist species, able to live and feed under a wide variety of conditions, but a specialist very highly adapted for one mode of life only.

The Giant Anteater walks on the knuckles of its hands, with the result that the four strong claws of the fore-limbs are kept sharp. If threatened, the animal uses these claws in self-defence, striking out boldly, but they are more usually employed in ripping open the tough muddy walls of the nests of the termites, or white ants, on which it feeds. Once the nest is open the Anteater's long, viscous tongue comes into play, rapidly transferring the insects to the toothless, elongated mouth. In zoos Anteaters are given a substitute diet consisting of raw minced meat, raw eggs and milk.

TAMANDUA

Tamandua tetradactyla

(Forests of Central and South America)

The Tamandua, or Lesser Anteater, bears some resemblance to its close relative the Giant Anteater, which it replaces in the more thickly forested areas from Mexico to Paraguay and Peru. It is about 40 inches long, including the tail which measures 16 inches. The head is considerably less elongated than that of the larger species, and the black marking on the throat and shoulders is less dramatic. The remainder of the coarse fur is very pale buff in colour. It is sometimes stated that the Tamandua has three toes on the front foot, while the animal's Latin name suggests that it has four. In fact there are five, although the first and especially the fifth are very much reduced.

As the illustration above shows, the Tamandua's long tail is prehensile, indicating that the animal is at least partly arboreal. In fact, it is as much at home in the trees as on the ground. By day it hides amongst thick vegetation, or in a hole in a mango tree, emerging at night to scour the forest for insects.

The mouth is toothless and is a mere tube through which the long tongue projects. The salivary glands in the floor of the mouth produce a copious secretion which keeps the tongue sticky. The dexterity with which this specialized organ can be used is remarkable. Once a termites' nest in a tree or on the ground has been ripped open, the tongue can be inserted this way and that along the narrow galleries, picking up thousands of the insects in the process. Over a pound of termites have been taken from one Tamandua's stomach.

DWARF ANTEATER

Cyclopes didactylus

(Forests of Central and South America)

The Dwarf Anteater is the least frequently encountered of the three South American species. It is little larger than a squirrel, and is exclusively arboreal, living high in the trees of the thickest forests, from Mexico to Trinidad, Brazil and Peru. It bears a family resemblance to its larger relatives, but even apart from its smaller size it has a relatively shorter head than that of the Tamandua, which in turn is relatively shorter than that of the Giant species. The fur of the Dwarf Anteater is yellowish and silky. Like the Tamandua, it has a prehensile tail but, unlike it, it has only two claws on its front limbs.

It feeds, like the others, on termites, raiding the nests that these insects build in the tree-tops. Not only is it able to ignore the retaliatory attacks of the termites as it destroys their nest, but it even shows signs that their attentions may be pleasantly stimulating.

If it is attacked by a larger predator, the Anteater adopts the posture shown below. The hind limbs and tail take a firm grip upon the branch, whilst the impressive claws on the fore-limbs are held ready for instant use. A very similar posture is adopted by the Tamandua if it is unable to scuttle to safety. The Dwarf Anteater makes use of the same position when it tears the termites' nest open with its claws.

Like all members of the family, this species normally has only one young at a time. This rides on the mother's back, clinging tightly until it is quite large. The young of the two larger species behave similarly.

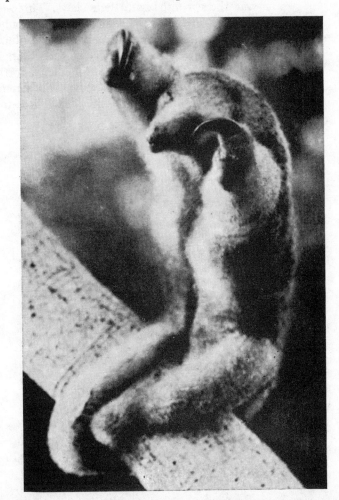

HOFFMAN'S SLOTH

Choloepus hoffmanni

(Forests of Central and South America)

Sloths are slow-moving tree-dwellers that hang upside down in the forests of tropical America. There are two basic kinds—the Two-toed, with two digits on the fore-limbs and three on the hind limbs, and the Three-toed, with three on all limbs. The fingers and toes are encased for most of their length in a common sheath of skin and muscle and are terminated by huge hooked claws.

The hair of the body lies in such a way that the tropical rain runs easily off the inverted body. The long, rough coat often looks greenish in the wild state due to the presence of algae. Mites, beetles and three species of small moths live in the hair as commensals, apparently feeding on these algae. Sloths rarely descend to the ground, where they can only move with difficulty although, incredibly, they are said to swim quite well.

The jaws are equipped with sharp cheek teeth well able to chew tough vegetation. Two-toed Sloths feed on a variety of leaves, stems and fruits, hooking leafy branches into their mouths with their claws. Three-toed Sloths, on the other hand, are more exacting in their requirements and eat only the leaves of cecropia, which is a tree related to the mulberry, and of the hog plum tree.

There are two species of Two-toed Sloths: one (*C. didactylus*) from Brazil and the other (Hoffmann's Sloth) from Ecuador north to Costa Rica. The Brazilian species has seven neck vertebrae like almost all other mammalian species, but Hoffmann's Sloth for some reason has only six. The Three-toed Sloths are even more unusual in this respect, having nine.

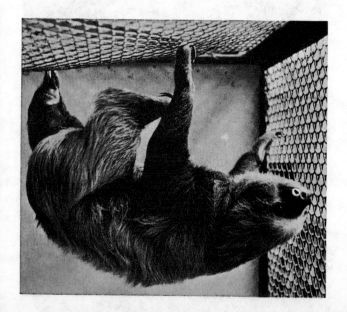

GIANT ARMADILLO

Priodontes giganteus

(Forests of South America)

Most armadillos inhabit grasslands but the largest species of all, the Giant Armadillo, is found deep in the South American forests. It can weigh as much as 100 lb. when fully grown and is about 4 feet long. Its legs, back, head and tail are all heavily armoured. There are five digits on both the front and hind feet, but those on the back feet are short, blunt nails, whereas the front claws are long and curved. The one on the third front digit is enormous. It is, in fact, the largest claw in the entire animal kingdom today and operates like a pick-axe, slashing into the termite colonies and ant-hills from which the Giant Armadillo obtains its basic food.

The elephantine hind legs are remarkably thick. On these, the animal sometimes walks bi-pedally, holding the front feet clear of the ground, with the long, stiff, tapering tail acting as a counterweight to balance the body.

When digging a burrow the front feet, hind feet and tail operate efficiently together as picks, shovels and a prop respectively. The front claws tear at the earth and throw it up and back. The heavy tail is pushed downward, tilting the rear end of the body up, and the massive hind legs shovel the earth backwards behind the animal. In this way a Giant Armadillo can disappear even into hard gravel at an alarming rate.

This species possesses more teeth than any other land mammal. They are small, rootless and peg-like and may number up to 100.

171

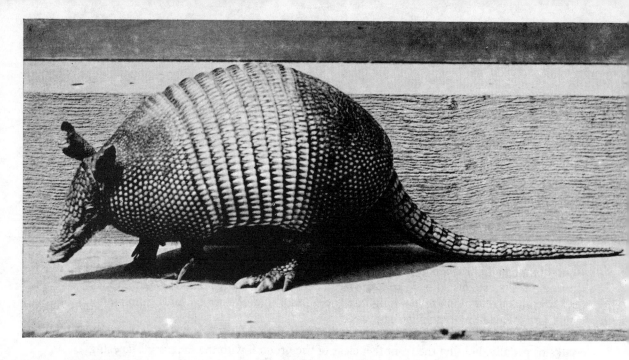

NINE-BANDED ARMADILLO

Dasypus novemcinctus

(South and Central America and Southern North America)

The Nine-banded Armadillo is widely distributed from the southern United States to Argentina. Like most armadillos, it rests during the day in a burrow which it excavates for itself using its strong front paws. Each animal has several burrows and these, in addition to the bony shell, serve to protect it from its many predators.

The shell itself is divided into a shoulder shield and a pelvic shield. In between these there is a series of moveable transverse bands. These bands (which vary in number in the different species) allow some degree of body curling and in some cases (*Tolypeutes*) the animals can roll right up into a tight ball. The Nine-banded Armadillo cannot do this but, when threatened, it makes rapidly for its burrow and arches its back to the maximum, wedging itself so that it cannot be pulled out. The tough shell is also useful when the animal plunges into thorny bushes.

It forages at night, shuffling along and ploughing up the litter of dead leaves with its nose. With its keen sense of smell it can locate grubs buried 6 inches deep. Periodically it rises to its hind legs and tests the air for the scent of its worst enemies, the Coyote and the Puma.

The food consists largely of beetles and other insects, but some earthworms and a few berries are eaten too. The young are born in a den at the end of a burrow. There are almost always four of them and they are identical quads, alike in every respect. They are well developed at birth and are weaned at the age of 2 months.

LESSER PICHICIEGO

Chlamyphorus truncatus

(Argentina and Bolivia)

This minute, pink-shelled, white-haired creature is the smallest of all the edentates, being little more than 5 inches long when fully adult. It is often called the Fairy Armadillo and is apparently as elusive and delicate as this name would suggest. It has seldom been seen alive in captivity.

Having adapted to a subterranean, mole-like existence it has small eyes and ears and heavy, powerful feet and claws. It digs with amazing rapidity, propping its body up with its stiff tail and shovelling the earth backwards as fast as possible. Authors differ as to whether insects or roots are its basic diet, but it almost certainly eats both.

Only the top of the head, the back, the rump and the tail are armoured, long silky hairs covering the rest of the body surface. In contrast to all other armadillos (including the Greater Pichiciego) the body armour is connected to the animal's back only down the mid-line. It is made up of approximately twenty uniform plates that stop abruptly above the rump. The latter is covered by a separate circular disc of armour. This is rigidly fused to the pelvic bones. When the Pichiciego flees into its tunnel it automatically plugs the exit with its own body, the bony rump-shield protecting its rear. The tail protrudes through a notch at the bottom of this shield and can be withdrawn forward out of harm's way. If the animal is caught away from its burrow it attempts to curl up into a ball like the more typical species.

173

H. PANGOLINS

Pangolins, or Scaly Anteaters, are found in Tropical Africa, southern Asia, Sumatra, Java, Borneo and the Philippines. There are four species in the African region and three in the Asiatic. They have aptly been described as looking like "animated pine cones".

The name Pholidota, given to this restricted order, means literally "scaly-ones", many of the hairs having changed during the course of evolution into large, flattened, overlapping scales of armour. The underside of the body, however, has remained soft and hairy and when defending itself the pangolin must curl up into a tight ball, like a hedgehog or an armadillo.

Teeth are completely absent and until comparatively recently it was thought that pangolins were close relatives of the also toothless anteaters of South America. It is now known that they are unrelated, the similarities between them being due to convergence, as a result of similar feeding habits.

Pangolins are unintelligent specialists and represent a small and unimportant, but nevertheless interesting mammalian offshoot. Their ancestry is virtually unknown.

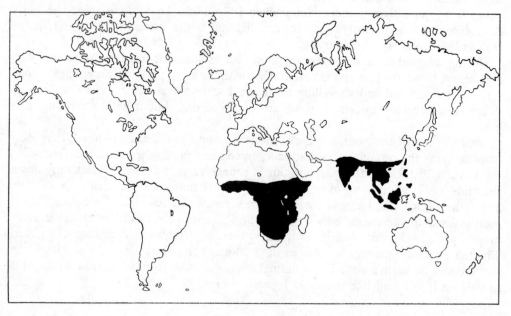

H. Order PHOLIDOTA.   Pangolins.

Family MANIDAE.

1	*Manis gigantea.*	**Giant Pangolin.** Cen. W. Africa. (A)
2 ►	*Manis temmincki.*	**Cape Pangolin.** Africa. (EMH)
3	*Manis tricuspis.*	**Tree Pangolin.** Africa. (EMH)
4	*Manis longicaudata.*	**Long-tailed Tree Pangolin.** Africa. (A)
5	*Manis pentadactyla.*	**Chinese Pangolin.** S.E. Asia. (EM)
6	*Manis crassicaudata.*	**Indian Pangolin.** S. Asia. (EM)
7	*Manis javanica.*	**Malayan Pangolin.** S. Asia, Sumatra, Borneo, Java, Philippines. (EM)

CAPE PANGOLIN

Manis temmincki

(South and East Africa)

Like all members of this order, the Cape Pangolin is found in the moist areas of its range. The head, tail, limbs, back and sides are completely covered with broad, horny scales and over the soft underside there are scattered a few bristle-like hairs. The elongated head is small and the mouth is situated at the tip of the slender snout. The Pangolin's tongue is almost a foot long and the animal has no teeth whatsoever. Each of the five digits on the hands and feet bears a large claw. Like its relatives, it possesses a pair of anal glands which give off a foul smell.

Pangolins are nocturnal and powerful diggers, scraping through the sides of termite mounds and tearing away the outer parts of ant-eaten trees to feed on the termites and ant larvae. They often move slowly along bi-pedally, with the fore-body lifted off the ground, and are capable of climbing well, using their prehensile tails and their sharp claws. Pangolins are seldom seen abroad in the light. They spend their days sleeping in their deep burrows which they seal off behind them. Both eyes and ears are very small but the sense of smell is apparently very good.

Pangolins bear one or two young in late winter. The offspring are born with soft scales which take several days to harden.

The largest member of the group is the Giant or Great Ground Pangolin (*Manis gigantea*) of Equatorial Africa which may be 6 feet long. Others include the long-tailed forms from West Africa and the edible Chinese Pangolin (*Manis pentadactyla*).

I. LAGOMORPHS

Lagomorphs have an almost world-wide distribution, being completely absent only in the Antarctic and the Australasian–New Zealand regions. (In the latter, they were, of course, introduced all too successfully by man during recent times.) There are two basic types, the rock-dwelling pikas, or conies, and the grassland rabbits and hares. There are fourteen species of pikas, twelve in Asia and two in North America. In general they are confined to the colder, more northerly and more mountainous regions. They all have short, rounded ears and rounded bodies and live in burrows under rocky outcrops. The fifty-two species of rabbits and hares are found in regions of intense cold in some cases and shimmering heat in others. They range from Scandinavia to Sumatra and from Alaska to Amazonia. There are twenty-eight species in the Old World and twenty-four in the New World. Their ears and limbs are longer than those of the pikas and they are extremely fast movers. Some burrow, others keep to the surface; some are solitary, others communal. All members of the order are short-tailed.

The name lagomorph means literally "hare-shaped" and gives us no clue concerning the diagnostic features of the group. These animals used to be placed within the rodent order, but it was later realized that their resemblances are largely superficial and due not to true affinity but to a similar way of life. Admittedly, they share much the same dental arrangements, with large, chisel-like, ever-growing incisors, no canines, and a gap, or diastema, between the front teeth and cheek teeth. But in detail even the teeth show striking differences. All rodents, for example, have a single upper and a single lower incisor on each side of the jaws. All lagomorphs, on the other hand, have two upper incisors on each side. The second one is small and situated just behind the first. There are also many additional differences in skeletal and other features, that come to light when a detailed comparison is made between the two groups.

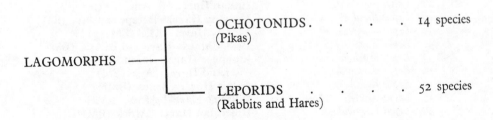

LAGOMORPHS

OCHOTONIDS. . . . 14 species
(Pikas)

LEPORIDS . . . . 52 species
(Rabbits and Hares)

I. Order LAGOMORPHA. Lagomorphs.
Family OCHOTONIDAE. Pikas.

1	*Ochotona pusilla.*	**Steppe Pika.** Asia. (EM)
2	*Ochotona thibetana.*	**Moupin Pika.** Asia. (EM)
3	*Ochotona roylei.*	**Royle's Pika.** Asia. (EM)
4	*Ochotona macrotis.*	**Large-eared Pika.** Asia. (EM)
5	*Ochotona daurica.*	**Daurian Pika.** Asia. (EM)
6	*Ochotona rufescens.*	**Afghan Pika.** Asia. (EM)
7	*Ochotona koslowi.*	**Koslow's Pika.** Asia. (EM)
8	*Ochotona alpina.*	**Altai Pika.** Asia. (EM)
9	*Ochotona hyperborea.*	**Northern Pika.** Asia. (EM)
10	*Ochotona pallasi.*	**Pallas's Pika.** Asia. (EM)
11	*Ochotona rutila.*	**Red Pika.** Asia. (EM)
12	*Ochotona ladacensis.*	**Ladak Pika.** Asia. (EM)
13	*Ochotona princeps.*	**American Pika.** N. America. (HK)
14 ►	*Ochotona collaris.*	**Alaskan Pika.** N. America. (HK)

Family LEPORIDAE. Rabbits and Hares.
Subfamily PALEOLAGINAE.

15	*Pentalagus furnessi.*	**Liukiu Rabbit.** Liukiu Islands (S. of Japan). (EM)
16	*Pronolagus marjorita.*	**African Grass Hare.** Africa. (EM)
17	*Pronolagus crassicaudatus.*	**Natal Red Hare.** Africa. (EMH)
18	*Pronolagus randensis.*	**Rand Red Hare.** Africa. (EMH)
19	*Pronolagus rupestris.*	**Smith's Red Hare.** Africa. (EMH)
20	*Romerolagus diazi.*	**Volcano Rabbit.** Cen. America. (HK)

Subfamily LEPORINAE.

21	*Caprolagus hispidus.*	**Assam Rabbit.** Asia. (EM)
22	*Lepus capensis.*	**Cape Hare.** Europe, Asia, Africa. (EM)
23	*Lepus atlanticus.*	**Lesser Moroccan Hare.** N. Africa. (EM)
24	*Lepus peguensis.*	**Burmese Hare.** S. Asia. (EM)
25	*Lepus arabicus.*	**Arabian Hare.** N. Africa. (EM)
26 ►	*Lepus europaeus.*	**European Hare.** Europe, Africa, W. Asia. (EM)
27	*Lepus siamensis.*	**Siamese Hare.** S. Asia. (EM)
28	*Lepus nigricollis.*	**Indian Hare.** S. Asia. (EM)
29	*Lepus timidus.*	**Varying Hare.** Europe and Asia. (EM)
30	*Lepus oiostolus.*	**Woolly Hare.** Asia. (EM)
31	*Lepus sinensis.*	**East Chinese Hare.** S.E. Asia. (EM)
32	*Lepus brachyurus.*	**Japanese Hare.** Japan. (EM)
33	*Lepus yarkandensis.*	**Yarkand Hare.** Asia. (EM)
34	*Lepus salai.*	**Sala's Hare.** Africa. (EMH)
35	*Lepus whytei.*	**Whyte's Hare.** Africa. (EMH)
36	*Lepus monticularis.*	**Bushman Hare.** Africa. (EMH)
37	*Lepus chadensis.*	**Lake Chad Hare.** Africa. (A)
38	*Lepus berberanus.*	**Berbera Hare.** Africa. (A)
39	*Lepus fagani.*	Africa. (A)
40	*Lepus raineyi.*	Africa. (A)
41	*Lepus crispii.*	Africa. (A)
42	*Lepus americanus.*	**Snowshoe Hare.** N. America. (HK)

178

43	*Lepus othus.*	**Alaskan Hare.** N. American Arctic. (HK)
44	*Lepus arcticus.*	**Arctic Hare.** N. American Arctic. (HK)
45	*Lepus townsendi.*	**White-tailed Jack Rabbit.** N. America. (HK)
46	*Lepus californicus.*	**Black-tailed Jack Rabbit.** N. America. (HK)
47	*Lepus insularis.*	**Black Jack Rabbit.** Espiritu Santo Island (N. America). (HK)
48	*Lepus mexicanus.*	**White-sided Jack Rabbit.** Cen. America. (HK)
49	*Lepus flavigularis.*	**Tehuantepec Jack Rabbit.** Cen. America. (HK)
50	*Lepus gaillardi.*	**Gaillard's Jack Rabbit.** N. America. (HK)
51	*Lepus alleni.*	**Antelope Jack Rabbit.** N. America. (HK)
52	*Sylvilagus idahoensis.*	**Pygmy Rabbit.** N. America. (HK)
53	*Sylvilagus brasiliensis.*	**Forest Rabbit.** N. and S. America. (HK/C2)
54	*Sylvilagus bachmani.*	**Brush Rabbit.** N. America. (HK)
55	*Sylvilagus mansuetus.*	**San José Brush Rabbit.** San José Island (N. America). (HK)
56	*Sylvilagus palustris.*	**Marsh Rabbit.** N. America. (HK)
57 ►	*Sylvilagus floridanus.*	**Eastern Cottontail.** N. and S. America. (HK/C2)
58	*Sylvilagus transitionalis.*	**New England Cottontail.** N. America. (HK)
59	*Sylvilagus nuttalli.*	**Nuttall's Cottontail.** N. America. (HK)
60	*Sylvilagus auduboni.*	**Desert Cottontail.** N. America. (HK)
61	*Sylvilagus aquaticus.*	**Swamp Rabbit.** N. America. (HK)
62	*Sylvilagus insonus.*	**Omilteme Cottontail.** Cen. America. (HK)
63	*Sylvilagus cunicularius.*	**Mexican Cottontail.** Cen. America. (HK)
64	*Sylvilagus graysoni.*	**Tres Marias Cottontail.** Tres Marias Islands (Cen. America). (HK)
65 ►	*Oryctolagus cuniculus.*	**European Rabbit** (and Domestic Rabbit). Europe and N. Africa. (EM
66	*Nesolagus netscheri.*	**Short-eared Rabbit.** Sumatra. (EM)

I 14 ALASKAN PIKA

Family OCHOTONIDAE

ALASKAN PIKA

Ochotona collaris

(North-west of North America)

There are two species of pikas in North America and twelve in Asia. The New World animals are confined to the rocky slopes of mountainous districts, one on the Rocky Mountains and the other (see above) in the highlands of Alaska and the Yukon. There, amongst the rock slides, they tunnel their underground homes.

They are gregarious, diurnal animals, smaller than rabbits, with short rounded ears and almost non-existent tails. Many local names have been given to them including Rock Rabbit, Slide Rat, Little Chief Hare, Mouse Hare, Coney, Haymaker, Squeak Rabbit, Whistling Hare and Calling Hare. As some of these suggest, they are well known for their high-pitched alarm calls.

Living in a bleak environment, the pikas are faced with a difficult winter survival problem. They solve it with an elaborate system of food storage. In the late summer they venture away from their rocky fortresses in search of green plants. These they cut off and carry back in their mouths. The freshly cut vegetation is then spread out on the rocks and left to dry in the sun. If the sun moves round so that the drying plants are shaded, the pikas shift them until they are once again exposed to its full glare. If a storm comes, they all dash out together, collect up the plants and carry them quickly out of the rain. When the vegetation is dried it is transported to special sites under overhanging rocks where "haystacks" are constructed. These may be several feet high and are often hollow inside, providing a winter restaurant for the pikas when both they and their rocky homes are hidden under deep snow.

EUROPEAN HARE

Lepus europaeus

(Europe, Africa and Western Asia)

The common European Hare is larger and more lanky than the European Rabbit, with longer legs and much bigger, black-tipped ears. Unlike rabbits, hares are solitary. They never burrow, but lie instead in shallow depressions called "forms". When danger approaches they crouch and freeze until the last moment. When they do flee they make frequent sudden changes in direction, leaping powerfully as they switch from one course to another. This helps to destroy their scent trail and confuse the pursuer.

The male hare is called a Jack, the female a Doe. In the spring the Jacks leap and kick, and fight one another by boxing with their front feet. When in pain, a hare emits a piercing scream sounding like a terrified child. Other noises include gruntings and teeth-gnashings and strange mating calls that are imitated by game-keepers or poachers to lure the animals towards them.

The young, known as leverets, are born fully furred and with their eyes open. They soon leave the mother's "form" and disperse. She then visits them one by one to feed them. In this way, even if a predator does find one, the others may escape. They are weaned after only 4 weeks.

Abandoned leverets are often bottle-fed and kept as pets. They grow up as remarkably inquisitive and intelligent household creatures, but they soon become destructive. In the wild they strip bark for food and in captivity this activity is directed towards furniture and wallpaper. If removed to a new home, such as a zoo, tame hares seem to be incapable of re-adjusting and usually die of shock.

EASTERN COTTONTAIL

Sylvilagus floridanus

(East of North America, Central America and North of South America)

The Eastern Cottontail is a woodland rabbit with a wide distribution from the Atlantic coast to the Rocky Mountains and from southern Ontario to Venezuela and Colombia. The race illustrated below is the White-browed form (*S.f. superciliaris*) from Colombia. In the more typical North American races the white eye marking is much less distinct.

During the summer months cottontails graze on the fresh green vegetation, but in the winter most of them must survive on nothing more than bark and twigs.

In certain respects they are intermediate between the European Hare and the European Rabbit. They do not make complex burrows like the Rabbit, but neither are the young well advanced at birth, like the Hare. The female Cottontail digs a shallow nest approximately 6 inches deep and lines it with dried grasses and with fur plucked from her own body. In this soft hole she gives birth to between four and seven blind, naked and helpless offspring. She then covers it over with more grasses and leaves. She does not stay near the nest, returning to it from time to time only to suckle the young. When entering it on these occasions she does not scrape the cover away but gently and carefully edges underneath it and then curves her body around the outside of the nest cavity, keeping the young in the middle.

After about 2 weeks, the developing Cottontails are furred and can see, and soon emerge from the nest. Throughout their lives their main enemies, apart from man, will be the Red Fox and the larger owls.

EUROPEAN RABBIT

Oryctolagus cuniculus

(Europe and North Africa)

The wild European Rabbit is a prolific, burrowing lagomorph that lives in large colonies in complex tunnel systems called warrens. It has a long breeding season in the spring, litters of five or more young being produced after a gestation period of only 29 days. The female mates again 12 hours after giving birth. When she becomes pregnant she digs a special breeding burrow away from the main warren. Into this she collects fragments of vegetation and constructs a nest. She lines it with fur plucked from her own body. The young, weighing only just over an ounce, are born blind, deaf and naked.

When it senses danger, a Rabbit alerts its companions by stamping its back feet. As it flees, the bobbing of its white tail adds a further, visual warning signal. The tail is also used by the male when courting the female. He makes ceremonial stiff-legged "false retreats" in front of her, with his tail flattened upward against his body. He also chases her in special non-aggressive "sexual pursuits", and performs enurination (the squirting over her of a jet of urine).

The grass and other foods eaten by wild Rabbits are not easy to digest. Ruminants, such as cattle and sheep, overcome this problem by regurgitation and by chewing the cud. Rabbits instead indulge in reingestion. When they are resting in their burrows they produce special soft droppings which each animal eats direct from its own anus. Only when they are out and about actively grazing do they produce the typical hard droppings. This means that all food is passed twice through the gut and the rabbit can extract the maximum possible amount of nourishment from its coarse diet.

J. RODENTS

Rodents are world-wide in distribution and proverbially numerous, both in numbers of specimens and numbers of species. It is often said that there are more rodent species than all the other mammal species put together, but this is something of an exaggeration. It is nevertheless true to say that two out of every five species of mammals are rodents. There are 1,729 species recognized at the present time. Until recent years there were far more, but hundreds of old species are now known to be no more than racial variations. As time goes on, with more and more specimens being examined, the number of rodent species will no doubt fall yet again, but for the present we must accept the latest figures as outlined here.

There are three main groups—the squirrel-like rodents, with 366 species, the rat-like with 1,183 species, and the porcupine-like with 180 species.

The name rodent is derived from the Latin verb *rodere* meaning to gnaw. It refers to the basic characteristic of the group; namely the use of the sharp, ever-growing, incisor teeth as instruments for attacking hard objects. These teeth are chisel-like in shape and action—the front surface being strong enamel and the rest softer dentine. As the tooth wears, the front edge lasts longer than the back and this gives the tip its chisel-like shape.

The second incisors, the canines and the front premolars are absent in all rodents and there is a gap, or diastema, between the front teeth and the cheek teeth. When the lower jaw is moved forward, the large incisors come into opposition and can act, but the cheek teeth do not meet. While this is happening, the back part of the mouth can be shut off completely by the drawing in of the cheeks in the diastema region. This means that the rodent can gnaw away for long periods without wearing out its cheek teeth and without swallowing chips of wood or lumps of earth.

If the animal is going to switch from gnawing to chewing, the lower jaw moves backwards and then the upper and lower cheek teeth can be opposed, but not the incisors, which now lie behind one another. Complex muscles have evolved in connection with these special jaw movements and detailed differences in these muscles and in the skull bones associated with them provide one of the most important sources of information for the complicated task of classifying the many rodent species.

With their adaptability and their dual-action mouths, rodents have been able to succeed in many environments that have proved too difficult for other species. They have spread everywhere and have filled almost every niche: they burrow, they run, they hop, they climb, they leap, they glide and they swim. They are found in the deserts and the rain forests, in the Arctic and on the Equator. As man has moved about the world, rodents have followed him in his camps and on his ships. Practically every form of vegetable food has been attacked by them at some point. From the moment man became an agricultural species, the rodents became one of his deadliest enemies. The battle still continues.

For some reason rodents have always remained small-bodied creatures. A mere handful of them have attained the size of small pigs, but nothing larger has been achieved and the vast majority of them are only a few inches in length.

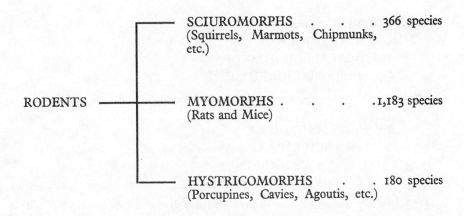

RODENTS — SCIUROMORPHS . . . 366 species
(Squirrels, Marmots, Chipmunks, etc.)

MYOMORPHS . . . .1,183 species
(Rats and Mice)

HYSTRICOMORPHS . . 180 species
(Porcupines, Cavies, Agoutis, etc.)

Classification Note

Owing to the huge number of species, it has only been possible to list the genera of rodents. In each case, however, the number of living species is given and, where there is only a single species in a genus, its full name is included. Ellerman's standard two-volume work on the rodents (E1 and E2) has been used as a basis for the present rodent list at the genus and species level. However, although his study was comprehensive it was not particularly selective. He himself modified it (E3) in certain respects and it has also been simplified in later regional works (EM, EMH, etc.). Where these later works have left his original species lists unaltered, only the E1 or E2 symbol is given. Where a later work has modified them, then its symbol is added to the E symbol (for example: E2/EM). In almost all cases the modification takes the form of a reduction of the number of accepted species in a genus.

J. Order RODENTIA. Rodents.

Suborder SCIUROMORPHA.

Superfamily APLODONTOIDEA.

Family APLODONTIDAE.

1 ►*Aplodontia rufa.*   **Mountain Beaver.** N. America. (E1)

Superfamily SCIUROIDEA.

Family SCIURIDAE. Squirrels.

Subfamily SCIURINAE.

Tribe SCIURINI.

2 ►*Sciurus* (37 species).   **Tree Squirrels.** Europe, Asia, N. and S. America. (E1/EM/C2/HK)

3 *Syntheosciurus* (2 species).   **Mountain Squirrels.** Cen. America. (E1/HK)
4 *Microsciurus* (3 species).   **Pygmy Squirrels.** Cen. and S. America. (E1/C2/HK)
5 *Sciurillus pusillus.*   **South American Pygmy Squirrel.** S. America. (E1/C2)
6 *Prosciurillus murinus.*   **Celebes Dwarf Squirrel.** Celebes. (E3)
7 *Rheithrosciurus macrotis.*   **Tufted-eared Ground Squirrel.** Borneo. (E1)

Tribe TAMIASCIURINI.

8 *Tamiasciurus* (2 species).   **American Red Squirrels.** N. America. (E1/HK)

Tribe FUNAMBULINI.

9 *Funambulus* (5 species).   **Palm Squirrels.** S. Asia. (E1/E3)
10 ►*Ratufa* (4 species).   **Giant Squirrels.** S. Asia, Sumatra, Java, Borneo. (E1/E3)
11 *Protoxerus stangeri.*   **African Giant Squirrel.** Africa. (E1)
12 *Myrsilus aubinnii.*   W. Africa. (E1)
13 *Epixerus* (2 species).   **African Palm Squirrels.** W. Africa. (E1)
14 *Funisciurus* (14 species).   **African Striped Squirrels.** Africa. (E1/EMH)
15 *Paraxerus* (11 species).   **Bush Squirrels.** S. and E. Africa. (E1/EMH)
16 *Heliosciurus* (7 species).   **Sun Squirrels.** Africa. (E1)
17 *Myosciurus pumilio.*   **African Pygmy Squirrel.** W. Africa. (E1)

Tribe CALLOSCIURINI.

18 *Callosciurus* (25 species).   **Common Oriental Squirrels.** Asia, Sumatra, Java, Borneo, Philippines. (E1/E3/EM/SA)
19 *Menetes berdmorei.*   **Berdmore's Squirrel.** S. Asia. (E1)
20 *Rhinosciurus laticaudatus.*   **Long-nosed Ground Squirrel.** S. Asia, Sumatra, Borneo. (E1)
21 *Lariscus* (2 species).   **Striped Ground Squirrels.** S. Asia, Sumatra, Java, Borneo. (E1)
22 *Dremomys* (4 species).   **Ground Squirrels.** S. Asia and Borneo. (E1/EM/CH)
23 *Sciurotamias* (2 species).   **Rock Squirrels.** E. Asia. (E1)
24 *Glyphotes simus.*   **Pygmy Ground Squirrel.** Borneo. (E1)
25 *Nannosciurus* (7 species).   **Oriental Pygmy Squirrels.** Sumatra, Java, Borneo, Philippines. (E1)
26 *Hyosciurus heinrichi.*   **Long-snouted Squirrel.** Celebes. (E1)

Tribe XERINI.

27	*Atlantoxerus getulus.*	**Barbary Ground Squirrel.** N.W. Africa. (E1)
28	*Xerus* (4 species).	**Bristly Ground Squirrels.** Africa. (E1)
29	*Spermophilopsis leptodactylus.*	**Long-clawed Ground Squirrels.** S. Asia. (E1/EM)

Tribe MARMOTINI.

30	*Marmota* (8 species).	**Marmots.** Europe, Asia, N. America. (E1/EM/HK)
31	►*Cynomys* (5 species).	**Prairie Marmots.** N. America. (E1)
32	►*Citellus* (34 species).	**Ground Squirrels.** E. Europe, Asia, N. America. (E1/EM/HK)
33	►*Tamias* (18 species).	**Chipmunks.** Asia and N. America. (E1) (E1/EM/HK)

Subfamily PETAURISTINAE.

34	►*Petaurista* (5 species).	**Giant Flying Squirrels.** Asia, Sumatra, Java, Borneo. (E1/E3/EM/CH)
35	*Aeromys* (2 species).	**Black Giant Flying Squirrels.** S. Asia, Borneo, Sumatra. (E1/CH)
36	*Eupetaurus cinereus.*	**Woolly Flying Squirrel.** S. Asia. (E1)
37	*Pteromys* (2 species).	**Smaller Flying Squirrels.** Europe and Asia. (E1)
38	*Glaucomys* (2 species).	**American Flying Squirrels.** Cen. and N. America. (E1)
39	*Eoglaucomys fimbriatus.*	**Small Kashmir Flying Squirrel.** S. Asia. (E1)
40	*Hylopetes* (8 species).	**Arrow-tailed Flying Squirrels.** S. Asia, Sumatra, Java, Borneo, Philippines. (E1/EM/CH)
41	*Petinomys* (8 species).	**Bearded Flying Squirrels.** S. Asia, Sumatra, Java, Borneo, Philippines. (E1) (E1/EM/CH)
42	*Aeretes melanopterus.*	**Grooved-toothed Giant Flying Squirrel.** E. Asia. (E3)
43	*Trogopterus xanthipes.*	**Complex-toothed Flying Squirrel.** Asia. (E1)
44	*Belomys pearsoni.*	**Hairy-footed Flying Squirrel.** S. Asia and Formosa. (E1)
45	*Pteromyscus pulverulentus.*	**Smoky Flying Squirrel.** S. Asia, Sumatra, Borneo. (E1)
46	*Petaurillus* (3 species).	**Pygmy Flying Squirrels.** S. Asia and Borneo. (E1)
47	*Iomys horsfieldi.*	**Horsfield's Flying Squirrel.** Sumatra, Java, Borneo. (E1)

Superfamily GEOMYOIDEA.

Family GEOMYIDAE.

Subfamily GEOMYINAE.   Pocket Gophers.

48	*Geomys* (7 species).	**Eastern Pocket Gophers.** N. America. (E1/HK)
49	*Thomomys* (6 species).	**Smooth-toothed Pocket Gophers.** N. America. (E1/HK)
50	*Pappogeomys* (2 species)	**Buller's and Alcorn's Pocket Gophers.** Cen. America. (E1)
51	*Cratogeomys* (7 species).	**Yellow Pocket Gophers.** N. America. (E1)
52	*Platygeomys* (5 species).	**Yellow Pocket Gophers.** Cen. America. (E1)
53	*Orthogeomys* (3 species).	**Giant Pocket Gophers.** Cen. America. (E1/HK)
54	*Heterogeomys* (2 species).	**Hispid Pocket Gophers.** Cen. America. (E1/HK)
55	*Macrogeomys* (6 species).	**Central American Pocket Gophers.** Cen. America. (E1/HK)
56	*Zygogeomys trichopus.*	**Michoacán Pocket Gopher.** Cen. America. (E1)

187

Family HETEROMYIDAE.
    Subfamily PEROGNATHINAE.

57 *Perognathus* (25 species).   **Pocket Mice.** N. America. (E1/HK)
58 *Microdipodops* (2 species).   **Kangaroo Mice.** N. America. (E1/E3)

    Subfamily DIPODOMYINAE.

59 ►*Dipodomys* (22 species).   **Kangaroo Rats.** N. America. (E1/HK)

    Subfamily HETEROMYINAE.

60 *Liomys* (11 species).   **Spiny Pocket Mice.** Cen. America. (E1)
61 *Heteromys* (11 species).   **Spiny Pocket Mice.** S. and Cen. America. (E1/HK)

Superfamily CASTOROIDEA.
    Family CASTORIDAE.   Beavers.
      Subfamily CASTORINAE.

62 ►*Castor fiber*.   **Beaver.** Europe, Asia, N. America. (E1/EM)

Superfamily ANOMALUROIDEA.
    Family ANOMALURIDAE.
      Subfamily ANOMALURINAE.

63 *Anomalurus* (3 species).   **Scaly-tailed Squirrels.** W. and Cen. Africa. (E1)
64 *Anomalurops beecrofti*.   **Beecroft's Scaly-tailed Squirrel.** W. and Cen. Africa. (E1)

      Subfamily ZENKERELLINAE.

65 *Idiurus* (3 species).   **Pygmy Scaly-tailed Squirrels.** Cen. Africa. (E1)
66 *Zenkerella insignis*.   **Non-flying Scaly-tailed Squirrel.** W. Africa. (E1)

    Family PEDETIDAE.

67 ►*Pedetes capensis*.   **Springhaas.** Africa. (E1/EMH)

Suborder MYOMORPHA.
    Superfamily MUROIDEA.
      Family CRICETIDAE.
        Subfamily CRICETINAE.
          Tribe HESPEROMYINI.   New World Mice.

68 *Oryzomys* (68 species).   **Rice Rats.** N. and S. America and Galapagos. (E2/C2/HK)
69 *Neacomys* (3 species).   **Bristly Mice.** Cen. and S. America. (E2/C2/HK)
70 *Scolomys melanops*.   **South American Spiny Mouse.** S. America. (E2/C2)
71 *Nectomys* (3 species).   **Water Rats.** Cen. and S. America. (E2/C2/HK)
72 *Rhipidomys* (6 species).   **Long-tailed Climbing Mice.** Cen. and S. America. (E2/C2/HK)

73	*Thomasomys* (25 species).	**Thomas' Paramo Mice.** S. America. (E2/C2)
74	*Phaenomys ferrugineus.*	**Rio Rice Rat.** S. America. (E2)
75	*Chilomys instans.*	**Colombian Forest Mouse.** S. America. (E2/C2)
76	*Tylomys* (8 species).	**Climbing Mice.** Cen. and S. America. (E2/C2/HK)
77	*Ototylomys* (3 species).	**Big-eared Climbing Mice.** Cen. America. (E2/HK)
78	*Nyctomys sumichrasti.*	**Sumichrast's Vesper Rat.** Cen. America. (E2)
79	*Otonyctomys hatti.*	**Yucatan Vesper Rat.** Cen. America. (HK)
80	*Rhagomys rufescens.*	**Brazilian Tree Mouse.** S. America. (E2)
81	*Reithrodontomys* (17 species).	**American Harvest Mice.** N. and S. America. (E2/C2/HK)
82	*Peromyscus* (57 species).	**White-footed Mice.** N. and Cen. America. (E2/HK)
83	*Baiomys* (2 species).	**Pygmy Mice.** N. and Cen. America. (E2)
84	*Onychomys* (2 species).	**Grasshopper Mice.** N. America. (E2)
85	*Akodon* (39 species).	**South American Field Mice.** S. America. (E2/C2)
86	*Zygodontomys* (6 species).	**American Cane Rats.** Cen. and S. America. (E2/C2/HK)
87	*Podoxymys roraimae.*	**Mount Roraima Mouse.** S. America. (E2/C2)
88	*Lenoxus apicalis.*	**Peruvian Rat.** S. America. (E2)
89	*Oxymycterus* (8 species).	**South American Burrowing Mice.** S. America. (E2/C2)
90	*Elarinomys breviceps.*	**Brazilian Shrew Mouse.** S. America. (E2)
91	*Notiomys* (6 species).	**Long-clawed Mice.** S. America. (E2/C2)
92	*Scapteromys* (5 species).	**South American Water Rats.** S. America. (E2)
93	*Wiedomys pyrrhorhinos.*	**Wied's Red-nosed Mouse.** S. America. (C2)
94	*Scotinomys* (4 species).	**American Brown Mice.** Cen. America. (E2/HK)
95	*Calomys* (10 species).	**Vesper Mice.** S. America. (E2/C2)
96	*Paralomys gerbillus.*	S. America. (C2)
97	*Pseudoryzomys wavrini.*	**Red-nosed Mouse.** S. America. (C2)
98	*Eligmodontia* (2 species).	**Highland Desert Mice.** S. America. (E2/C2)
99	*Phyllotis* (14 species).	**Long-eared Mice.** S. America. (E2/C2)
100	*Galenomys garleppi.*	S. America. (C2)
101	*Irenomys tarsalis.*	**Chilean Rat.** S. America. (E2/C2)
102	*Punomys lemminus.*	**Puna Mouse.** S. America. (E3)
103	*Chinchillula sahamae.*	**Chinchilla Mouse.** S. America. (E2)
104	*Neotomys ebriosus.*	**Andean Swamp Rat.** S. America. (E2/C2)
105	*Reithrodon physodes.*	**Pampas Gerbil.** S. America. (E2/C2)
106	*Euneomys* (4 species).	**Patagonian Chinchilla Mice.** S. America. (E2)
107	*Holochilus* (2 species).	**Web-footed Marsh Rats.** S. America. (E2/C2)
108	*Sigmodon* (14 species).	**Cotton Rats.** N. and S. America. (E2/C2/HK)
109	*Andinomys edax.*	**Andean Mouse.** S. America. (E2)
110	*Neotomodon alstoni.*	**Volcano Mouse.** Cen. America. (E2/HK)
111	*Neotoma* (20 species).	**Wood Rats.** N. and Cen. America. (E2/HK)
112	*Teanopus phenax.*	**Sonoran Wood Rat.** Cen. America. (E3)
113	*Hodomys alleni.*	**Allen's Wood Rat.** Cen. America. (E2/HK)
114	*Nelsonia neotomodon.*	**Diminutive Wood Rat.** Cen. America. (E2/HK)
115	*Xenomys nelsoni.*	**Magdalena Rat.** Cen. America. (E2)
116	*Ichthyomys* (2 species).	**Fish-eating Rats.** S. America. (E2/C2)
117	*Anotomys leander.*	**Ecuador Fish-eating Rat.** S. America. (E2)
118	*Daptomys venezuelae.*	**Aquatic Rat.** S. America. (E2)
119	*Rheomys* (4 species).	**Water Mice.** S. and Cen. America. (E2/HK)
120	*Neusticomys monticolus.*	**Fish-eating Mouse.** S. America. (E2)

Tribe CRICETINI. Hamsters.

| 121 | *Calomyscus bailwardi.* | **Mouse-like Hamster.** Asia. (E2) |
| 122 | *Phodopus* (2 species). | **Asian Hamsters.** Asia. (E2/EM) |

189

123	►*Cricetus cricetus.*	**Common Hamster.** Europe and W. Asia. (E2)
124	*Cricetulus* (9 species).	**Eurasian Hamsters.** Europe and Asia. (E2/EM)
125	*Mesocricetus auratus.*	**Golden Hamster.** E. Europe and W. Asia. (E2/EM)
126	*Mystromys* (2 species).	**White-tailed Rats.** S. and E. Africa. (E2)

Tribe MYOSPALACINI.   Mole Mice.

| 127 | *Myospalax* (5 species). | **Mole Mice.**   Asia. (E2/EM) |

Subfamily NESOMYINAE.   Malagasy Rats.

128	*Macrotarsomys bastardi.*	Madagascar. (E2/A)
129	*Nesomys* (3 species).	Madagascar. (E2)
130	*Brachytarsomys albicauda.*	Madagascar. (E2)
131	*Eliurus* (5 species).	Madagascar. (E2)
132	*Gymnuromys roberti.*	Madagascar. (E2)
133	*Hypogeomys antimena.*	Madagascar. (E2)
134	*Brachyuromys* (2 species)	Madagascar. (E2)

Subfamily LOPHIOMYINAE.

| 135 | ►*Lophiomys imhausi.* | **Maned Rat.**   E. Africa. (E1) |

Subfamily MICROTINAE.
Tribe LEMMINI.   Lemmings.

136	*Dicrostonyx* (4 species).	**Collared Lemmings.** Arctic Asia and Arctic America. (E2/EM/HK)
137	*Synaptomys* (2 species).	**Bog Lemmings.** N. America. (E2)
138	*Myopus schisticolor.*	**Wood Lemming.** N. Europe and N. Asia. (E2)
139	*Lemmus* (4 species).	**Lemmings.** N. Europe, N. Asia, N. of N. America. (E2/EM/HK)

Tribe MICROTINI   Voles.

140	*Clethrionomys* (5 species).	**Red-backed Voles.** Europe, Asia, N. America, Arctic. (E2/E3/EM/HK)
141	*Eothenomys* (5 species).	**Chinese Voles.** Asia. (E2/EM)
142	*Alticola* (4 species).	**Mountain Voles.** Cen. Asia. (E2/EM)
143	*Hyperacrius* (2 species).	**Kashmir Voles.** S. Asia. (E2/EM)
144	*Dolomys bogdanovi.*	**Martino's Snow Vole.** S. Europe. (E2/EM)
145	*Arvicola terristris.*	**Water Vole.** Europe and Asia. (E2/EM)
146	►*Ondatra* (2 species).	**Muskrats.** N. America. (E2/HK)
147	*Neofiber alleni.*	**Round-tailed Muskrat.** N. America. (E2)
148	*Phenacomys* (4 species).	**Heather Vole and Tree Mice.** N. America. (E2/HK)
149	*Pitymys* (11 species).	**Pine Voles.** Europe, S.W. Asia, N. America. (E2/HK/EM)
150	*Blanfordimys afghanus.*	**Afghan Vole.** Cen. Asia. (E2/EM)
151	►*Microtus* (42 species).	**Common Field Voles.** Europe, Asia, N. America, N. Africa. (E2/HK/EM)
152	*Orthriomys umbrosus.*	Cen. America. (E2)
153	*Herpetomys guatemalensis.*	Cen. America. (E2)
154	►*Lagurus* (3 species).	**Steppe Lemmings.** Asia and N. America. (E2/EM/HK)
155	*Prometheomys schaposchnikowi.*	**Long-clawed Mole Vole.** Asia. (E2)

Tribe ELLOBIINI.   Mole Lemmings.

156   *Ellobius* (3 species).   **Mole Lemmings.**   Asia. (E2/EM)

Subfamily GERBILLINAE.   Gerbils.

157	*Monodia mauritaniae.*	Africa. (HB)
158	*Gerbillus* (37 species).	**Smaller Gerbils.** S.W. Asia and Africa. (E2/EM/EMH)
159	*Tatera* (32 species).	**Larger Gerbils.** S. Asia and Africa. (E2/EMH)
160	*Taterillus* (16 species).	**Naked-soled Gerbils.** Africa. (E2)
161	*Desmodillus auricularis.*	**Cape Short-tailed Gerbil.** S. Africa. (E2)
162	*Desmodilliscus braueri.*	**Short-eared Rat.** C. Africa. (E2)
163 ►	*Pachyuromys duprasi.*	**Fat-tailed Gerbil.** N. Africa. (E2)
164	*Ammodillus imbellis.*	E. Africa. (E2)
165	*Meriones* (13 species).	**Jirds.** N. Africa and Cen. Asia. (E2/EM)
166	*Brachiones przewalskii.*	**Przewalski's Gerbil.** Cen. Asia. (E2/EM)
167	*Psammomys obesus.*	**Fat Sand Rat.** N. Africa and S.W. Asia. (E2/EM)
168	*Rhombomys opimus.*	**Great Gerbil.** Asia. (E2)

Family SPALACIDAE.   Palaearctic Mole Rats.

169   *Spalax* (3 species).   **Mole Rats.**   Asia and N. Africa. (E1/EM)

Family RHIZOMYIDAE.

170	*Tachyoryctes* (14 species).	**East African Mole Rats.** E. Africa. (E2)
171	*Rhizomys* (3 species).	**Bamboo Rats.** S. Asia and Sumatra. (E1/EM)
172	*Cannomys badius.*	**Lesser Bamboo Rat.** S. Asia. (E1)

Family MURIDAE.
Subfamily MURINAE.

173	*Vernaya fulva.*	**Vernay's Climbing Mouse.** S. Asia. (EM)
174	*Tokudaia osimensis.*	**Liukiu Spiny Rat.** Liukiu Islands. (EM)
175	*Hapalomys longicaudatus.*	**Marmoset Mouse.** S. Asia. (E2/EM)
176	*Vandeleuria oleracea.*	**Palm Mouse.** S. Asia. (E2/EM)
177	*Micromys minutus.*	**Harvest Mouse.** Europe and Asia. (E2)
178 ►	*Apodemus* (5 species).	**Field Mice.** Europe, Asia, N. Africa. (E2/EM)
179	*Thamnomys* (4 species).	**Thicket Rats.** Africa. (E2)
180	*Grammomys* (7 species).	**Forest Mice.** Africa. (E2/EMH)
181	*Carpomys* (2 species).	**Fruit Rats.** Philippines. (E2)
182	*Mindanaomys salomonseni.*	**Mindanao Rat.** Philippines. (SA1)
183	*Batomys* (2 species).	**Luzon Forest Rats.** Philippines. (E2)
184	*Pithecheir melanurus.*	**Red Tree Rat.** Sumatra and Java. (E2)
185	*Hyomys goliath.*	**New Guinea Giant Rat.** New Guinea. (E2/LH)
186	*Conilurus* (4 species).	**Rabbit Rats.** Australia. (E2)
187	*Zyzomys argurus.*	**White-tailed Rat.** Australia. (E2)
188	*Laomys* (2 species).	**Thick-tailed Rats.** Australia. (E2)
189	*Mesembriomys* (2 species).	**Rabbit Rats.** Australia. (E2)
190	*Oenomys* (2 species).	**Rufous-nosed Rats.** Africa. (E2)
191	*Mylomys cuninghamei.*	**African Groove-toothed Rat.** Africa. (E2)
192	*Dasymys* (2 species).	**African Water Rats.** Africa. (E2)

191

193 ►*Arvicanthis* (4 species).	**African Field Rats.** Africa. (E2)
194 *Hadromys humei.*	**Hume's Rat.** S. Asia. (E2)
195 *Golunda ellioti.*	**Indian Bush Rat.** S. Asia. (E2)
196 *Pelomys* (9 species).	**Creek Rats.** Africa. (E2/EMH)
197 *Lemniscomys* (6 species).	**Striped Mice.** Africa. (E2)
198 *Rhabdomys pumilio.*	**Four-striped Rat.** Africa. (E2)
199 *Hybomys* (2 species).	**Back-striped Mice.** Africa. (E2)
200 *Millardia* (3 species).	**Soft-furred Field Rats.** S. Asia. (E2)
201 *Dacnomys millardi.*	**Millard's Rat.** Asia. (E2)
202 *Eropeplus canus.*	**Celebes Grey Rat.** Celebes. (E2)
203 *Stenocephalemys albocaudata.*	**Narrow-headed Rat.** E. Africa. (E2)
204 *Aethomys* (6 species).	Africa. (E2)
205 *Thallomys* (5 species).	**White-bellied Tree Rats.** Africa. (E2)
206 *Tarsomys apoensis.*	Philippines. (E2)
207 ►*Rattus* (137 species).	**Rats.** Europe, Asia, Sumatra, Java, Borneo, Philippines, New Zealand, New Guinea, Australia, Africa. (E2/EM/ EMH/LH/A/CH)
208 *Limnomys* (3 species).	Philippines. (E2)
209 *Nilopegamys plumbeus.*	**Water Rat.** E. Africa. (E2)
210 *Tryphomys adustus.*	**Mearn's Luzon Rat.** Philippines. (E2)
211 *Gyomys* (8 species).	**Australian Native Mice.** Australia. (E2)
212 *Leporillus* (3 species).	**Stick-nest Rats.** Australia. (E2)
213 *Pseudomys* (11 species).	**Pseudo-rats.** Australia. (E2)
214 *Apomys* (8 species).	Philippines. (E2)
215 *Melomys* (25 species).	**Banana Rats.** Australia and New Guinea (E2/LH/T)
216 *Pogonomelomys* (4 species).	**Mosaic-tailed Rats.** New Guinea. (LH)
217 *Solomys* (3 species).	**Naked-tailed Rats.** Solomon Islands. (LH)
218 *Xenuromys barbatus.*	**New Guinea Giant Rat.** New Guinea. (TA4)
219 *Uromys* (8 species).	**Giant Naked-tailed Rats.** Australia, New Guinea, Solomon Islands. (E2/LH/T)
220 *Malacomys* (2 species).	**Milne-Edward's Swamp Rats.** Cen. and W. Africa. (E2)
221 *Haeromys* (2 species).	**Pygmy Tree Rats.** Borneo and Celebes. (E2)
222 *Chiromyscus chiropus.*	**Fea's Tree Rat.** S. Asia. (E2)
223 *Diomys crumpi.*	**Crump's Mouse.** S. Asia. (EM)
224 *Zelotomys* (2 species).	**Broad-headed Rats.** Africa. (E2/EMH)
225 *Hylenomys callewaerti.*	**Congo Mice.** Cen. Africa. (E2)
226 *Muriculus imberbis.*	**Striped-back Mice.** E. Africa. (E2)
227 *Mus* (27 species).	**House Mice.** Europe, Asia, Africa, Philippines. (E2/EM/ EMH)
228 *Mycteromys crociduroides.*	**Shrew Rat.** Sumatra and Java. (E2)
229 *Leggadina* (7 species).	**Australian Native Mice.** Australia. (E2)
230 *Colomys goslingi.*	**Gosling's Swamp Rat.** Cen. Africa. (E2)
231 *Nesoromys ceramicus.*	**Ceram Rat.** Ceram Island (off New Guinea). (E2)
232 *Crunomys* (2 species).	**Flat-headed Luzon Water Rats.** Philippines (E2)
233 *Macruromys* (2 species).	**New Guinea Jumping Rats.** New Guinea (E2)
234 *Lorentzimys nouhuysi.*	**New Guinea Jumping Mouse.** New Guinea. (E3)
235 *Lophuromys* (9 species).	**Harsh-furred Rats.** Africa. (E2/EMH)
236 *Leimacomys buttneri.*	**Groove-toothed Forest Mouse.** W. Africa. (E2)
237 *Notomys* (9 species).	**Australian Hopping Mice.** Australia. (E2/IT)
238 *Mastacomys fuscus.*	**Broad-toothed Rat.** Australia. (E2/IT)
239 *Echiothrix leucura.*	**Celebes Shrew Rat.** Celebes. (E2)
240 *Melasmothrix naso.*	**Lesser Shrew Rat.** Celebes. (LH)
241 ►*Acomys* (18 species).	**Spiny Mice.** Africa and S.W. Asia. (E2/EM/EMH)

242	*Uranomys* (5 species).	**African Big-toothed Mice.** Africa. (E2/EMH)
243	*Bandicota* (2 species).	**Bandicoot Rats.** S. Asia, Sumatra, Java, Formosa. (E2/EM)
244	*Nesokia indica.*	**Short-tailed Bandicoot Rat.** S. Asia. (E2)
245	*Beamys* (2 species).	**East African Long-tailed Pouched Rats.** E. Africa. (E2)
246	*Saccostomus campestris.*	**Cape Pouched Mouse.** Africa. (E2/EMH)
247 ►	*Cricetomys gambianus.*	**African Giant Rat.** Africa. (E2)
248	*Anisomys imitator.*	**New Guinea Giant Rat.** New Guinea. (E2)

Subfamily DENDROMURINAE. African Tree Mice.

249	*Dendromus* (15 species).	**African Climbing Mice.** Africa. (E2/EMH)
250	*Malacothrix typica.*	**Mouse Gerbil.** S. Africa. (E2)
251	*Prionomys batesi.*	**Bates' Tree Mouse.** Cen. and W. Africa. (E2)
252	*Petromyscus* (2 species).	**Rock Mice.** S.W. Africa. (E2/EMH)
253	*Delanymys brooksi.*	**Delany's Swamp Mouse.** Cen. E. Africa. (H2)
254	*Steatomys* (11 species).	**Fat Mice.** Africa. (E2/EMH)
255	*Deomys ferrugineus.*	**Congo Forest Mouse.** Cen. Africa. (E2)

Subfamily OTOMYINAE.

| 256 | *Otomys* (16 species). | **Vlei Rats.** Africa. (E2/EMH) |
| 257 | *Parotomys* (2 species). | **Karroo Rats.** S. Africa. (E2) |

Subfamily PHLOEOMYINAE.

258	*Lenomys* (2 species).	**Trefoil-toothed Giant Rats.** Celebes. (E2)
259	*Pogonomys* (9 species).	**Prehensile-tailed Rats.** New Guinea and Japan. (E2/LH)
260	*Chiropodomys* (9 species).	**Pencil-tailed Tree Mice.** S. Asia, Java, Borneo, Sumatra, Philippines. (E2)
261	*Mallomys rothschildi.*	**New Guinea Complex-toothed Rat.** New Guinea. (E2/LH)
262	*Papagomys armandvillei.*	**Flores Complex-toothed Rat.** Flores. (LH)
263	*Phloeomys* (2 species).	**Bushy-tailed Rats.** Philippines. (E2)
264	*Crateromys schadenbergi.*	**Bushy-tailed Rat.** Philippines. (E2)

Subfamily RHYNCHOMYINAE.

| 265 | *Rhynchomys soricoides.* | **Philippines Shrew Rat.** Philippines. (E2) |

Subfamily HYDROMYINAE. Water Rats.

266	*Chrotomys whiteheadi.*	**Back-striped Luzon Water Rat.** Philippines. (E2)
267	*Celaenomys silaceus.*	**Grey Luzon Water Rat.** Philippines. (E2)
268	*Crossomys moncktoni.*	**Monckton's Water Rat.** New Guinea. (E2)
269	*Xeromys myoides.*	**False Water Rat.** Australia. (E2)
270	*Hydromys chrysogaster.*	**Beaver Rat.** Australia and New Guinea. (E2)
271	*Parahydromys asper.*	**Mountain Water Rat.** New Guinea. (E2)
272	*Leptomys elegans.*	**New Guinea Water Rat.** New Guinea. (E2/LH)
273	*Paraleptomys* (2 species).	**New Guinea False Water Rats.** New Guinea. (LH)
274	*Pseudohydromys* (2 species).	**New Guinea Water Rats.** New Guinea. (E2/LH)
275	*Microhydromys richardsoni.*	**Lesser Water Rat.** New Guinea. (LH)

276	*Neohydromys fuscus.*	**New Guinea Water Rat.** New Guinea. (LH)
277	*Mayermys ellermani.*	**Shaw-Mayer's Mouse.** New Guinea. (LH)
278	*Baiyankamys shawmayeri.*	**Baiyanka Water Rat.** New Guinea. (LH)

Superfamily GLIROIDEA.
Family GLIRIDAE. Dormice.
Subfamily GLIRINAE. Eurasian Dormice.

279 ►*Glis glis.*	**Fat Dormouse.** Europe and Asia. (EI)
280 ►*Muscardinus avellanarius.*	**Common Dormouse.** Europe and Asia. (EI/EM)
281	*Eliomys* (2 species).	**Garden Dormice.** Europe, S.W. Asia, N.W. Africa. (EI/EM)
282	*Dryomys nitedula.*	**Forest Dormouse.** Europe and Asia. (EI/EM)
283	*Glirulus japonicus.*	**Japanese Dormouse.** Japan. (EI)
284	*Myomimus personatus.*	**Mouse-like Dormouse.** S.W. Asia. (EI)

Subfamily GRAPHIURINAE. African Dormice.

| 285 | *Graphiurus* (21 species). | **African Dormice.** Africa. (EI/EMH) |

Family PLATACANTHOMYIDAE. Spiny Dormice.

| 286 | *Platacanthomys lasiurus.* | **Malabar Spiny Dormouse.** S. Asia. (EI) |
| 287 | *Typhlomys cinereus.* | **Chinese Pygmy Dormouse.** S.E. Asia. (EI) |

Family SELEVINIIDAE.

| 288 | *Selevinia betpakdalaensis.* | **Betpakdala Dormouse.** Cen. Asia. (EM) |

Superfamily DIPODOIDEA.
Family ZAPODIDAE. Jumping Mice.
Subfamily SICISTINAE.

| 289 | *Sicista* (6 species). | **Birch Mice.** N. Europe and Asia. (EI/EM) |

Subfamily ZAPODINAE.

290	*Zapus* (3 species).	**American Jumping Mice.** N. America. (EI/HK)
291	*Eozapus setchuanus.*	**Szechuan Jumping Mouse.** E. Asia. (EI)
292	*Napaeozapus insignis.*	**Woodland Jumping Mouse.** N. America. (EI)

Family DIPODIDAE. Jerboas.
Subfamily DIPODINAE.

293	*Dipus sagitta.*	**Northern Three-toed Jerboa.** Asia. (EI)
294	*Paradipus ctenodactylus.*	**Comb-toed Jerboa.** Cen. Asia. (EI)
295	*Jaculus* (4 species).	**Jerboas.** N. Africa and S.W. Asia. (EI/EM)
296	*Stylodipus telum.*	**Thick-tailed Three-toed Jerboa.** Asia. (EI/EM)
297 ►*Allactaga* (10 species).	**Five-toed Jerboas.** N. Africa and Asia. (EI)
298	*Alactagulus pumilio.*	**Little Earth Hare.** Cen. Asia. (EI)
299	*Pygeretmus* (2 species).	**Fat-tailed Jerboas.** Cen. Asia. (EI)

Subfamily CARDIOCRANIINAE.

300 *Cardiocranius paradoxus.* **Satunin's Pygmy Jerboa.** Cen. Asia. (E1)
301 *Salpingotus* (3 species). **Pygmy Jerboas.** Cen. Asia. (E1)

Subfamily EUCHOREUTINAE.

302 *Euchoreutes naso.* **Long-eared Jerboa.** E. Asia. (E1)

Suborder HYSTRICOMORPHA.
Superfamily HYSTRICOIDEA.
Family HYSTRICIDAE. Old World Porcupines.
Subfamily HYSTRICINAE.

303 *Thecurus* (2 species). **Indonesian Porcupines.** Borneo, Sumatra, Philippines. (E1/CH)
304 ►*Hystrix* (8 species). **Large Porcupines.** Africa, S. Europe, S. Asia, Sumatra, Java, Borneo. (E1/E3/EM/EMH)

Subfamily ATHERURINAE. Brush-tailed Porcupines.

305 *Atherurus* (4 species). **Brush-tailed Porcupines.** Africa, S. Asia, Sumatra. (E1)
306 *Trichys lipura.* **Long-tailed Porcupine.** Borneo and Sumatra. (E1/CH)

Superfamily ERETHIZONTOIDEA.
Family ERETHIZONTIDAE. New World Porcupines.
Subfamily ERETHIZONTINAE.

307 ►*Erethizon dorsatum.* **North American Porcupine.** N. America. (E1/HK)
308 ►*Coendou* (8 species). **Tree Porcupines.** Cen. and S. America. (E1/HK/C2)
309 *Echinoprocta rufescens.* **Upper Amazon Porcupine.** S. America. (E1)

Subfamily CHAETOMYINAE.

310 *Chaetomys subspinosus.* **Thin-spined Porcupine.** S. America. (E1)

Superfamily CAVOIDEA.
Family CAVIIDAE.
Subfamily CAVIINAE. Cavies.

311 ►*Cavia* (6 species). **Cavies** (including Domestic Guinea Pig—*C. porcellus*). S. America. (E1/C2)

312 *Kerodon rupestris.* **Rock Cavy.** S. America. (E1/C2).
313 *Galea* (3 species). **Cavies.** S. America. (E1/C2)
314 *Microcavia* (3 species). **Mountain Cavies.** S. America. (E1/C2)

Subfamily DOLICHOTINAE.

315 ►*Dolichotis patagonum.* **Mara.** S. America. (E1/C2)
316 *Pediolagus salinicola.* **Salt-desert Cavy.** S. America. (C2)

195

Family HYDROCHOERIDAE.

317 ►*Hydrochoerus hydrochaeris.*   **Capybara.**   Cen. and S. America. (E1/C2)

Family DINOMYIDAE.

318   *Dinomys branickii.*   **Paca-rana.**   S. America. (E1)

Family DASYPROCTIDAE.
Subfamily CUNICULINAE.

319 ►*Cuniculus paca.*   **Paca.**   Cen. and S. America. (E1/C2)
320   *Stictomys taczanowskii.*   **Mountain Paca.**   S. America. (E1/C2)

Subfamily DASYPROCTINAE.

321 ►*Dasyprocta* (13 species).   **Agoutis.**   Cen. and S. America. (E1/C2/HK)
322 ►*Myoprocta* (2 species).   **Acouchis.**   S. America. (E1/C2)

Superfamily CHINCHILLOIDEA.
Family CHINCHILLIDAE.

323 ►*Lagostomus maximus.*   **Viscacha.**   S. America. (E1/C2)
324   *Lagidium* (3 species).   **Mountain Chinchillas.**   S. America. (E1/C2)
325 ►*Chinchilla* (2 species).   **Chinchillas.**   S. America. (E1/C2)

Superfamily OCTODONTOIDEA.
Family CAPROMYIDAE.

326   *Capromys* (4 species).   **Long-tailed Hutias.**   Cuba. (E1)
327   *Geocapromys* (3 species).   **Short-tailed Hutias.**   W. Indies. (E1)
328   *Procapromys geayi.*   **Venezuelan Hutia.**   S. America. (E1)
329   *Plagiodontia* (2 species).   **Zagoutis.**   Cen. America. (E1)
330 ►*Myocastor coypus.*   **Coypu.**   S. America. (E1)

Family OCTODONTIDAE.

331   *Octodon* (3 species).   **South American Bush Rats.**   S. America. (E1/C2)
332   *Octodontomys gliroides.*   **Boris.**   S. America. (E1)
333   *Spalacopus cyanus.*   **Cururo.**   S. America. (E1/C2)
334   *Aconaemys fuscus.*   **South American Rock Rat.**   S. America. (E1/C2)
335   *Octomys mimax.*   **Viscacha Rat.**   S. America. (E1)
336   *Tympanoctomys barrerae.*   S. America. (C2)

Family CTENOMYIDAE.

337 ►*Ctenomys* (27 species).   **Tucotucos.**   S. America. (E1/C2)

Family ABROCOMIDAE.

338   *Abrocoma* (2 species).   **Rat Chinchillas.**   S. America. (E1)

Family ECHIMYIDAE. Spiny Rats.
Subfamily ECHIMYINAE.

339 *Proëchimys* (12 species). **Spiny Rats.** S. America. (E1/C2)
340 *Hoplomys gymnurus.* **Armoured Rat.** Cen. and S. America. (E1)
341 *Euryzygomatomys spinosus.* **Suira.** S. America. (E1/C2)
342 *Clyomys laticeps.* **Spiny Rat.** S. America. (E1)
343 *Carterodon sulcidens.* **Spiny Rat.** S. America. (E1)
344 *Cercomys cunicularis.* **Punare.** S. America. (E1/C2)
345 *Mesomys* (3 species). **Hedgehog Rats.** S. America. (E1/C2)
346 *Lonchothrix emiliae.* **Spiny Rat.** S. America. (E1)
347 *Isothrix* (3 species). **Arboreal Rats.** S. America. (E1/C2)
348 *Diplomys* (2 species). **Arboreal Spiny Rats.** Cen. and S. America. (E1/C2)
349 *Echimys* (11 species). **Crested Spiny Rats.** S. America. (E1/C2)

Subfamily DACTYLOMYINAE.

350 *Dactylomys* (3 species). **Arboreal Rats.** S. America. (E1)
351 *Kannabateomys amblyonyx.* **Tree Rat.** S. America. (E1)
352 *Thrinacodus* (2 species). **Arboreal Rats.** S. America. (E1/C2)

Family THRYONOMYIDAE.

353 ►*Thryonomys* (2 species). **African Cane Rats.** Africa. (E1/EMH)

Family PETROMYIDAE.

354 *Petromus typicus.* **Rock Rat.** Africa. (E1)

Superfamily BATHYERGOIDEA.
Family BATHYERGIDAE. African Mole Rats.

355 *Georychus capensis.* **Blesmol.** Africa. (E1)
356 ►*Cryptomys* (10 species). **Mole Rats.** Africa. (E1/EMH)
357 *Heliophobius* (3 species). **Silvery Mole Rats.** Africa. (E1)
358 *Bathyergus suillus.* **Cape Mole Rat.** S. Africa. (E1/EMH)
359 *Heterocephalus glaber.* **Naked Mole Rat.** Africa. (E1)

Superfamily CTENODACTYLOIDEA.
Family CTENODACTYLIDAE. Gundis.

360 *Ctenodactylus gundi.* **Gundi.** N. Africa. (E1/EM)
361 *Pectinator spekei.* **East African Gundi.** N.E. Africa. (E1)
362 *Massoutiera mzabi.* **Lataste's Gundi.** N. Africa. (E1/EM)
363 *Felovia vae.* **West African Gundi.** W. Africa. (E1)

J 1 Family APLODONTIDAE

MOUNTAIN BEAVER

Aplodontia rufa

(West of North America)

The Mountain Beaver is known by several names including Boomer, Whistler and Sewellel. All are misleading, since it is not confined to the mountains, it is not closely related to the true Beaver, it does not boom, it does not whistle, and the Indian word Sewellel refers not to the animal but to the native garment fashioned from its pelts. However, Mountain Beaver is the most widely used name and so it is retained here.

It is the only living representative of its rather isolated family. A stocky, almost tailless rodent, it has small ears and eyes, coarse fur and large feet and claws. It is approximately 12 inches long and in the field it roughly resembles a tailless Muskrat. Its dentition is unusual, the simple cheek teeth growing throughout life.

The Mountain Beaver lives only in the extreme west of North America, along the Pacific coast from the south of British Columbia to central California. It occurs in humid regions at anything from sea-level to 9,700 feet. It feeds on succulent vegetation and is more active by night, spending most of the day underground in its highly complex tunnel systems. These colonial burrows, with their food storage chambers and sleeping quarters, may run for as far as 300 yards.

Although it is primarily a fossorial species, the Mountain Beaver is reported to be a good swimmer and even to climb trees in search of food.

There is only a single litter each year, two to three young being born in April, after a gestation period of 30 days.

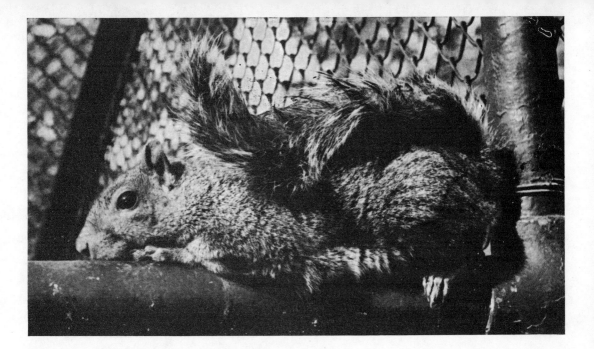

Family SCIURIDAE

GREY SQUIRREL

Sciurus carolinensis

(East of North America)

This is a typical example of the successful tree squirrels that are to be found in almost all parts of the world. They are acrobatic climbers, nesting in enlarged hollows or in specially built "dreys" of twigs and leaves, lodged in the fork of a tree.

Nuts form the Grey Squirrel's basic diet, but it will also eat buds, fruit, berries, insects and even young birds. The latter it attacks in the head region, cracking open the skull as if it were a nut.

Their main enemies are owls, foxes, bobcats and man. Early hunters shot thousands in America, as many as 100 sometimes being bagged in half a day's hunt, but the species is still holding its own.

There are two breeding seasons—in spring and summer. The young can breed themselves when they are 18 months old. The litter of three to four blind and hairless offspring, each weighing half an ounce, are savagely protected by the female, who drives the male away from the nest until weaning is completed after a period of 10 weeks.

Several strange calls can be heard during the mating season—a ticking and a long eerie cry and, during courtship itself, soft mutterings and growlings. The courting male also gnashes his teeth, strikes the branch with his front feet, fluffs his tail and vibrates it at the female. If rebuffed, he chews vigorously at a patch of bark.

The Grey Squirrel is active throughout the winter, when it relies largely on stored food that it has buried in scattered sites in the ground during the autumn.

INDIAN GIANT SQUIRREL

Ratufa indica

(India)

Sometimes known as the Malabar Squirrel, this species is a true giant among squirrels, reaching an overall length of nearly 3 feet. It is a deep chestnut brown, black and cream in colour. In captivity it has lived for as long as 16 years. In general it seems to prefer fruit to nuts, but like most squirrels it eats a wide range of different food-stuffs.

It is known locally as the "tree-dog" and is reputed always to build seven nests. In fact it does seem to construct and use several at once, although the reason for this is not known. The nests are built of twigs and branches and lined with green leaves, like an outsized version of an ordinary squirrel's drey. In these the Indian Giant will sleep away much of the day, coming out in the cool of the evening to search for food.

The call of this species has been described as a loud, shrill cackle. It is apparently a solitary animal, but is sometimes seen in pairs. Little is known about its breeding cycle. It seems likely that the litter is small, possibly only a single young one being born, or occasional twins.

It is extremely rapid when jumping through the trees and is reputed to take leaps of up to 20 feet at a time, when passing from tree to tree. Like most climbing squirrels, however, its first reaction to danger is to hide by pressing its body close to the branch, on the side farthest from the source of the alarm. It "freezes" in this position until the danger has passed, or until it is forced to flee.

BLACK-TAILED PRAIRIE MARMOT

Cynomys ludovicianus

(Central North America)

Known popularly as the Prairie Dog because of its barking alarm cry, this well-known rodent once lived in vast colonies of millions of individuals in the open prairies of North America. Their numbers have been drastically reduced in recent times, not by hunters as is usually the case, but by farmers. The Prairie Marmots fed on the forage that cattle-men needed for their herds and so they were attacked extensively, being poisoned with strychnine in untold numbers.

A Prairie Marmot "town" is a complex underground burrow system that in some instances has been known to extend for miles, with hundreds of entrances and cross-connections. One of the reasons for the enormous spread of these colonies is that rattlesnakes use the burrows each year as ideal hibernating quarters and the rightful owners must then move on to new grounds. The fact that the snakes usurp the rodents' burrows in this way has led to the myth that the two forms live happily together, but this is not the case.

One of the marmot's great architectural problems is how to prevent flooding of the burrow system. It does this in a remarkable way. When the humidity of the air increases, it scrapes up earth near the rim of each tunnel entrance and then proceeds to butt this down hard with its nose, packing it tight around the edge of the hole. In this way a raised lip is created. Eventually this hardens and, when the floods come, most of the water swills past the entrance rather than into it.

201

EUROPEAN SOUSLIK

Citellus citellus

(Europe and Asia)

This is the common ground squirrel of central and eastern Europe, but its range also extends far into the Asiatic region. Apart from the Spotted Souslik (*Citellus suslicus*), that reaches the extreme east of Europe, it is the only ground squirrel indigenous to the European region. Its close relatives in the New World are sometimes known as gophers.

The European Souslik is a small, plainly marked, yellowish-brown creature with a short tail (turned towards us in the photograph), large eyes and very small external ears. Like all sousliks it prefers dry, open country, keeping largely to the plains and avoiding the forests and damper, swampy areas.

It constructs large burrows that descend as much as 8 feet into the ground. In the depths of these it passes the winter, feeding on its extensive hoards of stored seeds, roots and berries, that it has carried below in its large cheek pouches. Sousliks are said to use only a single entrance to their burrows but apparently make a special exit tunnel just before retiring for their winter sleep. This new tunnel does not reach right to the surface, but is broken through in the spring and becomes the new entrance, the old one having been blocked up.

Although sousliks in general tend to avoid the warmer climates, those individuals that do inhabit hotter regions retire to their burrows for a long sleep, not in the depth of winter, but in the height of summer.

Sousliks are said to be rather more carnivorous than most rodents, eating not only insects, but also small birds, voles, mice and even small squirrels.

EASTERN CHIPMUNK

Tamias striatus

(East of North America)

The chipmunks, of which there are eighteen species, are very similar in many respects to the sousliks, but prefer to live in more wooded country where they can make large collections of nuts for their winter hoards. They have been observed to carry as many as seventeen hazel nuts in their large cheek pouches at one time. These hoards are made in special storage chambers in the animals' burrows, near the sleeping-quarters at the bottom of the 3-foot long, sloping entrance tunnels. When excavating these burrows, chipmunks are apparently careful to remove the tell-tale heap of earth from outside the entrance and scatter it around in the bushes near by. As a further precaution, they will sometimes securely plug up the entrance to the tunnels.

With a snug nest below the frost-line and with a vast store of nuts, seeds, dried fruits and berries to see them through the cold winter months, the chipmunks do not need to go into full hibernation, but they sleep for long periods and do not emerge until the early spring, when mating occurs.

Five weeks after mating, the litters of six or more young begin to appear. Blind at birth, they open their eyes after 1 month and after 3 months they are independent.

Chipmunks climb little, spending most of their time near the ground, although usually not actually on it. They prefer to sit on outcrops of some kind—rocks, walls, fallen trees, or low branches, using the ground itself largely as a pathway to and from their burrows and feeding sites.

203

RED AND WHITE FLYING SQUIRREL

Petaurista alborufus

(East Asia)

There are thirty-seven species of flying squirrels today, concentrated almost entirely in the Asiatic region, with only two species in North America and one that extends into north-eastern Europe. All of them have evolved gliding membranes, as a development of their self-defence technique of taking huge leaps when fleeing from their pursuers. These membranes are thin flaps of skin that are stretched out tight when all the animal's legs are fully extended (as they are in a normal leap). The relaxed edge of the gliding membrane of the giant Red and White Flying Squirrel can be clearly seen in the photograph below as a white line along its flank. With its legs outstretched, a flying squirrel can sail through the air for long distances but, although it may guide its direction slightly using its powerful tail as a rudder, it never attempts to gain height by actively flapping its legs. It would perhaps be more correct therefore to refer to these animals as gliding squirrels rather than flying squirrels.

The small American species have become familiar in recent years as pets. The less familiar giant Asiatic forms are more beautifully marked, the species illustrated below having conspicuous reddish-brown eye-rings that contrast vividly with the white of its face.

Like its close relatives, the Red and White Flying Squirrel spends its days curled up asleep or, if the temperature is too high, stretched out on a branch with its extended membranes acting as an aid to cooling. At dawn and dusk it moves leisurely about in search of fruits, berries, nuts and insects.

HEERMANN KANGAROO RAT

Dipodomys heermanni

(West of North America)

Kangaroo rats are North American desert rodents with stocky bodies, short front legs, very long back legs, and long, hairy tails. When moving about they do not run, but hop like miniature kangaroos. These hopping movements are well adapted to the sandy surface, and the long tails act as balancers and rudders when fleeing at high speed. When the animals are stationary they are used as props.

In most kangaroo rats, the tail is dark above and below with contrasting white stripes on either side. The ears are small, the eyes and whiskers large.

Kangaroo rats are active food-hoarders, with a complex system of drying their seeds. When these are fresh they are not always taken straight to the burrow but may be buried in separate, scattered, shallow pits on the home range. Lying hidden just below the surface, they are dried by the sun. When the process is complete, they are dug up and carried below to the winter food-store. This prevents the vital larder contents from becoming mouldy during the storage period. This system of winter food preparation was discovered by marking buried seeds, re-burying them, and then tracing their subsequent removal to the burrow.

Kangaroo rats never drink. They obtain all their liquid from their food. Apart from seeds this also includes small, juicy tubers dug up from just below the surface.

When they come into conflict with one another, they fight largely by kicking with the powerful back feet. The females are attentive mothers and in an emergency will carry their babies to safety by holding them in their arms.

BEAVER

Castor fiber

(Europe, Asia and North America)

The well-known but seldom encountered Beaver is one of the largest of all rodents. From nose to tail it measures over 3 feet and can weigh up to 60 lb. Hunted for its fur, it has become rare over much of its range, but is still holding out in the wilder, more northerly parts of both the Old and New World. It is easily recognized by its expansive, flattened, black tail. This is used, not only in swimming, but also as a warning device, the animal slapping it hard against the water surface as it dives.

A large house, or lodge, is built in the water, using twigs and branches. These are cemented together with mud. A living chamber is constructed inside, just above water-level, with tunnels sloping downward away from it towards the submerged entrances. It is vital for the Beaver to keep the water-level constant around its home and this is managed by building dams in the stream, both above and below the home site. The dams may be up to 100 yards across and are made of branches and mud, reinforced with stones.

Many more branches are cut, carried and anchored in the bottom of the stream as a winter food supply. The Beaver collects the wood for the lodge, the dams and the food store, from the river-banks near by, gnawing saplings and branches into sections and then carrying the cut pieces through elaborately constructed canal systems to their appropriate positions.

It is now generally accepted that all living Beavers belong to a single species, despite slight differences between the American and Eurasian forms.

SPRINGHAAS

Pedetes capensis

(Southern and Eastern Africa)

At first sight, the Springhaas appears to be a strange kind of kangaroo. It moves in the same way, leaping along on its enormous back feet and balancing itself with its long, black-tipped tail. But the resemblance is entirely superficial. The Springhaas is a true rodent and is distantly related to the squirrels. It has no close relatives, there being only the one species in the family.

It is a shy, retiring creature that never emerges from its sandy burrows during daylight hours, coming out only at night to search for bulbs and roots. These it digs up with the long curved claws of its front feet. Its enormous eyes are extremely sensitive to small movements in very dim light and if panic seizes it, it can flee at an incredible pace taking huge leaps of many feet. In a single night it may travel as much as 6 miles in search of food and water. In cultivated areas it has frequently done serious damage to crops.

Each pair lives in a separate burrow system, but in close proximity to other burrows. These warrens may hold altogether twenty or thirty individuals. When they go to earth in the morning, they plug the entrances with earth. If they have been seriously disturbed just before entering their home, they may make several such plugs, one after the other. The animals sleep curled up in a ball, in a highly characteristic posture, but they never lie down on their sides. The litter normally only consists of a single offspring. The name Springhaas derives from the Boers and means "jumping hare".

J 123

COMMON HAMSTER

Cricetus cricetus

(Europe and Western Asia)

The Common or European Hamster is an aggressive, solitary, burrowing rodent with characteristic markings on its reddish brown coat. On each side of the body there are four white patches—on the nose, the cheek, the throat and the flank. As with many specialized burrowers, the tail has become much shortened during the course of evolution. Underneath the hair on each flank there is a small scent gland. This the hamster rubs against the vertical features of its territory, such as tussocks of grass, stones, or the tunnel-walls of its burrows. The scent deposited in this way acts as a warning to other hamsters that they are trespassing on someone else's domain. When a male is courting a female, he rubs his way around her territory, adding his own personal scent to hers. After mating, she attacks him and drives him away. She rears the young hamsters without his help.

The closely related, but smaller and paler Golden Hamster (*Mesocricetus auratus*) has become a popular pet during recent years, but nothing is known of its life in the wild as the entire domestic stock has originated from three members of a single family of thirteen that were dug up in 1930 at Aleppo in Syria. It has apparently not been found alive in the wild before or since.

Hamsters collect seeds and grain in their large cheek pouches and hurry below ground to disgorge them into their vast food stores. This they do by repeatedly pushing at their bulging cheeks with their front feet, at the same time gaping their jaws wide.

208

Family CRICETIDAE

MANED RAT

Lophiomys imhausi

(East Africa)

This unusual, large, black and white rodent, also known as the Crested Hamster or the African Crested Rat, has a long strip of erectile hairs down the middle of its back. When it is alarmed these hairs stand on end, forming a distinctive crest, as shown in the above photograph. On either side of the body there is a broad band of short stiff hairs that become more completely exposed as the longer softer hairs become erect. These flank bands appear to be glandular and the display is therefore not only visual but also olfactory. Both above and below the flank bands there are white stripes. There are further white markings on the face and ears.

Little is known about the animal's life in the wild. It is nocturnal and lives in the highlands in forest country, where it is said to make burrows in the sides of the steep valleys or at the bottom of big trees. It is reputed to be partially arboreal and to include a considerable number of insects in its diet.

One of the strange anatomical features of the Maned Rat is the arrangement of certain of its skull bones. Those that form the greater part of the roof of the brain-case have grown outwards to form a bony sheath covering the great temporal muscles. The outer surfaces of these and certain other skull bones are studded with small tubercles. These unique skeletal features have resulted in the Maned Rat being placed in a family by itself. The only other rodent possessing similar skull characters is the unrelated Paca (*Cuniculus paca*) of South America.

Family CRICETIDAE

MUSKRAT

Ondatra zibethica

(North America)

This commercially famous rodent, sometimes known by its native Indian name of "Musquash", has a natural range covering most of North America, but has also been introduced by man into a number of other countries. It has been important for many years in the fur trade as a source of comparatively cheap pelts. During the nineteenth century 160 million Muskrat skins were shipped to the London fur markets. The trade peak was reached in the early part of the present century when more than 7 million Muskrats were killed for their pelts in a single year.

Muskrats were brought to Britain in 1929 by fur-farmers, but soon escaped and became established in many regions. They were registered as pests and were successfully exterminated by 1939.

They are large (10 to 14 inches) water-rats with a dense, brown coat and a long (8 to 11 inches), black, naked tail that is flattened from side to side. When inhabiting marshes they make canal systems (but never dams like Beavers) and build houses out of large mounds of vegetation that may be as much as 3 to 4 feet high and 8 to 9 feet wide. In streams where there is a high bank they simply make tunnels into the earth. In both cases, the entrances are below water-level and the tunnels slope upward towards the living chamber. Food is stored in these homes for the long winter period.

In March the male becomes very active, moving about in search of females. There are two or three litters a year, with five to nine young in each litter. The last litter of the season is allowed to over-winter in the parental home.

Family CRICETIDAE

ORKNEY VOLE
Microtus orcadensis
(Orkney Islands)

Careful examination of fossil evidence has revealed that the ancestors of the Orkney Vole were once widespread in the British Isles, but were ousted from the mainland by later arrivals, the ancestors of the common Field Vole (*Microtus agrestis*). The latter apparently did not invade until after the Orkney Islands were cut off by the sea. In the absence of competition there, the less successful Orkney Voles were able to survive to the present time. However, as the Orkney species is not only larger, but also more aggressive than its victorious successor, its mainland defeat is difficult to understand.

Voles in general are characterized by their short tails, rounded stumpy bodies and inconspicuous ears. They feed mainly on grass stems and leaves and, in agricultural areas, can become a serious pest. They construct elaborate tunnel systems just below the earth and these are connected to complex networks of surface tracks. These pathways are not open to the sky and are therefore hidden from birds of prey. Nevertheless owls and other predators take a heavy toll.

In places where man has reduced the numbers of killers there have sometimes been dramatic increases in the vole populations. Even without this interference, however, vole communities experience considerable cyclical rises and falls in population density. By rapid breeding, groups "over-stock" themselves and they then suffer from the various effects of over-crowding. A natural population crash follows.

Breeding nests connected to the pathway systems are constructed with shredded leaves and stems and in these the female bears and rears (in less than 3 weeks) her large (5 to 7) litters.

J 154 Family CRICETIDAE

STEPPE LEMMING

Lagurus lagurus

(Asia)

The Steppe Lemming illustrated above comes from the grasslands of southern Russia and western Siberia. Farther east, in the Mongolian region, it has a paler relative, the Yellow Steppe Lemming (*L. luteus*) and in the west of North America there is a third species known locally as the Sagebrush Vole (*L. curtatus*). These and the various other species of lemmings are, in fact, close relatives of the voles and, like them, have rounded heads, small ears, short legs and short tails.

All lemmings breed rapidly and every so often there is a population "explosion". The numbers become so great that vast hordes of them emigrate. In the case of the famous Norway Lemming (*Lemmus lemmus*) "Lemming Years" occur two or three times each decade. Some of the emigrating animals reach the coast and, instead of turning back, take to the water and swim on and on until, exhausted, they die. This has led to the popular idea that lemmings commit suicide. An earlier myth was that they purposefully sally forth to find their original homeland—the submerged continent of Atlantis—and perish in the attempt. In fact, of course, the population explosion leads to frenzied locomotory activity that drives the animals off in all directions, but this only leads to a spectacular result in the case of those that happen to meet the sea. To give some idea of just how impressive this spectacle can be, one need only cite the instance of the 1868 emigration when, in the sea off Trondheim, a steamer took a full quarter of an hour to pass through a vast swarm of swimming lemmings.

FAT-TAILED GERBIL

Pachyurcmys duprasi

(North Africa)

All the 106 species of gerbils have fur that is characteristically pale, soft and silky to the touch. Found in the hot, dry regions of Asia and Africa, they prefer to live in sandy soil and can survive in even the most arid desert conditions, as well as on the open plains and in savannah country. In a sense they are like less extreme versions of jerboas (the names gerbil and jerboa have the same origin). Their back legs are longer than their front legs, but the difference is far less marked than in their kangaroo-like relatives and, although they can hop like the jerboas, they are more likely to run in the typical rodent fashion.

Most species have slightly hairy tails with some degree of tufting at the tip, but the unusual species illustrated above has a fat, naked, sausage-shaped tail of a very distinctive kind. It is essentially a food-storage organ, containing a vital fat reserve that helps its owner through difficult periods when food is in short supply. In this respect it is similar to the tails of the Stump-tailed Skink (*Tiliqua rugosa*), the Fat-tailed Marsupial Mouse (*Antechinus macdonnellensis*), the Fat-tailed Sminthopsis (*Sminthopsis crassicaudatus*), the Fat-tailed Lemur (*Cheirogaleus medius*) and a number of other unrelated species.

Another special feature of the Fat-tailed Gerbil is its enormously inflated ear-bones.

Gerbils in general are gregarious burrowers. In captivity they never seem to stop tunnelling, always enlarging and changing their intricate system of underground passageways. They never climb and, rather strangely, they never bite the human handler. Their food consists of seeds and roots.

213

J 178   Family MURIDAE

LONG-TAILED FIELD MOUSE

Apodemus sylvaticus

(Europe, Asia and North Africa)

The big-eared, pop-eyed Field Mouse prefers succulent foods to the drier grains and seeds. It is therefore a pest of horticulture rather than agriculture. It is particularly fond of such things as peas, beans, strawberries and bulbs and is not exactly the gardener's favourite visitor.

As can be guessed from the large sensitive eyes, it is strictly nocturnal, spending the day below ground with the hoarded spoils of the previous nights. The enlarged chamber at the end of its tunnel is lined with shredded grasses and is big enough to house several adults, for it is apparently a rather sociable species.

An incredibly fast mover, it is capable of jumping as high as 3 feet if suddenly surprised. When fleeing, it often takes a series of huge leaps to escape, instead of running away. Because of this people have sometimes reported finding a "jerboa" or "kangaroo mouse" in their kitchen, for in the country the Field Mouse sometimes boldly advances into the domain of the more familiar House Mouse (*Mus musculus*).

Despite these sorties, the overall area covered by a foraging Field Mouse is limited. By trapping, marking, releasing and re-trapping it has been possible to establish that they keep very much to a small home range—a journey of 200 yards being exceptional.

The breeding season extends from March to November. Gestation lasts 26 days. There are on the average five young to a litter and a female can produce six litters in a year. The young can breed when only a few months old, but life expectancy is little more than a year.

214

AFRICAN FIELD RAT

Arvicanthis abyssinicus

(Africa)

In almost every part of the world there are nondescript rodents that can be described as large mice or small rats. They are greyish-brown in colour, usually rather coarse-furred, and have long, naked, or slightly hairy tails. Except for various detailed skeletal differences they are all much the same in general appearance and habits. They live in grasslands or woodlands, feeding mainly on seeds, and make burrows in the earth. Although they are extremely common in each Continent they are so unspecialized and unremarkable that they are seldom studied, except as economic pests.

A typical example is the African Field Rat illustrated above. Little seems to have been recorded of its natural history, although it apparently occurs in large numbers in the areas where it is found. Judging by its distribution it appears to be capable of living independently of a water supply, obtaining all the liquid it requires from the grain, seeds and roots it eats. In some regions it is known as the Great Field Rat; in others as the Grass Mouse, Grass Rat, or Kusu. Its equivalents in the New World are the American Cotton Rats.

Four species have been described: *Arvicanthis abyssinicus*, with twenty races, from Abyssinia, Kenya, Uganda, Tanganyika, eastern Congo, and Northern Rhodesia; *A. lacernatus* from Abyssinia; *A. somalicus*, with three races, from Somaliland and Kenya; and *A. niloticus*, with twelve races from North, East and West Africa.

There is very little difference between the species, let alone the races, and further collections of specimens may reveal intermediates that make some of the present distinctions meaningless.

215

J 207

BLACK RAT

Rattus rattus

(World-wide today, but originally Asiatic)

The rat is one of the most successful of all mammals. Like the House Mouse (*Mus musculus*), it owes this achievement to its ability to associate with man. Wherever we have gone the rat has followed. Like ours, its distribution today is almost world-wide. The most successful of the 137 species of the genus *Rattus* have been the Black Rat (illustrated above) and the Brown Rat (*Rattus norvegicus*). There are many races of both, the one shown above being Sladen's Rat (*Rattus rattus sladeni*) from south-east Asia.

The Black Rat is more of a town-dweller than its brown relative, which is found both in cities and in the country, where it becomes a serious pest of farmers. The Black Rat, on the other hand, is the better sailor, being the classic "ship rat". Strict fumigation regulations are however now curtailing its travelling activities to a large degree.

Breeding continues throughout the year in favourable conditions, but reaches a peak in the spring. The gestation period is about 3 weeks and the average litter size is seven to eight. The young animals breed at 3 to 4 months, but have a life expectancy of only 2 to 3 years.

The Black Rat had apparently already reached Europe from its original Asiatic home by the thirteenth century. It was followed some centuries later by the Brown Rat. The latter has a slightly heavier build, smaller ears and is more aggressive. It has ousted its black relative from many of its former strongholds.

The Black Rat is a better climber and probably originally nested in trees. The Brown Rat is a better burrower and usually nests underground.

216

CAIRO SPINY MOUSE

Acomys cahirinus

(Southern Asia and Africa)

The self-protection device of developing sharp prickles from soft hairs has evolved a number of times in different groups of mammals. Amongst the insectivores, there are the hedgehogs and the tenrecs; in the monotremes, the echidnas. Amongst the rodents, the phenomenon has occurred in seven different families. Only where the development has been extreme is it well known, as in the case of the fifteen species of Old World porcupines (Hystricidae) and the eleven species of New World porcupines (Erethizontidae). But spiny hair has also evolved in twenty-two species of Spiny Pocket Mice (Heteromyidae) in Central and South America and thirty-three species of Spiny Rats (Echimyidae) in the same region; in the South American Spiny Mouse (Cricetidae); in the Malabar Spiny Dormouse of southern Asia (Platacanthomyidae); in the Spiny Rat of the Liuikiu Islands (Muridae) and the eighteen species of Afro-Asian Spiny Mice (also Muridae).

The representative of these prickly rodents illustrated above is the Cairo Spiny Mouse belonging to the last group. It was first named from specimens found in the Cairo district at the beginning of the nineteenth century, but has since been shown to have a wide range, extending from India through south-west Asia to much of Africa. Spiny Mice are terrestrial and nocturnal, living usually in woodland undergrowth. Of the eighteen recorded species, probably only a few are valid. The Golden Spiny Mouse (*A. russatus*) from north-east Africa and south-west Asia, distinguishable by the black soles to its feet, is considered to be a truly separate species, however, as is the less prickly Cape Spiny Mouse (*A. subspinosus*) from South Africa.

AFRICAN GIANT RAT

Cricetomys gambianus

(Tropical Africa)

This species is impressive because, although in general appearance it is similar to an ordinary Brown Rat, it is several times bigger, measuring as much as 32 inches from nose to tail-tip. Apart from its size, it can be distinguished by the dark hair around its eyes (not strongly marked in the individual shown above), the sharp division of the nose into a dark upper and a pale lower region, and the division of the tail into a dark (proximal) section and a pale (distal) section.

The African Giant Rat is sometimes known as the Gambian Pouched Rat and in captivity it can often be seen sitting up and ramming large food objects into its spacious cheek pouches. When these are full it returns to its nest and disgorges them into its food larder.

In the wild this animal is found largely in forest regions or heavily wooded areas where it makes its burrows at the foot of a tree. Its natural food appears to consist largely of seeds and one of the strangest features of its existence is its unique parasitization by a weird, wingless cockroach (*Hemimerus talpoides*). This insect, nearly 1 inch in length, infests the African Giant Rat like lice, but apparently feeds, not on its blood, but on its stored seeds. It is found on no other host species.

In and around African towns the Giant Rat has been able to adapt to life in the sewers and rubbish dumps, but it does comparatively little damage. It is hunted, not so much as a pest, but as an item of food.

Family GLIRIDAE

FAT DORMOUSE

Glis glis

(Europe and Western Asia)

This is the largest member of the dormouse family. It is found throughout continental Europe and parts of western Asia in deciduous and mixed forests. It has been artificially introduced into south-east England.

Leaves, buds, bark, seeds, acorns, insects and fruits are all included in its diet. The fruits it skins before eating. Before hibernating in September the animal hoards a large quantity of food and also becomes immensely fat. Courtship begins in May. The male pursues the female, squeaking at her. At first she attacks him, but later allows him to approach and perform a circular dance which leads to the actual mating.

When aggressive, the Fat Dormouse purrs, beats with its fore-paws, jumps up and down on the spot and gnashes its teeth. If attacked by a predator and grabbed by the tail, this species uses a defence technique more commonly associated with lizards than with rodents. The tail skin breaks off at a special point and slips clean away from the vertebral column. The naked bony spike that remains is later amputated by the dormouse itself. The predator wins only a fluffy tail-sheath, while the dormouse survives, tailless but otherwise unharmed.

This species lives for as long as 8 years in captivity. The young are weaned after 7 weeks, but do not usually breed until the second year. The nestling dormice not only drink their mother's milk, but also her saliva, by repeatedly licking her mouth.

The Fat Dormouse was popular in ancient Rome as a food delicacy. They were bred in a special outdoor pen (*Glirarium*) and fattened for the table in a clay container (*Dolium*).

COMMON DORMOUSE

Muscardinus avellanarius

(Europe and Western Asia)

The Common Dormouse looks like a mouse with a bushy tail. Its front legs (see photograph) are much shorter than its hind legs. Its thumbs are rudimentary and its big toes are reduced and clawless.

It is becoming rare in many parts of its range but can still be found in many copses and hedgerows. There the Dormouse (dor- from French *dormir*, to sleep) slumbers soundly throughout the day. Even in the summer months the Dormouse's sleep is heavy and it is difficult to arouse it. This predisposition leads, in the winter, to full hibernation, the animal becoming cold-blooded, with reduced heart-beat and respiration rate. It curls up into a tight ball with its chin on its belly and its tail wrapped round over its face. Prior to hibernating, it becomes extremely fat, but by the spring it will have lost almost half of its autumn body weight. It occasionally wakes up during the winter recess and eats some of the hoarded nuts in its carefully prepared food store. The winter nest is made out of leaves and grasses and is usually situated under litter or deeper in the ground.

In the spring, each animal constructs a summer sleeping nest for itself. Dormice being good climbers, these are typically off the ground, in low bushes or dense tangles of vegetation. They are spherical structures made of grasses and lined with leaves and mosses. The breeding nest is larger, more compact and nearer to ground level.

The Dormouse feeds largely on nuts, especially hazel nuts and the haws of whitethorn, but it also devours insects, berries and seeds of various kinds.

EUPHRATES JERBOA

Allactaga euphratica

(South-west Asia)

There are twenty-five species of jerboas alive today. Twenty-two of these are confined to Asia, but three occur in North Africa (The Egyptian Four-toed Jerboa, *Allactaga tetradactyla*; The Lesser Egyptian Jerboa, *Jaculus jaculus*; and The Greater Egyptian Jerboa—the "Desert Rat" of the Second World War—*Jaculus orientalis*). The species illustrated above is found in the desert lands of Arabia. Like all jerboas it has pale, sandy-coloured fur, large eyes and ears, minute front legs and huge back feet.

Although only a few inches long it can jump as much as 6 feet in a single bound. The long balancing tail has a characteristic black and white tuft at its tip. This is no doubt used as some form of signalling device in jerboa sign language. When they are standing still the tail acts as a prop (see photograph).

Despite the fact that they live in intensely hot desert regions, jerboas cannot endure high temperatures for any length of time. They survive by retreating during the day to their comparatively cool underground tunnels. The hot air is kept out by tightly plugging the entrance to the burrow. This is done in the early morning after their nightly food forays, before the arrival of the hot sun.

They sleep standing up, but rolled forward into a ball, with the ears folded down. They become rather cramped in this position and their first action on breaking through the entrance barrier is to roll and stretch on the sand. They clean themselves vigorously, grooming each of the large hind toes individually.

221

INDIAN CRESTED PORCUPINE

Hystrix indica

(Southern Asia)

The members of the genus *Hystrix* are the largest of all the spiny mammals, a fully-grown specimen weighing as much as 40 to 60 lb. and measuring over 3 feet in length. The huge spines are driven into the flesh of the porcupine's enemies by a special defensive action. The animal first issues a warning by shaking and rattling its short tail. If, despite this, the enemy continues to advance, the porcupine runs rapidly and suddenly backwards towards it, impaling it on the now stiffly erected spines. Only a starving, desperate carnivore would seriously attempt to tackle one.

Unlike the American Porcupines, these Old World species do not climb. They make extensive burrows, where a number of individuals may live peacefully together. In the evening they wander far and wide in search of bulbs, roots, bark and fallen fruits.

The eight members of the genus are very similar to one another. The Indian species shown above is found in the centre of the *Hystrix* range, in south and south-west Asia. Farther east, in Malaya, Borneo and Sumatra, there is the Malayan Porcupine (*H. brachyura*), the crestless Chinese Porcupine (*H. hodgsoni*) and the Javan Porcupine (*H. javanica*). Farther west, there is the North African Crested Porcupine (*H. cristata*), which is also still to be found in Italy and Sicily. This animal probably also extends into East Africa, but two separate species (*H. stegmanni* and *H. galeata*) are still recognized from that region. On further investigation, they may well turn out to be no more than races of *H. cristata*. In South Africa there is a distinct species, the Cape Porcupine (*H. africaeaustralis*).

Family ERETHIZONTIDAE

NORTH AMERICAN PORCUPINE

Erethizon dorsatum

(North America)

This is the only member of the North American fauna that possesses a covering of long sharp spines. In the cold winter months it does not hibernate, but survives entirely on bark stripped from the upper branches of evergreen trees. During this period it must stay deep in the forest, but in the warmer months of the year it may wander farther afield in search of other foods. It climbs well, but favours a hole in the ground or a rocky cavity as its resting place. The single, well-developed offspring weighs as much as one pound at birth.

When threatened, this species arches its body, erects its spines and turns its rear-end towards its enemy. If further agitated, it backs up to the foe and delivers a swift blow with its short spiky tail. Even if it does not actually make contact and drive some of its sharp quills home, some of the more loosely attached ones may fly off (like moulted hairs) and strike the enemy in the face. This action has led to the myth that the porcupine can "fire" its quills.

During the winter period the soft hair that grows in between the hard spines becomes extremely lengthy and conceals all but the longest quills. With this heavy, insulating coat the animal can withstand even the most intense blizzards. The species is, in fact, more vulnerable to heat than cold, rapidly-spreading forest fires overtaking and killing many of them during the dry summers.

In the north, the Wolverine is its most feared predator, the Wolf, Coyote and Northern Lynx attacking it only as a last resort.

BRAZILIAN TREE PORCUPINE

Coendou prehensilis

(South America)

When cornered, many mammals experience a tightening of their hair muscles, so that their fur stands on end and they appear to be bigger than they really are. Porcupines, however, have taken this defence technique a step further. When their spiny hair stands on end it is more than bluff. Normally the spines lie smoothly backwards against the body, but when the animals are threatened the would-be predator is suddenly confronted with a sea of sharp spikes. Any attempt to bite into it is not only intensely painful but also dangerous, for few killers are equipped with the kind of grasping hands that are needed to pull long thin quills out of the flesh of the snout and mouth. Agonized rubbing and wiping only helps to break them off, leaving the embedded points in wounds that may soon fester and swell.

In the case of the New World porcupines, such as the South American tree porcupines, or coendous, there is an added torture for the hapless carnivore, for the spines are minutely barbed and tend to work themselves deeper and deeper into the flesh.

Unlike other porcupines, the coendous have long tails that are powerfully prehensile. The lower part of the tail tip is naked and can grasp a branch so firmly that the creature can hang from it with ease. There are eight species of coendous in Central and South America, some of them having long, soft hairs that nearly conceal their sharp spines, whilst others, like the one illustrated below, carry all their white-tipped spines fully exposed, even when they are at rest.

224

Family CAVIIDAE   J 311

RESTLESS CAVY

Cavia porcellus

(South America)

The main claim to fame of this short-legged, round-bodied, tailless rodent is that it is the wild ancestor of the Guinea-pig. It is known that domesticated cavies already existed in several colour varieties in Inca times, and that the Incas bred them as a food delicacy and even sacrificed them to the gods. The animal was brought to Europe in the late sixteenth century and the earliest reference we have to it is in Topsell (1607). He referred to it as the Indian Little Pig Coney. There are several theories as to how it acquired the name of Guinea-pig. It could be a corruption of the name Coney-pig, or Guiana-pig, or the animals could have arrived from ships whose last stop had been in African Guinea.

In the wild, cavies live in a wide variety of habitats but prefer dense vegetation, where they use regular beaten tracks. They keep in touch with one another by frequent high-pitched squeaking. The young are born in an advanced state after a gestation period of 66 to 72 days. Average litter size is three to four. They are suckled by the mother for approximately 2 weeks, but if she is killed during that time other mothers are reputed to feed the abandoned litter. After 3 weeks the mother ignores her offspring and is soon ready to mate again. The young are capable of eating solids when only 48 hours old. Length of life in captivity is 6 to 8 years. They should be fed on bran, oats, hay and various green foods.

225H

MARA

Dolichotis patagonum

(South of South America)

The Mara, or Patagonian Cavy, is the most hare-like of all the rodents. It is a dry-country animal, living in groups of ten to thirty on the pampas of the Argentine and the stony wastes of Patagonia. When alarmed it does not go to earth in its burrows, but instead flees at high speed on the surface. Its long legs can quickly carry it to safety, but usually it stops every 50 to 100 yards and turns to look back at its pursuer.

The Mara is active only during the day but spends a great deal of time basking in the sun. When doing so, it either squats down with its front legs extended (as above), or sprawls out on its side with its back legs fully stretched, in a posture that is rarely seen in rodents. Its long eyelashes protect its eyes from the sun's glare. At night it retires to its burrows to sleep.

Its body is 2 to 3 feet long and 1 foot high. The coat is pale with a vivid white rump patch that flashes as a danger signal to other Maras as it flees. It feeds on grasses, roots and stems. During courtship the male squirts a jet of urine at the female, an action also found in certain porcupines, the cavies, the agoutis and the acouchis, and the rabbits and hares. Two litters are reared each year. The two to five young are born inside the burrows.

There is a smaller species, the Salt Desert Cavy (*Pediolagus salinicola*), found only in the salt deserts of southern Argentina. This species lacks the white rump patch.

Family HYDROCHOERIDAE

CAPYBARA

Hydrochoerus hydrochaeris

(Central and South America)

Looking rather like a cross between a Guinea-pig and a Hippopotamus, the Capybara is the largest of all the 1,729 species of living rodents. Extinct forms of this animal were even bigger, but the pig-sized, surviving specimens can reach an adult weight of more than 100 lb., an overall length of 4 feet and a shoulder height of 21 inches.

It lives in large groups along the river banks, where it grazes peacefully on the lush grasses and the aquatic vegetation. It comes out on to dry land to rest and bask in the sun but at the first hint of danger the whole troop dashes into the water. Its worst enemies are the Puma and the Jaguar.

Capybaras inhabiting the colder regions of South America have a long shaggy coat, but the typical form has the short, pale and rather coarse hair that can be seen in the above photograph. The face is very deep, the ears and tail are small and the feet are slightly webbed. There is a large bump in the middle of the top of the nose, which appears to be a scent gland of some kind.

Capybaras adapt easily to life in captivity and become remarkably friendly. They are rather vocal for rodents, often giving vent to a series of strange clicks, squeaks and grunts. It is important that they should be provided with a pool, as they appear to have a strong resistance to defecating or mating on dry land. The gestation period is approximately 4 months and maximum longevity about 10 years.

227

J 319

PACA

Cuniculus paca

(Central and South America)

A large, fat, spotted rodent that is found from Mexico in the north, to Paraguay in the south, the Paca or Spotted Cavy, is one of the favourite items of diet of the local carnivores. Its white flesh is so tasty that the Indians also make special efforts to hunt it down using dogs.

A shy forest dweller, it prefers to live in swampy ground, or near a river or stream, and when pursued it attempts to take to the water. It lives and breeds in burrows, in holes in the banks of rivers, or in old tree roots. The male and female are usually found together in the 4- to 5-foot deep burrows, which are equipped with two entrance tunnels. One or two young are born in the underground nest during the summer. There is apparently a long suckling period lasting 2 to 3 months. The female has two pairs of teats placed far apart, a similar arrangement to that found in the closely related agoutis and acouchis.

The skull of the Paca is unusual, possessing bony cheek expansions that ensheath some of the jaw muscles. This condition is known in only one other rodent, the un-related Maned Rat (*Lophiomys*) from Africa.

There is a small relative, the Mountain Paca, or Taczanowski's Paca (*Stictomys*) that is found at 6,000 to 10,000 feet in the highlands of Ecuador.

The False Paca, or Paca-rana (*Dinomys*), also known as Branick's Paca, is a rare creature from the Andes that is less closely related, but has a similarly marked coat, with long rows of white spots and a heavy, stocky body. Unlike the Paca, however, it has a 6-inch-long, bushy tail.

ORANGE-RUMPED AGOUTI

Dasyprocta aguti

(North of South America)

The agoutis are active, long-legged rodents that have come to look and live like miniature ungulates. They are highly-strung and flee in panic at the slightest alarm. They climb and burrow very little, being essentially specialized as surface-dwellers in the tropical Amazonian forest regions. They feed on fruits, berries, nuts and roots. When eating they sit up (see photograph) and hold the food delicately between their front feet. If the food object has an outer skin, this is peeled off carefully before they start their meal.

Agoutis store food by burying it in small holes scattered all over their communal home range. These hoards are usually situated near to special landmarks, but the animals do not make a typical, large "larder hoard" in one particular place, like so many other species.

These creatures have been described as the "basic diet of the South American carnivores". Although they are eaten in large numbers by a wide variety of species, including man, they are still extremely common and have a wide range that includes parts of the West Indies.

The coat in the rump region is much longer than on other parts of the body. When an agouti is alarmed or is engaging in combat, it erects these elongated rump-hairs to a remarkable degree. In some species this part of the coat is brightly coloured and the erection display therefore produces a sudden, dramatic increase in the size of the coloured region. The common species, found in much of Brazil and the Guianas, has orange-coloured rump hairs. Amongst the other species, one has a pure white rump and another a black one.

229

J 322

GREEN ACOUCHI

Myoprocta pratti

(North-west of South America)

It is difficult to decide whether the acouchis are dwarf agoutis, or the agoutis are giant acouchis. They are certainly very closely related and have many behaviour patterns in common. Both have basically the same feeding habits, the same foot-stamping alarm signals and rapid fleeing reactions. Both bury food in scattered positions by digging a hole (see photograph), dropping the food in, stamping it down and covering it over. Both have extremely precocious young that are born after a long gestation period and can run around within hours of birth and start feeding on solids within a few days.

The most important difference between the agoutis and the acouchis concerns their tails. The agoutis have a brief, black stump of a tail, whereas the acouchis are equipped with a slender, white-tipped appendage that is used as an important sexual signalling device. A courting male acouchi wags his tail rapidly as he follows the female around. If he is bold, he holds his tail straight up in the air as it wags to and fro. If he is scared, he wags it in a downward position. A female indicates her readiness to mate by erecting her tail and holding it stiffly upward as she arches her back downward.

Another difference between agoutis and acouchis is that the latter never have coloured rump patches, even though they show the full rump-hair-erection display during combat.

There are two species, the Green Acouchi and the Red Acouchi (*M. acouchy*). The latter is found in the north-east of South America. It has an orange-tipped coat and a more slender build.

230

VISCACHA

Lagostomus maximus

(South of South America)

On the open, exposed pampas of the Argentine, the gregarious Viscachas live in small colonies of twenty to thirty individuals. They inhabit complex warrens called "visca-cheras". A typical warren comprises twelve to fifteen burrows and covers 100 to 200 square feet. The earth that is brought up to the surface by the tunnelling activities of the colony can be seen from a distance as a large raised mound. The tunnel entrances are as much as three feet across and a number of other creatures make their homes inside. There is a passerine bird (*Geositta*), for example, that constructs its breeding holes in the sides of the burrows. When deserted they are taken over by a swallow-like bird (*Atticora*). Burrowing Owls (*Speotyto*) are also often present.

The whole region around the burrow is cleared of all vegetation and this is then heaped up near the entrances. In the same way, any strange object found by the Viscachas is transported to the burrow entrances and added to the heaps of rubbish there. Bones, whips, watches and even boots have been treated in this way. Travellers often mysteriously lose certain of their belongings when camping on the pampas, only to find them again amongst the Viscachas' strange hoard.

Viscachas are close relatives of the chinchillas, but are much larger, the head and body being nearly 2 feet long. They are nocturnal and feed on a wide variety of grasses, roots and seeds. They are not prolific breeders, producing a litter of two to three young only once a year, and taking 2 years to reach maturity.

The Mountain Chinchillas (*Lagidium*) are sometimes referred to as Mountain Viscachas.

Family CHINCHILLIDAE

SHORT-TAILED CHINCHILLA

Chinchilla brevicaudata

(Mountains of Argentina, Bolivia and Peru)

The Chinchilla possesses the finest and most valuable fur in the animal kingdom. As soon as this fact was discovered, an intensive slaughter of the wild populations began, bringing them to the verge of extinction in the early part of this century. Since then they have been successfully kept and bred in captivity and the wild stock is strictly protected.

The coat is silvery blue-grey and incredibly soft to the touch. The animal lives at high altitudes in the semi-arid regions of the Andes, making its home amongst the rocks and emerging at dawn and dusk to bask in the sun. It is active at night, feeding on hardy grasses and herbs and occasionally catching insects.

It is a gregarious creature and the females, which are larger, are said to dominate the males. They are very vocal animals, uttering a long warning cry that alerts the group to danger, a softer cooing sound when mating, and a hiss-and-spit when aggressive.

There are two species of Chinchilla, the Short-tailed and the Long-tailed (*C. laniger*) from Chile. The Short-tailed (seen above) also has shorter ears and a slightly larger body. Nearly all the Chinchillas that have been domesticated in North America have been Long-tailed, whereas nearly all those kept in captivity in South America have been Short-tailed. Hybrids from the two species are sterile in the case of males, but fertile in the case of females back-crossed with either parent species. Many of the male offspring of such back-crosses are, however, also infertile. The gestation period of *C. brevicaudata* is 128 days, that of *C. laniger* is 111 days.

232

COYPU

Myocastor coypus

(South America)

The Coypu is a large aquatic rodent looking rather like a smallish beaver with an un-flattened, rat-like tail. It has a long dense coat, a large blunt head, huge whiskers and bright orange front teeth. Its hind feet are webbed. It constructs its burrows in the banks of rivers and feeds largely on aquatic vegetation. An adult can weigh as much as 20 lb. The body length is 2 feet, the naked scaly tail stretching a further 18 inches.

The long brown outer fur hides a much softer greyish under fur. This is of some importance commercially, where it is known as Nutria. Fur farmers have imported the Coypu into Europe where, after repeated escapes in various countries, it has established itself successfully despite the colder climate. In some countries it has been welcomed, but in Great Britain it is now considered as a pest and its numbers are being reduced.

As with most hystricomorph rodents, the litters (of five to eight young) are born after a long (130 days) gestation period, and are able to swim and feed on solids within a day or two of birth. The young animals are said to take rides on their mother's back when she swims. They are capable of breeding at the age of 5 months.

All rodents spend a great deal of time grooming themselves, but the Coypu excels in this respect. After swimming, it sits up and laboriously cleans itself for long periods, combing the fur vigorously with its front claws.

The Coypu's only close relatives are the hutias of Central America and the West Indies.

J 337

TUCOTUCO

Ctenomys mendocinus

(South of South America)

The Tucotuco is a specialized burrower with short, powerful, long-clawed feet and a stocky (8 to 12 inch) body. Its external ears are reduced to little more than apertures, and the tail is short. Most authorities also insist that the animal exhibits another special subterranean feature, namely reduction in the size of the eyes. These are usually said to be "minute", but the photograph above indicates that this is an error. The soft fur is greyish-brown and the feet are fringed with long bristles.

Twenty-seven species, with a total of fifty-two races, have been recorded, but it is agreed that the family requires a serious revision. When this has been done it will no doubt emerge that there are in reality only a few valid species. Different forms are found from Brazil to Tierra del Fuego in the extreme south, but the main concentration is in the Argentine, where no less than twenty-nine races, belonging to fifteen different species have been recorded, including all nine races of the species shown above.

The Tucotucos live in large colonies, especially in sandy soil, where whole sections of land can become undermined by their long, shallow tunnels. The courses of these tunnels are indicated by lines of hillocks, like mole-hills, and in certain regions the Tucotuco is referred to as the South American Mole Rat. Their Guarani Indian name of Tucotuco (sometimes spelled Tucutucu) refers to their often repeated cry. This underground call is resonant and loud and sounds like a succession of hammer blows on an anvil, as if an army of midgets were building an underground city.

234

GREAT CANE RAT

Thryonomys swinderianus

(Tropical Africa)

With its short tail, small ears and heavy, stocky body, the Great Cane Rat, or Cutting Grass, looks rather like an African equivalent of the South American Cavy. It has enormous incisor teeth, bright orange in colour, that can deal with even the toughest vegetation. The body is over 12 inches in length, the tail a further 6 inches.

Its enemies are many and include leopards, eagles and pythons. Its flesh is also eaten by man and is said to resemble sucking pig. When alarmed, the Cane Rat gives a strange booming grunt and stamps its hind feet hard on the ground. When fleeing, it can run extremely fast, but will take to the water if given a chance. The animal's favourite habitat is, in fact, the dense lush vegetation along the banks of rivers and streams. It is most common in swampy areas where there are tall reed-beds. Its presence can be detected by searching for small piles of finely chopped grass stems. It feeds on a variety of grasses, reeds, roots and bulbs.

The Cane Rat does not appear to burrow. It relies on the dense vegetation to hide it from its enemies. The young are born in a shallow depression, deep in the reed-beds. These nests are lined with grasses and shredded reeds. The offspring are well developed at birth, fully furred and with their eyes open.

As its name suggests, it is fond of sugar cane, and can become a serious nuisance in plantation regions. There is a second, smaller species, the Lesser Cane Rat (*T. gregorianus*) in Central Africa.

235

J 356

ZECH'S MOLE RAT
Cryptomys zechi
(West Africa)

Like the true moles, the Mole Rat lives out its life almost entirely below ground level, throwing up small mounds of earth at irregular intervals as it excavates its subterranean tunnel systems. Also like the moles, it has no external ears, there being a simple, round ear aperture, as shown clearly in the above photograph. The eyes are minute, the legs short and the feet powerful. The tail is reduced to a stump. This is the body design of the specialized burrower.

It differs from the true moles most strikingly in its diet and its teeth. The food consists entirely of subterranean vegetation and the incisor teeth are huge and protrude forward out of the mouth to a startling degree. It prefers to live in comparatively loose, sandy soil, but it can be destructive in agricultural areas, being fond of potatoes, sweet potatoes, bulbs and root vegetables of various kinds. It never drinks, obtaining all its liquid from its food.

Zech's Mole Rat is one of the sixteen species of the Tropical African family Bathyergidae. There are three other species of Mole Rats in the Palaearctic region (The Russian Mole Rat, the Lesser Mole Rat of eastern Europe and western Asia, and the Palestine Mole Rat of south-west Asia and North Africa; *Spalax microphthalmus, leucodon,* and *ehrenbergi* respectively) and fourteen species of East African Mole Rats (*Tachyoryctes*), but these are not closely related to the Bathyergids, having independently taken up a similar way of life.

The strangest of the tropical forms is the Naked Mole Rat (*Heterocephalus glaber*) from the hot Somali deserts, with its almost hairless, wrinkled skin.

K. CETACEANS

The ninety-two species of whales, dolphins and porpoises are world-wide in distribution, being found in virtually all marine waters and also in many of the larger rivers. They fall into two distinct groups: the toothed whales, of which there are eighty species, and the whalebone whales, of which there are twelve. Amongst the latter is to be found the largest of all mammals, the great Blue Whale, attaining a length of nearly 100 feet and a weight of over 100 tons. (The Blue Whale record stands at 136·4 tons.) It is doubtful if any creature has ever lived on this planet that has exceeded these enormous proportions.

The name cetacean is derived from the Greek word *ketos* meaning simply a whale. This group of mammals has become so strongly adapted to life in the sea that there are many striking diagnostic features. Firstly, for example, there are no hind limbs, the fore-limbs have become flippers and the tail has been horizontally flattened. There is no neck in the ordinary sense and no external ears. The nasal opening or openings are located on top of the head, there being a single blow-hole in toothed whales and a double one in whalebone whales. There are no sweat glands and a hairy covering to the body is also absent, although a few isolated bristles usually remain as remnant structures. These bristles are found on the chin and the snout, but they are few in number: for example, a Greenland Whale has only 250, a Rorqual sixty and a Dolphin no more than eight. Some whales, such as the Narwhal are completely hairless. In all species the skin is smooth and thick and beneath it is a characteristic fat layer of insulating blubber.

Whales are highly vocal creatures and communicate a great deal by the use of sound signals. They can also navigate by echo-sounding, using a kind of natural sonar system. This is basically the same navigation technique as that used in the air by bats.

They migrate for long distances, but never come up on to dry land like most other aquatic mammals, except when they are accidentally washed ashore, in which case they die rapidly. The young whale is born at sea and is pushed up to the surface by its mother and other adults in the school, thus enabling it to take its first breath. Sick whales are apparently helped in the same way by their companions. Social co-operation of this sort seems to have been developed to a remarkable degree in this order of mammals.

The toothed whales, which include the many species of dolphins and the porpoises, may have as many as 260 teeth (the mammalian record), in some species, or as few as a single pair, in others. The teeth are usually simple in structure, although in the case of the extraordinary Narwhal the left upper canine extends forwards in the males as a formidable coiled tusk, reaching a length of 8 feet or more.

Toothed whales feed on a wide variety of fish, a few marine mammals and some of the larger invertebrates. The whalebone whales, by contrast, filter-feed on the minute organisms that make up marine plankton. In place of teeth, they possess whalebone, or baleen. There is a row of transverse plates of baleen (horny outgrowths from the roof of the mouth) hanging down from each side of the palate. The inner edges of these plates are fringed and act as sieves, straining off the plankton. When water enters the mouth it has to escape through these sieves and the thousands of small organisms are trapped. Then the mouth shuts and the huge, fixed tongue fills the cavity of the mouth and automatically squeezes the plankton down the whale's throat. To give some idea of the scale of this operation, it may help to record that the tongue of a large Blue Whale weighs 4 tons, or as much as an average sized elephant.

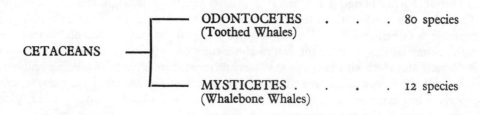

K. Order CETACEA. Whales.

Suborder ODONTOCETI. Toothed Whales.

Superfamily PLATANISTOIDEA. River Dolphins.

Family PLATANISTIDAE.

Subfamily PLATANISTINAE.

1 *Platanista gangetica.* **Gangetic Dolphin.** Rivers of S. Asia. (EM)

Subfamily INIINAE.

2 *Inia geoffrensis.* **Geoffroy's Dolphin.** Rivers of N. of S. America. (C2)
3 *Lipotes vexillifer.* **Chinese River Dolphin.** Rivers of S.E. Asia. (EM)

Subfamily STENODELPHININAE.

4 *Stenodelphis blainvillei.* **La Plata Dolphin.** Rivers of S. America. (C2)

Superfamily PHYSETEROIDEA.

Family ZIPHIIDAE. Beaked Whales.

5 *Mesoplodon bidens.* **Sowerby's Whale.** N. Atlantic and European waters. (EM)
6 *Mesoplodon gervaisi.* **Gervais' Beaked Whale.** N. Atlantic. (EM)
7 *Mesoplodon mirus.* **True's Beaked Whale.** N. Atlantic. (EM)
8 *Mesoplodon grayi.* **Gray's Beaked Whale.** S. Pacific. (EM)
9 *Mesoplodon densirostris.* **Blainville's Beaked Whale.** World-wide. (EM)
10 *Mesoplodon stejnegeri.* **Stejneger's Beaked Whale.** N. Pacific. (EM)
11 *Mesoplodon layardi.* **Strap-toothed Whale.** New Zealand, Australia, S. America, S. Africa. (EMH)
12 *Mesoplodon pacificus.* **Longman's Beaked Whale.** Australia. (IT)
13 *Ziphius cavirostris.* **Cuvier's Beaked Whale.** World-wide. (EM)
14 *Tasmacetus shepherdi.* **New Zealand Beaked Whale.** S. Pacific. (OL)
15 *Berardius bairdi.* **Baird's Beaked Whale.** N. Pacific. (EM)
16 *Berardius arnouxi.* **Arnoux's Beaked Whale.** S. Pacific. (C2)
17 *Hyperoodon ampullatus.* **Bottlenose Whale.** Waters of N. Hemisphere. (EM)
18 *Hyperoodon planifrons.* **Southern Bottlenose Whale.** Waters of S. Hemisphere. (C2)

Family PHYSETERIDAE. Sperm Whales.

Subfamily PHYSETERINAE.

19 *Physeter catodon.* **Sperm Whale.** World-wide. (EM)

Subfamily KOGIINAE.

20 *Kogia breviceps.* **Pygmy Sperm Whale.** World-wide. (EM)

Superfamily MONODONTOIDEA.

Family MONODONTIDAE.

21 *Delphinapterus leucas.* **White Whale.** Arctic and northern waters. (EM)
22 *Monodon monoceros.* **Narwhal.** Arctic and northern waters. (EM)

Superfamily DELPHINOIDEA.

Family STENIDAE.

23	*Steno bredanensis.*	**Rough-toothed Dolphin.** World-wide. (EM)
24	*Sousa sinensis.*	**Chinese White Dolphin.** Coast of S. Asia. (EM/FCF)
25	*Sousa plumbea.*	**Plumbeous Dolphin.** Indian Ocean. (EM/FCF)
26	*Sousa borneensis.*	**Malaysian Dolphin.** Malaysian Waters. (CH/FCF)
27	*Sousa lentiginosa.*	**Speckled Dolphin.** Indian Ocean and Australian waters. (EM/IT/FCF)
28	*Sousa teuszii.*	**West African White Dolphin.** W. Africa. (A)
29	*Sotalia fluviatilis.*	**Amazonian White Dolphin.** Rivers of N. of S. America. (C2)
30	*Sotalia guianensis.*	**Guiana White Dolphin.** Coast of N.E. of S. America. (C2)

Family DELPHINIDAE. Dolphins.

Subfamily DELPHININAE.

31	*Stenella malayana.*	**Malay Dolphin.** Indian Ocean and S. Pacific. (EM)
32	*Stenella frontalis.*	**Bridled Dolphin.** Atlantic and Indian Oceans. (EM)
33	*Stenella caeruleoalbus.*	**Blue-white Dolphin.** S. America and Japan. (EM)
34	*Stenella styx.*	**Euphrosyne Dolphin.** Atlantic and N. Pacific. (EM)
35	*Stenella alope.*	**Ceylon Dolphin.** Ceylon. (EM)
36	*Stenella attenuata.*	**Narrow-snouted Dolphin.** Pacific. (EMH)
37	*Stenella longirostris.*	**Long-beaked Dolphin.** Pacific. (EMH)
38	*Stenella graffmani.*	**Graffman's Dolphin.** Pacific. (HK)
39	*Stenella microps.*	**Small-headed Dolphin.** Pacific. (HK)
40	*Stenella plagiodon.*	**Spotted Dolphin.** Atlantic. (HK)
41	*Stenella roseiventris.*	**Torres Strait Dolphin.** Torres Strait. (IT/FP)
42 ►	*Delphinus delphis.*	**Common Dolphin.** World-wide. (EM)
43	*Delphinus capensis.*	**Cape Dolphin.** S. Africa and Japan. (EM)
44	*Delphinus bairdi.*	**Pacific Dolphin.** Pacific. (HK)
45	*Delphinus boryi.*	**Bory's Dolphin.** Australia. (IT)
46	*Grampus griseus.*	**Risso's Dolphin.** World-wide. (EM)
47 ►	*Tursiops truncatus.*	**Bottlenosed Dolphin.** World-wide. (EM)
48	*Tursiops aduncus.*	**Red Sea Bottlenosed Dolphin.** Red Sea, Indian and Pacific Oceans. (EM)
49	*Tursiops gilli.*	**Gill's Bottlenosed Dolphin.** Pacific. (HK)
50	*Tursiops nuuana.*	**Pacific Bottlenosed Dolphin.** Pacific. (HK)
51	*Tursiops maugeanus.*	**Tasmanian Bottlenosed Dolphin.** Tasmania. (IT)
52	*Lagenorhynchus acutus.*	**White-sided Dolphin.** N. Atlantic. (EM)
53	*Lagenorhynchus albirostris.*	**White-beaked Dolphin.** N. Atlantic and European waters. (EM)
54	*Lagenorhynchus electra.*	**Indian Broad-beaked Dolphin.** Indian, Atlantic and Pacific Oceans. (EM)
55	*Lagenorhynchus obliquidens.*	**Pacific White-sided Dolphin.** N. Pacific. (EM)
56	*Lagenorhynchus thicolea.*	**Gray's White-sided Dolphin.** Pacific. (HK)
57	*Lagenorhynchus obscurus.*	**Gray's Dolphin.** Waters of S. Hemisphere. (EMH)
58	*Lagenorhynchus australis.*	**Peale's Dolphin.** Waters of S. Hemisphere. (C2)
59	*Lagenorhynchus cruciger.*	**Cruciger Dolphin.** Waters of S. Hemisphere. (C2)
60	*Lagenodelphis hosei.*	**Bornean Dolphin.** Borneo waters. (FR1)

Subfamily CEPHALORHYNCHINAE.

61 *Cephalorhynchus commersoni.* **Commerson's Dolphin.** S. America. (C2)
62 *Cephalorhynchus eutropia.* **Black Dolphin.** S. America. (C2)
63 *Cephalorhynchus heavisidei.* **Tonine.** S. Pacific and Cape Seas. (EMH)

Subfamily ORCINAE.

64 ►*Orcinus orca.* **Killer Whale.** World-wide. (EM)
65 *Pseudorca crassidens.* **False Killer.** World-wide. (EM)
66 *Orcaella brevirostris.* **Irrawaddy Dolphin.** Indian and S. Pacific Oceans. (EM)
67 *Globicephala melaena.* **Pilot Whale.** European Waters, Pacific, Atlantic. (EM)
68 *Globicephala macrorhyncha.* **Indian Pilot Whale.** Atlantic, Indian and Pacific Oceans. (EM)
69 ►*Globicephala scammoni.* **Pacific Pilot Whale.** Pacific. (HK)
70 *Globicephala edwardi.* **Southern Pilot Whale.** S. African Seas. (EMH)
71 *Feresa attenuata.* **Pygmy Killer.** Tropical Atlantic and S. Pacific. (HK/FR2)

Subfamily LISSODELPHINAE.

72 *Lissodelphis peroni.* **Southern Right Whale Dolphin.** S. Pacific. (EMH)
73 *Lissodelphis borealis.* **Northern Right Whale Dolphin.** N. Pacific. (EM)

Family PHOCAENIDAE. Porpoises.

74 *Phocaena phocoena.* **Porpoise.** Waters of N. Hemisphere. (EM)
75 *Phocaena vomerina.* **Pacific Harbour Porpoise.** Pacific. (HK)
76 *Phocaena dioptrica.* **Bi-coloured Porpoise.** S. America. (C2)
77 *Phocaena spinipinnis.* **Burmeister's Porpoise.** S. America. (C2)
78 *Phocaenoides dalli.* **Dall's Porpoise.** N. Pacific. (HK)
79 *Phocaenoides truei.* **True's Porpoise.** Japanese waters. (RCA)
80 *Neomeris phocaenoides.* **Black Finless Porpoise.** Pacific and Indian Oceans. (EM)

Suborder MYSTICETI. Whale-bone Whales.

Family ESCHRICHTIDAE.

81 *Eschrichtius glaucus.* **Californian Grey Whale.** Atlantic, N. Pacific. (HK/MK)

Family BALAENOPTERIDAE.

82 *Balaenoptera acutorostrata.* **Lesser Rorqual.** World-wide. (EM)
83 *Balaenoptera borealis.* **Sei Whale.** World-wide. (EM)
84 *Balaenoptera physalus.* **Common Rorqual.** World-wide. (EM)
85 *Balaenoptera musculus.* **Blue Whale.** World-wide. (EM)
86 *Balaenoptera brydei.* **Bryde's Whale.** S. African Seas. (EMH)
87 *Megaptera novaeangliae.* **Humpback Whale.** World-wide. (EM)

Family BALAENIDAE.

88 *Balaena mysticetus.* **Greenland Right Whale.** Arctic waters. (EM)
89 *Eubalaena glacialis.* **Black Right Whale.** N. Atlantic. (EM)
90 *Eubalaena sieboldi.* **Pacific Right Whale.** N. Pacific. (EM)
91 *Eubalaena australis.* **Southern Right Whale.** S. Hemisphere. (EMH)
92 *Caperea marginata.* **Pygmy Right Whale.** Southern waters. (EMH)

241

COMMON DOLPHIN

Delphinus delphis

(World-wide)

The Common Dolphin is frequently seen, as in the photograph above, leaping from the water at the bows of a ship. Unlike the Bottlenosed Dolphin shown on the next page, it prefers deep water and it is probably for this reason that it is less able to adjust to life in captivity.

Dolphins can be distinguished from porpoises by their head shape: the mouth of a dolphin is a clearly demarcated narrow beak (in the photograph this is just below the surface), whereas the mouth of a porpoise is blunt. Dolphins are also slightly larger, a typical common specimen being 7 to 8 feet long, while an adult porpoise is usually less than 6 feet. There is a further difference in the shape of the dorsal fin, that of the dolphin curving backwards to a sharp point, while that of the porpoise is more triangular.

Dolphins surface every few minutes to take in air through the dorsal "blow-hole". This is, in fact, the animal's nose. In almost all whales the nostrils have migrated to the very top of the head. In some species (the whalebone whales) they have remained separate, resulting in a double blow-hole, but in this species (and all other toothed whales) there is only a single aperture. It is wide open and taking in a deep breath in the photograph above.

When a cetacean "spouts", it is expelling moist, expended air through its blow-hole in a mighty exhalation immediately after surfacing. This is then followed by the inhalation of fresh air before the dive.

BOTTLENOSED DOLPHIN

Tursiops truncatus

(World-wide)

The Bottlenosed Dolphin has become famous in recent years as the star of the American Oceanarium exhibitions. At Marineland of the Pacific, they have been taught to perform a number of complicated routines in their 500,000 gallon tank including basket-ball, leaping through flaming hoops, towing boats and various acrobatics and formation high jumps. The animals have displayed a remarkable degree of intelligence and a constant need for novelty and activity.

It has been reported recently that they not only make a variety of strange noises, but are imitative and can apparently copy human voices. If this is true they are unique amongst mammals. It is further claimed that, unlike talking birds, the dolphins can quickly learn to link a particular utterance with a relevant situation. One individual, for example, is reputed to call its human companions by their names and to demand "more fish" when it is hungry. When it has finished feeding, but is offered another fish, it says "no". It can also speak the numbers one to ten. Over a period of time in captivity dolphins manage to improve the quality of their imitations by reducing the pitch of their vocalizations more and more. Even at their lowest pitch, however, they still sound like tiny children.

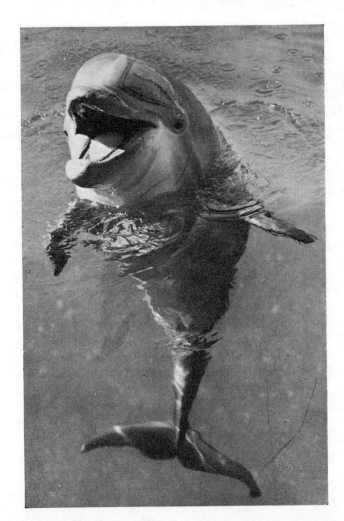

Their extraordinary vocal communication abilities appear to have evolved as an aid to intelligent, co-operative action demanded by the hazards of their marine environment.

On a more mundane level, dolphins are gregarious fish-eaters that move about in small schools searching for their preferred prey species. They are restricted largely to the warmer waters of the world. Sharks are their worst enemies.

243

KILLER WHALE

Orcinus orca

(World-wide)

The 30-foot long Killer Whale is without doubt the most fearsome predator of the high seas. By comparison, the shark is a harmless midget. For example, the stomach of one Killer Whale caught in the Bering Sea was found to contain thirty-two adult seals. Another 21-foot long specimen was found with no less than 13 complete porpoises and 14 seals inside it.

Killers prefer to attack aquatic mammals such as dolphins, porpoises, seals, sealions, sea otters, narwhals and small whales, but they also eat penguins, squid and occasionally fish. They have even been known to attack the huge Blue Whale. They assault the adults in bands of three to forty individuals, tearing at the giant's fins and lips until the victim bleeds to death and can be eaten in safety. They sometimes attack young Walruses, but are said to avoid the sharp-tusked adults. In some areas they have become a serious pest of the fishing waters and have been successfully driven away only after the dropping of depth-charges from aircraft.

The markings of the Killer Whale are easy to recognize. The upper surface is black and the lower white. There is a characteristic white patch on each side, above and behind the eyes, and the white underside extends on to the flanks in an oval patch just behind the huge dorsal fin. The bulls are much bigger than the cows and have a larger, more pointed and more vertical dorsal fin. Both sexes can be seen in the photograph above.

The gestation period is reported to be approximately 1 year, the young Killer Whale measuring 7 feet at birth.

Family DELPHINIDAE

PACIFIC PILOT WHALE
Globicephala scammoni
(Pacific Ocean)

Like all toothed whales, the Pacific Pilot Whale has teeth designed for holding its prey and not for chewing. These teeth, usually conical, vary in number from species to species.

Whales, which may attain a speed of 15 knots under water, are streamlined in many ways. Their bodies are almost hairless, their external ears are missing, their neck vertebrae are telescoped and the highly efficient tail fluke, unlike that of fish, is horizontal. The insulating blubber under the skin is apparently insufficient to maintain the body temperature, so whales must keep moving.

The toothed whales produce a variety of sounds which vary from bellowing to whistling. Many of the smaller species use supersonic sounds for echo-location.

Second only to domestic animals in their usefulness to man, whales have been hunted for centuries. The gregarious Sperm Whale (*Physeter catodon*), the hero of *Moby Dick*, possesses a mass of loose fibrous tissue in the head, which is the spermaceti used in candles and cosmetics. Ambergris, a perfume fixative, is made by bacteria in the whale's intestines. The Sperm Whale can remain submerged for an hour at a time and may sound to a depth of 3,000 feet.

The white Whale (*Delphinapterus leucas*) of the Arctic has no dorsal fin and is the noisiest of all. The Narwhal (*Monodon monoceros*) sports a frontal tusk formed by the left upper canine.

The Pacific Pilot Whale is the only species of whale (excluding dolphins and porpoises) that has been trained to give performances in captivity. The 3,400 lb. male shown above at Marineland of the Pacific is 18 feet long.

245

L. CARNIVORES

The 252 species of carnivores cover much of the land surface of the globe. Before the advent of man, members of this order were absent from Australia and New Zealand. Today they run wild even in these areas, early man having introduced the dingo to Australia and later colonists having taken foxes and other species. If this invasion had occurred naturally, millions of years earlier, the slow-witted marsupial fauna of Australia might well have perished long ago, for modern carnivores are fast, intelligent killers, well equipped with powerful weapons and with efficient brains to put them into action. In other regions of the world where they were on the prowl in a variety of forms, the prey species were forced to become more and more efficient at escape and defence.

Modern carnivores fall into seven natural groupings. The central type, similar in some respects to the ancestral carnivores, are the mustelids—the weasels, stoats and martens. There are sixty-eight species alive today, distributed right across the Old and New World. In general they are smallish, long-tailed, short-legged creatures with long, low bodies. Closely related, but more sensitive and cat-like, are the eighty-two species of viverrids—the genets, civets and mongooses. An important difference is that the mustelids have fixed, dog-like claws, whereas the viverrids typically have semi-retractile claws approaching the feline condition. Viverrids have a more limited distribution covering only Africa, southern Europe and southern Asia. Apparently they cannot survive a colder climate like the mustelids. Their place is taken in the New World by sixteen species of procyonids—the raccoons, coatis and kinkajous. These are more closely related to the canine groups of the carnivores, and are represented in the Old World only by the strange and limited pandas (two species).

Closely related to the viverrids are the four species of Afro-Asian hyaenas. Although superficially dog-like in appearance they belong on the feline side of the carnivore family tree. The seven species of bears, on the other hand, have stronger bonds with the canine side of the order, being little more than massive, omnivorous dogs. They are found in both the Old and the New World, but for some reason have failed to colonize Africa.

Finally, we come to the two extreme groups of the carnivores—the cats (thirty-six species) and the dogs (thirty-seven species). In both cases the groups are virtually world-wide and in a sense they represent peaks of predatory evolution.

The name carnivore means literally flesh-eater and, with a few exceptions, such as the Kinkajou and the Giant Panda, this is a precise enough description of the group. The jaws are strong, the skull powerful, the teeth large and sharp, capable of rapidly tearing to pieces the flesh of the prey. The incisors are sharp for nipping, the canines huge and pointed for stabbing. Some of the cheek teeth have become sharper too, acting as shears that chop up the meat quickly, instead of grinding it slowly. These cutting teeth are called carnassials.

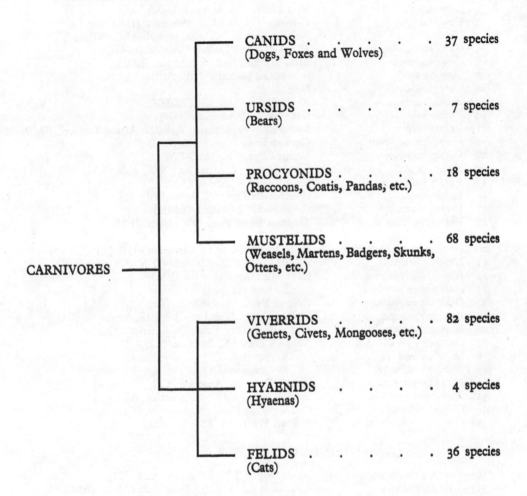

CARNIVORES

CANIDS . . . . . 37 species
(Dogs, Foxes and Wolves)

URSIDS . . . . . 7 species
(Bears)

PROCYONIDS . . . . 18 species
(Raccoons, Coatis, Pandas, etc.)

MUSTELIDS . . . . 68 species
(Weasels, Martens, Badgers, Skunks, Otters, etc.)

VIVERRIDS . . . . 82 species
(Genets, Civets, Mongooses, etc.)

HYAENIDS . . . . 4 species
(Hyaenas)

FELIDS . . . . . 36 species
(Cats)

L. Order CARNIVORA. Carnivores.

Superfamily CANOIDEA.

Family CANIDAE. Dogs.

Subfamily CANINAE.

1 ►*Canis lupus.*	**Wolf.** Europe, Asia, N. America, Arctic. (EM/HK)
2 *Canis niger.*	**Red Wolf.** N. America. (HK)
3 ►*Canis latrans.*	**Coyote.** N. and Cen. America. (HK)
4 *Canis aureus.*	**Asiatic Jackal.** S. Asia and N. Africa. (EM)
5 ►*Canis mesomelas.*	**Black-backed Jackal.** Africa. (EMH)
6 *Canis adustus.*	**Side-striped Jackal.** Africa. (EMH)
7 *Canis simensis.*	**Simenian Jackal.** N.E. Africa. (A)
8 *Canis familiaris.*	**Dog.** (Domestic)
9 ►*Alopex lagopus.*	**Arctic Fox.** Arctic. (EM/HK)
10 *Vulpes velox.*	**Kit Fox.** N. America. (HK)
11 ►*Vulpes vulpes.*	**Red Fox.** N. America, Asia, N. Africa, Europe. (EM/HK)
12 *Vulpes corsac.*	**Corsac Fox.** Cen. Asia. (EM)
13 *Vulpes bengalensis.*	**Bengal Fox.** S. Asia. (EM)
14 *Vulpes ruppelli.*	**Sand Fox.** N. Africa and S.W. Asia. (EM)
15 *Vulpes pallida.*	**Pale Fox.** N. Africa. (A)
16 *Vulpes cana.*	**Blanford's Fox.** S. Asia. (EM)
17 *Vulpes chama.*	**Cape Fox.** S. Africa. (EMH)
18 *Vulpes ferrilata.*	**Tibetan Sand Fox.** Cen. Asia. (EM)
19 ►*Fennecus zerda.*	**Fennec Fox.** N. Africa and S.W. Asia. (EM)
20 *Urocyon cinereoargenteus.*	**Grey Fox.** N. and S. America. (HK/CI)
21 *Urocyon littoralis.*	**Island Grey Fox.** Islands off N. America. (HK)
22 ►*Nyctereutes procyonoides.*	**Raccoon Dog.** E. Asia. (EM)
23 *Dusicyon culpaeolus.*	S. America. (CI)
24 *Dusicyon culpaeus.*	**Colpeo Fox.** S. America. (CI)
25 *Dusicyon fulvipes*	**Chiloé Fox.** Island of Chiloé (S. America). (CI)
26 *Dusicyon griseus.*	**Argentine Grey Fox.** S. America. (CI)
27 *Dusicyon gymnocercus.*	**Azara's Fox.** S. America. (CI)
28 *Dusicyon inca.*	S. America. (CI)
29 *Dusicyon sechurae.*	S. America. (CI)
30 *Dusicyon vetulus.*	**Hoary Fox.** S. America. (CI)
31 *Atelocynus microtis.*	**Small-eared Fox.** S. America. (CI)
32 *Cerdocyon thous.*	**Crab-eating Fox.** S. America. (CI)
33 ►*Chrysocyon brachyurus.*	**Maned Wolf.** S. America. (CI)

Subfamily SIMOCYONINAE.

34 ►*Speothos venaticus.*	**Bush Dog.** S. and Cen. America. (CI)
35 ►*Cuon alpinus.*	**Asiatic Wild Dog.** Asia, Sumatra, Java. (EM/CH)
36 ►*Lycaon pictus.*	**Hunting Dog.** Africa. (EMH)

Subfamily OTOCYONINAE.

37 ►*Otocyon megalotis.*	**Bat-eared Fox.** Africa. (A)

Family URSIDAE. Bears.

38 ►*Tremarctos ornatus.*	**Spectacled Bear.** S. America. (CI)
39 ►*Selenarctos thibetanus.*	**Asiatic Black Bear.** Asia. (EM)

248

40 ►*Ursus arctos.*	**Brown Bear.**	N. America, Europe, Asia. (HK/EM)
41 ►*Ursus americanus.*	**American Black Bear.**	N. America. (HK)
42 ►*Thalarctos maritimus.*	**Polar Bear.**	Arctic. (HK/EM)
43 ►*Helarctos malayanus.*	**Sun Bear.**	S. Asia, Sumatra, Borneo. (EM)
44 ►*Melursus ursinus.*	**Sloth Bear.**	S. Asia. (EM)

Family PROCYONIDAE. Raccoons.
Subfamily PROCYONINAE.

45 ►*Bassariscus astutus.*	**North American Cacomistle.**	N. America. (HK)
46 *Bassariscus sumichrasti.*	**Central American Cacomistle.**	Cen. America. (HK)
47 *Procyon lotor.*	**North American Raccoon.**	N. and Cen. America. (HK)
48 *Procyon insularis.*	**Tres Marias Raccoon.**	Tres Marias Islands (N. America). (HK)
49 *Procyon maynardi.*	**Bahaman Raccoon.**	Bahamas (W. Indies). (HK)
50 *Procyon pygmaeus.*	**Cozumel Island Raccoon.**	Cozumel Island (Cen. America). (HK)
51 *Procyon minor.*	**Guadeloupe Raccoon.**	Guadeloupe Island (W. Indies). (HK)
52 *Procyon gloveralleni.*	**Barbados Raccoon.**	Barbados (W. Indies). (HK)
53 ►*Procyon cancrivorus.*	**Crab-eating Raccoon.**	Cen. and S. America. (HK/CI)
54 ►*Nasua nasua.*	**Coati.**	Cen. and S. America. (HK/CI)
55 *Nasua nelsoni.*	**Cozumel Island Coati.**	Cozumel Island (Cen. America). (HK)
56 *Nasuella olivacea.*	**Mountain Coati.**	S. America. (CI)
57 ►*Potos flavus.*	**Kinkajou.**	Cen. and S. America. (HK/CI)
58 *Bassaricyon gabbii.*	**Bushy-tailed Olingo.**	Cen. and S. America. (HK/CI)
59 ►*Bassaricyon alleni.*	**Allen's Olingo.**	S. America. (CI)
60 *Bassaricyon beddardi.*	**Beddard's Olingo.**	S. America. (CI)

Subfamily AILURINAE. Pandas.

61 ►*Ailurus fulgens.*	**Red Panda.**	Asia. (EM)
62 ►*Ailuropoda melanoleuca.*	**Giant Panda.**	Asia. (EM)

Family MUSTELIDAE.
Subfamily MUSTELINAE.

63 ►*Mustela erminea.*	**Stoat.**	N. America, Europe, Asia, Arctic. (HK/EM)
64 *Mustela rixosa.*	**Pygmy Weasel.**	N. America. (HK)
65 *Mustela frenata.*	**Long-tailed Weasel.**	N. and S. America. (HK/CI)
66 *Mustela nigripes.*	**Black-footed Ferret.**	N. America. (HK)
67 ►*Mustela vison.*	**American Mink.**	N. America. (HK)
68 ►*Mustela nivalis.*	**Weasel.**	Europe, N. and Cen. Asia, N. Africa. (EM)
69 *Mustela altaica.*	**Alpine Weasel.**	Asia. (EM)
70 *Mustela kathiah.*	**Yellow-bellied Weasel.**	Asia. (EM)
71 *Mustela sibirica.*	**Siberian Weasel.**	Asia. (EM)
72 *Mustela lutreola.*	**European Mink.**	Europe and W. Asia. (EM)
73 *Mustela strigidorsa.*	**Back-striped Weasel.**	S. Asia. (EM)

74 ►*Mustela putorius.*	**European Polecat** (and Domestic Ferret). Europe, Asia, N. Africa. (EM)
75 *Mustela lutreolina.*	**Java Weasel.** Java. (CH)
76 *Mustela nudipes.*	**Bare-footed Weasel.** Sumatra, Borneo, S. Asia. (CH/EM)
77 *Grammogale africana.*	S. America. (CI)
78 *Vormela peregusna.*	**Marbled Polecat.** Asia. (EM)
79 *Martes martes.*	**Pine Marten.** Europe and Asia. (EM)
80 *Martes foina.*	**Stone Marten.** Europe and Asia. (EM)
81 *Martes melampus.*	**Japanese Marten.** E. Asia. (EM)
82 *Martes zibellina.*	**Sable.** Asia. (EM)
83 *Martes flavigula.*	**Yellow-throated Marten.** Asia. (EM)
84 *Martes gwatkinsi.*	**South Indian Yellow-throated Marten.** S. Asia. (EM)
85 ►*Martes americana.*	**American Marten.** N. America. (HK)
86 *Martes pennanti.*	**Fisher.** N. America. (HK)
87 ►*Eira barbara.*	**Tayra.** Cen. and S. America. (CI)
88 *Galictis vittata.*	**Allamand's Grison.** Cen. and S. America. (CI)
89 ►*Galictis cuja.*	**Lesser Grison.** S. America. (CI)
90 *Lyncodon patagonicus.*	**Patagonian Weasel.** S. America. (CI)
91 ►*Ictonyx striatus.*	**Zorilla.** Africa. (EMH)
92 *Poecilictis libyca.*	**Libyan Striped Weasel.** N. Africa. (EM)
93 *Poecilogale albinucha.*	**White-naped Weasel.** Africa. (EMH)
94 ►*Gulo gulo.*	**Wolverine.** N. America, N. Asia, N. Europe, Arctic. (EM/HK)

Subfamily MELLIVORINAE.

95 ►*Mellivora capensis.*	**Ratel.** Africa and S. Asia. (EM)

Subfamily MELINAE.   Badgers.

96 ►*Meles meles.*	**Eurasian Badger.** Europe and Asia. (EM)
97 ►*Arctonyx collaris.*	**Hog Badger.** S. Asia and Sumatra. (EM)
98 *Mydaus javanensis.*	**Malay Badger.** S. Asia, Borneo, Java, Sumatra. (CH)
99 *Suillotaxus marchei.*	**Philippines Badger.** Philippines. (SA)
100 *Taxidea taxus.*	**American Badger.** N. America. (HK)
101 ►*Melogale moschata.*	**Chinese Ferret Badger.** S. Asia. (EM)
102 *Melogale personata.*	**Burmese Ferret Badger.** S. Asia. (EM)
103 *Melogale orientalis.*	**Javan Ferret Badger.** Java and Borneo. (CH)

Subfamily MEPHITINAE.   Skunks.

104 ►*Mephitis mephitis.*	**Striped Skunk.** N. America. (HK)
105 *Mephitis macroura.*	**Hooded Skunk.** N. and Cen. America. (HK)
106 *Spilogale putorius.*	**Spotted Skunk.** N. and Cen. America. (HK)
107 *Conepatus leuconotus.*	**Hog-nosed Skunk.** N. and Cen. America. (HK)
108 *Conepatus semistriatus.*	**Amazonian Skunk.** Cen. and S. America. (CI/HK)
109 *Conepatus castaneus.*	**Cordovan Skunk.** S. America. (CI)
110 *Conepatus chinga.*	**Argentine Skunk.** S. America. (CI)
111 *Conepatus humboldti.*	**Patagonian Skunk.** S. America. (CI)
112 *Conepatus rex.*	S. America. (CI)

Subfamily LUTRINAE.   Otters.

113	*Lutra lutra.*	**Eurasian Otter.** Europe, Asia, Java, Sumatra, N. Africa. (EM)	
114	*Lutra canadensis.*	**North American Otter.** N. America. (HK)	
115	*Lutra annectens.*	**Central American Otter.** Cen. and S. America. (CI/HK)	
116	*Lutra enudris.*	S. America. (CI)	
117	*Lutra felina.*	S. America. (CI)	
118	*Lutra incarum.*	S. America. (CI)	
119	*Lutra platensis.*	S. America. (CI)	
120	*Lutra provocax.*	S. America. (CI)	
121	*Lutra maculicollis.*	**Spotted-necked Otter.** Africa. (EMH)	
122	*Lutra perspicillata.*	**Smooth Indian Otter.** S. Asia. (EM)	
123	*Lutra sumatrana.*	**Hairy-nosed Otter.** S. Asia, Sumatra, Borneo. (EM)	
124 ►	*Pteronura brasiliensis.*	**Giant Otter.** S. America. (CI)	
125	*Aonyx cinerea.*	**Oriental Small-clawed Otter.** S. Asia, Borneo, Java, Sumatra, Philippines. (EM/TAY)	
126 ►	*Aonyx capensis.*	**Cape Clawless Otter.** Africa. (EMH)	
127	*Paraonyx philippsi.*	**Philip's Otter.** Cen. Africa. (A)	
128	*Paraonyx microdon.*	**Cameroons Otter.** Cen. Africa. (A)	
129	*Paraonyx congica.*	**Congo Otter.** Cen. Africa. (A)	
130 ►	*Enhydra lutris.*	**Sea Otter.** N. Pacific Coasts. (HK/EM)	

Superfamily FELOIDEA.

Family VIVERRIDAE.

Subfamily VIVERRINAE.

Tribe VIVERRINI.

131	*Poiana richardsoni.*	**African Linsang.** Africa. (A)
132	*Genetta genetta.*	**Small-spotted Genet.** Africa and S. Europe. (EM)
133	*Genetta abyssinica.*	**Abyssinian Genet.** Africa. (A)
134	*Genetta maculata.*	**Forest Genet.** Cen. W. Africa. (A)
135	*Genetta servalina.*	**Servaline Genet.** Cen. W. Africa. (A)
136 ►	*Genetta tigrina.*	**Blotched Genet.** Africa. (EMH)
137	*Genetta rubiginosa.*	**Rusty-spotted Genet.** Africa. (EMH)
138	*Genetta victoriae.*	**Giant Genet.** Cen. Africa. (A)
139	*Genetta deorum.*	E. Africa. (FS)
140	*Genetta lehmanni.*	**Lehmann's Genet.** Africa. (KU)
141	*Viverricula indica.*	**Small Indian Civet.** S. Asia, Sumatra, Java. (EM/LH)
142	*Osbornictis piscivora.*	**Water Civet.** Cen. Africa. (A)
143 ►	*Viverra civetta.*	**African Civet.** Africa. (EMH)
144	*Viverra zibetha.*	**Large Indian Civet.** S. Asia. (EM)
145	*Viverra megaspila.*	**Large-spotted Civet.** S. Asia. (EM)
146	*Viverra tangalunga.*	**Malay Civet.** S. Asia, Borneo, Sumatra, Celebes, Philippines. (LH/CH)

Tribe PRIONODONTINI.

147	*Prionodon linsang.*	**Banded Linsang.** S. Asia, Sumatra, Java, Borneo. (EM/CH)
148	*Prionodon pardicolor.*	**Spotted Linsang.** S. Asia. (EM)

251

Subfamily PARADOXURINAE.
Tribe NANDINIINI.

149 *Nandinia binotata.*   **Two-spotted Palm Civet.**   Africa. (EMH)

Tribe ARCTOGALIDIINI.

150 *Arctogalidia trivirgata.*   **Small-toothed Palm Civet.**   S. Asia, Sumatra, Java, Borneo. (EM/CH)

Tribe PARADOXURINI.

151 *Paradoxurus hermaphroditus.*   **Common Palm Civet.**   S. Asia, Java, Sumatra, Philippines, Borneo, Celebes and Pacific Islands. (EM/LH/CH)
152 *Paradoxurus zeylonensis.*   **Golden Palm Civet.**   Ceylon. (EM)
153 *Paradoxurus jerdoni.*   **Jerdon's Palm Civet.**   S. Asia. (EM)
154 ►*Paguma larvata.*   **Masked Palm Civet.**   S. Asia, Sumatra, Borneo. (EM/CH)
155 *Macrogalidia musschenbroeki.*   **Brown Palm Civet.**   Celebes. (LH)
156 ►*Arctictis binturong.*   **Binturong.** S. Asia, Java, Borneo, Sumatra, Philippines. (EM/CH)

Subfamily HEMIGALINAE.
Tribe FOSSINI.

157 *Fossa fossa.*   **Malagasy Civet.**   Madagascar. (A)

Tribe HEMIGALINI.

158 *Hemigalus derbyanus.*   **Banded Palm Civet.**   S. Asia, Sumatra, Borneo. (EM/CH)
159 *Hemigalus hosei.*   **Hose's Palm Civet.**   Borneo. (CH)
160 *Chrotogale owstoni.*   **Owston's Banded Civet.**   S. Asia. (EM)

Tribe CYNOGALINI.

161 ►*Cynogale bennetti.*   **Otter Civet.**   S. Asia, Sumatra, Borneo. (EM/CH)

Tribe EUPLERINI.

162 *Eupleres goudoti.*   **Falanouc.**   Madagascar. (A)
163 *Eupleres major.*   Madagascar. (A)

Subfamily GALIDIINAE.   Malagasy Mongooses.

164 *Galidia elegans.*   **Ring-tailed Mongoose.**   Madagascar. (A)
165 *Galidictis fasciata.*   Madagascar. (A)
166 *Galidictis ornata.*   Madagascar. (A)
167 *Galidictis striata.*   **Broad-striped Mongoose.**   Madagascar. (A)
168 *Mungotictis lineata.*   **Narrow-striped Mongoose.**   Madagascar. (A)
169 *Mungotictis substriata.*   Madagascar. (A)
170 *Salanoia olivacea.*   Madagascar. (A)
171 *Salanoia unicolor.*   **Brown-tailed Mongoose.**   Madagascar. (A)

Subfamily HERPESTINAE.
Tribe SURICATINI.

172 ▶ *Suricata suricatta.*   **Slender-tailed Meerkat.**   S. Africa. (EMH)

Tribe HERPESTINI.   Mongooses.

173	*Herpestes ichneumon.*	**Egyptian Mongoose.** Africa and S. Europe. (EM)
174	*Herpestes naso.*	**Cameroons Mongoose.** W. Africa. (A/IS)
175	*Herpestes sanguineus.*	**Slender Mongoose.** Africa. (EMH)
176	*Herpestes pulverulentus.*	**Cape Grey Mongoose.** S. Africa. (EMH)
177	*Herpestes ochracea.*	**Ochraceous Mongoose.** Cen. Africa. (A)
178	*Herpestes dentifer.*	E. Africa. (A)
179	*Herpestes granti.*	E. Africa. (A)
180	*Herpestes javanicus.*	**Javan Mongoose.** S. Asia and Java. (EM)
181	*Herpestes auropunctatus.*	**Small Indian Mongoose.** S. Asia. (EM)
182	*Herpestes edwardsi.*	**Indian Grey Mongoose.** S. Asia. (EM)
183	*Herpestes smithi.*	**Ruddy Mongoose.** S. Asia. (EM)
184	*Herpestes fuscus.*	**Indian Brown Mongoose.** S. Asia. (EM)
185	*Herpestes vitticollis.*	**Striped-necked Mongoose.** S. Asia. (EM)
186	*Herpestes urva.*	**Crab-eating Mongoose.** S. Asia. (EM)
187	*Herpestes semitorquatus.*	**Collared Mongoose.** Sumatra and Borneo. (CH)
188	*Herpestes brachyurus.*	**Short-tailed Mongoose.** S. Asia, Borneo, Sumatra, Philippines. (CH/SA)
189	*Herpestes hosei.*	**Hose's Mongoose.** Borneo. (CH)
190	*Helogale parvula.*	**Dwarf Mongoose.** Africa. (EMH)
191	*Helogale hirtula.*	E. Africa. (A)
192	*Helogale macmillani.*	E. Africa. (A)
193	*Helogale percivali.*	**Percival's Dwarf Mongoose.** E. Africa. (A)
194	*Helogale vetula.*	E. Africa. (A)
195	*Helogale victorina.*	**Lake Victoria Dwarf Mongoose.** E. and Cen. Africa. (A)
196	*Dologale dybowskii.*	Cen. Africa. (A)
197 ▶	*Atilax paludinosus.*	**Marsh Mongoose.** Africa. (EMH)
198	*Mungos mungo.*	**Banded Mongoose.** Africa. (EMH)
199	*Mungos gambianus.*	**Gambian Kusimanse.** Cen. W. Africa. (A/H)
200	*Crossarchus ansorgei.*	**Angolan Kusimanse.** Cen. Africa. (A)
201	*Crossarchus alexandri.*	**Congo Kusimanse.** Cen. Africa. (A)
202	*Crossarchus obscurus.*	**Kusimanse.** Cen. W. Africa. (A)
203	*Liberiictis kuhni.*	**Kuhn's Kusimanse.** Cen. W. Africa. (HI)
204	*Ichneumia albicauda.*	**White-tailed Mongoose.** Africa. (EM)
205	*Bdeogale crassicauda.*	**Bushy-tailed Mongoose.** E. Africa. (EMH)
206	*Bdeogale tenuis.*	**Zanzibar Mongoose.** Zanzibar Island. (A)
207	*Bdeogale nigripes.*	**Black-footed Mongoose.** Cen. Africa. (A/IS)
208	*Rhynchogale melleri.*	**Meller's Mongoose.** Africa. (EMH)
209	*Rhynchogale caniceps.*	Cen. Africa. (A)
210	*Cynictis penicillata.*	**Yellow Mongoose.** S. Africa. (EMH)
211	*Paracynictis selousi.*	**Selous' Meekat.** Africa. (EMH)

Subfamily CRYPTOPROCTINAE.

212 ▶ *Cryptoprocta ferox.*   **Fossa.**   Madagascar. (A)

253

Family HYAENIDAE.
Subfamily PROTELINAE.

213 ►*Proteles cristatus.*   **Aardwolf.** S. Africa. (EMH)

Subfamily HYAENINAE. Hyaenas.

214 ►*Crocuta crocuta.*   **Spotted Hyaena.** Africa. (EMH)
215 *Hyaena brunnea.*   **Brown Hyaena.** S. Africa. (EMH)
216 ►*Hyaena hyaena.*   **Striped Hyaena.** N. Africa and S. Asia. (EM)

Family FELIDAE. Cats.

217 ►*Felis silvestris.*   **European Wild Cat.** Europe and W. Asia. (EM)
218 *Felis libyca.*   **African Wild Cat.** Africa and Asia. (EM)
219 *Felis catus.*   **Cat.** (Domestic)
220 *Felis margarita.*   **Sand Cat.** N. Africa and S.W. Asia. (EM)
221 *Felis chaus.*   **Jungle Cat.** Asia and N. Africa. (EM)
222 *Felis bieti.*   **Chinese Desert Cat.** Cen. Asia. (EM)
223 *Felis bengalensis.*   **Leopard Cat.** S. Asia, Sumatra, Java, Borneo, Philippines. (EM)
224 *Felis rubiginosa.*   **Rusty-spotted Cat.** S. Asia. (EM)
225 *Felis planiceps.*   **Flat-headed Cat.** S. Asia, Borneo, Sumatra. (EM/CH)
226 *Felis badia.*   **Bay Cat.** Borneo. (CH)
227 *Felis nigripes.*   **Black-footed Cat.** S. Africa. (EMH)
228 *Felis caracal.*   **Caracal Lynx.** Africa and Asia. (EM)
229 ►*Felis lynx.*   **Northern Lynx.** Europe, N. Asia, N. America. (EM/HK)
230 ►*Felis rufa.*   **Bobcat.** N. America. (HK)
231 *Felis manul.*   **Pallas's Cat.** Asia. (EM)
232 ►*Felis serval.*   **Serval.** Africa. (EMH)
233 *Felis marmorata.*   **Marbled Cat.** S. Asia, Sumatra, Borneo. (EM)
234 *Felis aurata.*   **African Golden Cat.** Africa. (A)
235 ►*Felis temmincki.*   **Temminck's Golden Cat.** S. Asia and Sumatra. (EM)
236 *Felis viverrina.*   **Fishing Cat.** S. Asia, Sumatra, Java. (EM)
237 ►*Felis pardalis.*   **Ocelot.** Cen. and S. America. (C1/HK)
238 *Felis wiedi.*   **Margay Cat.** Cen. and S. America. (C1/HK)
239 *Felis tigrina.*   **Tiger Cat.** Cen. and S. America. (C1/HK)
240 *Felis jacobita.*   **Mountain Cat.** S. America. (C1)
241 *Felis geoffroyi.*   **Geoffroy's Cat.** S. America. (C1)
242 *Felis guigna.*   **Kodkod.** S. America. (C1)
243 ►*Felis yagouaroundi.*   **Jaguarondi.** Cen. and S. America. (C1/HK)
244 *Felis colocolo.*   **Pampas Cat.** S. America. (C1)
245 ►*Felis concolor.*   **Puma.** N. and S. America. (C1/HK)
246 ►*Neofelis nebulosa.*   **Clouded Leopard.** S. Asia, Borneo, Sumatra, Java. (EM)
247 ►*Panthera leo.*   **Lion.** S. Asia and Africa. (EM)
248 ►*Panthera tigris.*   **Tiger.** Asia, Sumatra, Java. (EM)
249 ►*Panthera pardus.*   **Leopard.** Africa, Asia, Java. (EM/CH)
250 ►*Panthera onca.*   **Jaguar.** N. and S. America. (C1/HK)
251 ►*Panthera uncia.*   **Snow Leopard.** Asia. (EM)
252 ►*Acinonyx jubatus.*   **Cheetah.** S. Asia and Africa. (EM)

WOLF

Canis lupus

(Forests of Europe, Asia, and North America)

The Wolf is closely related to the domestic dog, and the two species readily inter-breed. A fully-grown Wolf is about 31 inches tall at the shoulder, weighs about 100 lb., and resembles a dog with erect ears, having the long muzzle and non-retractile claws typical of the family.

Originally Wolves were found in most temperate parts of the Northern Hemisphere, but in many areas they have now been exterminated. The last Wolves in Britain, for example, were killed in the eighteenth century. Wolves from different parts of the world have their own racial characteristics, but the differences involved are slight. As is usually the case, the larger animals with heavier coats tend to be found in the cooler climates.

The cubs are born in late spring or early summer and, like puppies, they are at first blind and helpless. At this time, and throughout the summer, the adults hunt singly on behalf of the family group. In the autumn the parents and their litter hunt together, and a typical Wolf-pack is a family group like this, made up of about five individuals. During a hard winter these small packs tend to join together, but a pack of over thirty Wolves is unusual.

When hunting, a Wolf-pack may travel as much as 40 miles in a day in search of deer, smaller animals, carrion, and even some fruits. The pack tends to travel in a large circle covering the same ground every 15 or 20 days, ranging more widely when food is scarce.

255

COYOTE

Canis latrans

(Grasslands of Central and North America)

The Coyote lives on the open plains, deserts and prairies of North America, and is sometimes called the Prairie Wolf to distinguish it from its close relative, the true Wolf of North America, which is called the Timber Wolf. Coyotes are smaller than Wolves, being about 24 inches tall at the shoulder and weighing about 40 lb. when adult. When the animals are running, the tail of a Coyote points downward, but that of a Wolf points upward or is horizontal.

Coyotes hunt smaller game than Wolves, feeding on insects, rodents, especially Prairie Marmots, and occasionally larger animals, such as deer and Pronghorn Antelopes. To catch Pronghorns, Coyotes will work as a group, taking turns to chase the prey until it is exhausted. Usually, however, the Coyote hunts alone, making good use of its keen sense of smell, its excellent vision, and its ability to run at well over 30 miles per hour when necessary.

The den is adapted from the burrow of a badger, skunk, or fox, being enlarged and thoroughly cleaned out by its new owner, for Coyotes are remarkable for their attention to den sanitation. In such a den the litter, usually consisting of from five to seven cubs, is born between April and June.

Inevitably, during the last 100 years the numbers of this species have been reduced as a result of the changes which have taken place in North America. The Coyote is, however, an adaptable animal and is still quite common. The mournful howl which it utters at night is known to millions, if only through the medium of Western films.

Family CANIDAE

BLACK-BACKED JACKAL

Canis mesomelas

(Grasslands of East and South Africa)

The Black-backed Jackal is a little more lightly built than the Coyote, its narrow muzzle looking rather like that of a fox. As the name suggests, it has a saddle of black hair on its back. The sides of the body and the legs are orange-brown.

By day the Black-backed Jackal usually lies concealed in a thicket, or amongst long grass, venturing out at night in search of food. It often hunts on its own, but frequently several will join together and follow hunting Lions on the off-chance of sharing in the kill. In addition to carrion, it hunts and kills its own food, including mammals such as rats and mice, and even young antelopes; also various birds and reptiles. A large python may be attacked if the Jackal finds it when it is stretched out digesting its last meal. On the other hand, a hungry and active python is quite capable of eating a Jackal.

There are four species of jackals. The Side-striped Jackal (*C. adustus*), which also comes from Africa, is a little larger, but lacks the courage of its near relation. The very large Simenian Jackal (*C. simensis*) from Abyssinia is rare and little known. The more plainly marked Golden Jackal (*C. aureus*) is found in North Africa and southern Asia. All are closely related to the domestic dog and can inter-breed with it, and with the Wolf. All four species eat basically the same type of food as the Black-backed Jackal, but those from Asia are more sociable and usually live and hunt in small packs.

The natural enemy of the Jackal is the Leopard.

I

ARCTIC FOX

Alopex lagopus

(Arctic regions of Europe, Asia and North America)

Seen below is an Arctic Fox in its long winter coat. During the summer the same animal would look very different, the coat being a dark, slaty grey and shorter in length, giving the animal a more spidery, long-legged appearance. Some of the Arctic Foxes of Greenland, Iceland and Canada have grey winter coats, and these are sometimes specially bred for their fur, being known as Blue Foxes.

To most Arctic Foxes, however, a white coat is obviously extremely valuable, as it helps its owner to conceal itself in the snows of the northern winter. It is important, too, that the coat should be thick. Wild Arctic Foxes have been known to sleep peacefully, curled up in burrows in the snow and using their tails as mufflers, while the thermometer dropped to 50°C. below zero outside. Even in the depths of winter, Arctic Foxes do not hibernate, although they do bury some food in the "deep-freeze" of the snow which can be eaten should hunting become too difficult.

The diet is largely carnivorous, and consists of sea birds, ptarmigan, fish, Arctic hares, seal pups, and, above all, lemmings. When these rodents are abundant, Arctic Foxes become numerous. The Blue Foxes of West Greenland, where lemmings do not occur, rely solely on birds, fish and hares.

Arctic Foxes normally live on land, but when food is scarce they may venture on to the edge of the pack-ice in search of the remains of a seal abandoned by a Polar Bear. Sometimes several can be seen following a bear in exactly the same way that Jackals follow a Lion.

RED FOX

Vulpes vulpes

(North America, Europe, Asia and North Africa)

Of all the members of the dog family, the foxes are the most cat-like in their habits. They never normally collect in packs, while in their hunting they rely on stealth and cunning. Their behaviour is adaptable, and foxes of different kinds, instantly recognizable by the characteristic face, rather short legs, and bushy tail, are to be found in most parts of the world.

Of all the large carnivores the Red Fox has best survived the changes man has wrought in Europe during the last 2,000 years. Although forests have dwindled, the Fox still lurks by day in an underground den, coming out at night in search of any prey from insects and mice to rabbits and chickens. The food is usually taken back to the den, which soon becomes smelly and littered with bones and feathers. The Fox is wary and seldom seen, but its raids on poultry cannot escape attention, and the animal owes its survival at least in part to the fact that it is protected by those who enjoy fox-hunting.

The cubs, five or six in number, and with woolly, greyish coats, are born in April. The male helps the vixen to feed her family when they are weaned, at 8 weeks old, by which time they have the characteristic red coat. Later they accompany him on the hunt, and by the autumn they can begin to fend for themselves.

Very closely-related Red Foxes are found in North America. These are sometimes referred to as *Vulpes fulva*, but are now generally accepted as being the same species as *Vulpes vulpes*.

259

FENNEC FOX

Fennecus zerda

(Deserts of North Africa and Arabia)

The Fennec Fox, or Desert Fox, is a diminutive species with a fluffy, creamy-coloured coat. This is not surprising, for most animals from desert regions are lighter in colour than their relatives from more hospitable areas. The tip of the nose is black, and the eyes are rather large, but the Fennec Fox's most remarkable features are its ears, which are huge. Again, this is understandable, for in the Sahara and Arabian Deserts where this animal lives, the day-time temperatures are so high that it is unable to hunt during daylight hours. It is only able to venture out at night, when keen hearing is all important, and the big ears must pick up every minute sound.

During the day the Fennec Fox remains in the shelter of burrows which it digs with its rather large paws. Towards evening it emerges and sits in the shade of stunted desert plants, protecting its head from the heat with its bushy tail. After dark it hunts, trotting briskly, but quietly, and often pausing to listen for the insects, lizards, birds or desert rats upon which it feeds. Once food is detected, the fox disdains stealth and rushes straight at it. Any meat which cannot be eaten immediately is buried, for food is not so plentiful that it can afford to be wasteful.

It then drinks at a waterhole, often meeting there the other Fennecs which use the burrows adjoining its own. Eventually it returns to rest again in its clean, snug, sleeping-chamber, lined with dried plant material, feathers and hair.

Should a Fennec Fox be surprised in the open, it burrows so rapidly that it almost seems to sink vertically into the ground.

RACCOON DOG

Nyctereutes procyonoides

(Eastern Asia)

This broad, squat animal looks like a raccoon on dog's legs. The face is particularly raccoon-like. This is partly because on each side of the small pointed muzzle there is a large dark patch, so that the Raccoon Dog, like the raccoons, appears to be masked.

Raccoon Dogs are found in eastern Russia and northern China, living in woods and copses close to rivers and lakes, or sometimes by the shores of the Sea of Japan. Their principal food is frogs, but they also eat shellfish, insects, fish, rodents, and some fruit. They are active mainly at night and, except when breeding, they roam for considerable distances, moving at a steady walk with the head held low in search of food.

Pairing takes place in the spring. At this time fights between rival males are said to be frequent. About half a dozen young, blind and covered with soft black fur, are born in a burrow which is sometimes shared with a badger or fox. The family stays together at least until the early autumn, by which time the young are full sized and able to look after themselves. In the late autumn Raccoon Dogs become very fat, and they spend the worst part of the winter in hibernation. In this respect they are unique amongst canids.

The natural enemies of this species are the Wolf, Wolverine, Lynx, Golden Eagle, and Man, who hunts the animal for its fur which is known as "Japanese Fox" or "Ussurian Raccoon". Recently Raccoon Dogs have been deliberately introduced into many parts of Russia, and this animal is therefore now to be found in certain areas of eastern Europe.

MANED WOLF

Chrysocyon brachyurus

(Wooded areas of Central South America)

The most striking member of the dog family, the Maned Wolf, looks rather like a giant fox on stilts. It has a pointed muzzle, very large, erect ears, a body covered with long reddish-brown hair, and a white-tipped tail which resembles the "brush" of a fox. The incredibly elongated limbs are black and are so long that, as the photograph shows, when the tail is hanging straight down it reaches only just over half the distance from the body to the ground. On the neck there is a mane of longer fur that is erected when the animal is excited.

It comes from southern Brazil, Paraguay, and the north of the Argentine, in regions where small areas of forest are interspersed with more open country. It is seldom seen because it is solitary and secretive, usually hunting at night. The long legs enable it to run at extremely high speeds.

Like all other members of the family, the Maned Wolf is predominantly a meat-eater, feeding on insects, birds, rodents, and larger mammals including sometimes sheep. Snails and rodents are dug up from the ground in an unusual way, the animal using its teeth rather than its feet. It is, in fact, claimed that it never digs with its feet in any situation. If this is true then it is unique in this respect amongst the canids. In addition to meat it also feeds on some plant matter, including fruits and sugar cane.

It is the largest member of the dog family apart from the true Wolves of the Northern Hemisphere.

Family CANIDAE

BUSHDOG

Speothos venaticus

(Forests of Central and South America)

This is superficially the most terrier-like wild member of the dog family. The head and body together are about 2 feet long, but the legs are very short, the height at the shoulder being only about a foot.

The tail is less than 6 inches long. This squat shape is perhaps not so much an adaptation to burrowing, as to hunting in the dense forests, where the thick vegetation would hamper the movement of a taller animal. The muzzle is rather short, the back molar teeth being absent. The Bushdog is dark brown in colour, parts of the back sometimes being lighter, while the lower surface is sometimes darker.

During the day it sleeps in burrows, often on the banks of rivers or at the edge of the forest, emerging to hunt at dusk. It often hunts in packs of up to twelve animals, eating any small creature which the group can overcome. Rodents, in particular, form an important part of the diet, especially the large Paca (*Cuniculus paca*). Bushdogs are, in fact, normally found wherever Pacas occur.

In parts of Brazil young Bushdogs are caught and raised as pets. They are said to become tame readily, and to be intelligent. As is so often the case with animals from the Amazon forests, a great deal remains to be discovered about the habits of this species in the wild. From studies of captive specimens, however, we know that they have particularly interesting facial expressions, including a strange greeting gesture that consists of opening the corners of the mouth while keeping the front parts of the lips tightly shut.

263

ASIATIC WILD DOG

Cuon alpinus

(Forests of Central and South-east Asia, Sumatra and Java)

Like the African Hunting Dogs, to which they are related, the Asiatic Wild Dogs are fierce, running hunters. They differ from the typical members of the dog family in having fewer molar teeth in the lower jaw. They also have a larger number of nipples. All races of the species are reddish-brown, but those from Malaya, Sumatra and Java are brightest in colour.

They are gregarious animals, hunting in packs, each group consisting of one or more families. It is said that there is virtually no species which a large pack will not tackle. By day they scour the open forests or, in western Tibet, the rocky uplands, searching for their prey.

When Wild Boar, Spotted Deer, Musk Deer, or Markhor are located they attack from all directions, those approaching the prey from the rear leaping at the vulnerable flanks. In attacking bigger game, such as Gaur or Banteng, they stampede the herd and then single out the younger or weaker members as their quarry. Hungry Asiatic Wild Dogs are known to have eaten both Sloth Bears and Asiatic Black Bears, and even, on one occasion, a Tiger, which at first prudently took refuge in a tree, but later leapt down in an attempt to escape, when it was instantly pulled down and eaten.

A pack of Asiatic Wild Dogs will soon clear a small district of all game, frightening away everything that they do not kill, and each pack must therefore roam over a large area in search of food. In India this species is known as the Dhole. It is becoming rare in many regions.

Family CANIDAE

HUNTING DOG

Lycaon pictus

(Grasslands of East and South Africa)

The domestic dog and its closest wild relatives have five toes on their front feet, but the African Hunting Dog has only four. Another peculiarity of this powerful, long-legged killer is the irregularity of the black, yellow and white blotching of its strangely marked coat. These markings vary considerably from individual to individual, but the white tip to the tail appears to be fairly constant. (In the photograph above the tail is in the act of swinging towards the camera.)

Hunting Dogs sleep in packs which may consist of up to sixty individuals. At first light they move off at a trot, with their short, broad muzzles held low and their large, rounded ears cocked. When they discover their prey, which may be any of the antelopes from a small Duiker to a large Eland, they attempt to encircle it before dashing in for the kill. Should this fail they lope along after the quarry, each dog in turn increasing speed to leap at its flanks, ripping and tearing with their long canine teeth. When the prey is weakened by exhaustion and loss of blood the whole pack closes in for the kill.

After feeding, they drink and then rest through the heat of the day, possibly venturing forth for more food in the cool of the evening. Few animals willingly remain close to Hunting Dogs, and when they descend upon an area it is rapidly cleared of game. Like the Asiatic Wild Dogs, they are therefore forced to roam far in search of food. It is claimed that a single pack may wander at irregular intervals over an area as large as 1,500 square miles.

BAT-EARED FOX

Otocyon megalotis

(Dry regions of East and South Africa)

The Bat-eared Fox is also known as Delalande's Fox or the Draaijakkals. It is not quite as strongly built as the European Fox, having rather a slender body, but is a little taller. The muzzle is pointed, and the ears äre very large, although relatively not quite as big as those of the Fennec Fox. In colour it is a light grey-brown, with darker hair at the end of, and along the upper surface of the long tail. There are also dark patches around the eyes and on the nose.

An important difference between the Bat-eared Fox and all other members of the dog family is to be found in the number of teeth. Bat-eared Foxes have forty-eight or even fifty rather small teeth, whereas other species have no more than forty to forty-four. Mammals that eat insects are remarkable for having either no teeth at all or a great many, and the Bat-eared Fox is an insect-eater, feeding mainly upon termites. Other insects, small vertebrates, and even fruit are also eaten.

In the dry uplands that this animal inhabits, from Somalia to South Africa, it is active at night, resting during the day in a crevice among rocks. In such a den the young, three to five in number, are born. At first they are blind and helpless, but they grow rapidly, becoming adult when a year old. The gestation period of typical canids is 63 days, but that of Bat-eared Foxes is slightly longer, averaging about 70 days.

266

SPECTACLED BEAR

Tremarctos ornatus

(South America)

The Spectacled Bear is the only member of its family that is found in the Southern Hemisphere. It is a small bear, standing no more than 2 feet 3 inches high at the shoulder. Like the smallest of the Old World bears, the Sun Bear, it comes from the tropics. It is found in the cooler forests on the foothills of the Pacific slopes of the Andes in South America, from northern Chile, Bolivia and Peru to Colombia. It is sometimes known as the Andean Bear.

The coat is black, rather shaggy and markedly less dense than those of bears from temperate regions. On the muzzle the hair is light yellowish buff in colour, and lines of this shade extend to encircle each eye, giving the animal the bespectacled appearance from which it derives its name. A patch of hair of the same colour forms a mark of indistinct outline on the chest.

Remarkably little is known about the habits of Spectacled Bears in the wild, although these animals have been kept in zoological gardens for many years and have several times bred in captivity. Wild Spectacled Bears are said to be largely herbivorous, feeding on leaves, fruits and nuts. Like most bears they are nimble climbers despite their heavy bodies.

In zoos they are certainly omnivorous, but show rather less liking for meat than any other bears. Although the feeding habits of captive animals are by no means a perfectly reliable reflection of the food preferences of their wild counterparts, it seems probable that the Spectacled Bear is the least carnivorous of all bears.

267

ASIATIC BLACK BEAR

Selenarctos thibetanus

(Forests of Central and Eastern Asia)

The Himalayan, or Asiatic Black Bear, sometimes also known as the Moon Bear, replaces the Brown Bear in parts of Persia, the Himalayas, China and Japan. It is a slightly smaller animal, black in colour, and, as the illustration clearly shows, has a pale V-shaped mark on the chest. Those from the Himalayas are about 30 inches at the shoulder when in their normal posture, on all fours, but the bears of Japan are considerably smaller.

In its habits the Himalayan Bear is very similar to the Brown Bear except that it is a better climber. It is to be found in forests of various types, such as coniferous, mixed, deciduous, or dwarf rhododendron forest. In the Himalayas it spends the winter in the forests of the foothills, but during the summer is to be found at heights of up to 12,000 feet above sea-level. It is particularly common in leafy forests close to

running water where hollow poplar trees are to be found.

In such a tree the bear sleeps for much of the winter, usually at a height of about 15 feet above the ground. Before hibernation all rotten wood is carefully removed from the cavity. The bear is said to sleep in a sitting position.

In such a den the cubs, one or two in number, are born in January or February. Like all bear cubs, they are relatively tiny at birth, being no bigger than average-sized rats. They grow rapidly, being able to look after themselves by the following autumn, although they are not fully mature until they are 3 years old.

BROWN BEAR

Ursus arctos

(Temperate forests of the Northern Hemisphere)

Most of the Brown Bears which formerly inhabited much of western Europe have been killed, but a few survive in small pockets in the Pyrenees and in Scandinavia, and members of this species are still to be found in eastern Europe, northern and central Asia, and in North America.

There is considerable variation in the size and coat colour of Brown Bears coming from different parts of the world. For example, those from Syria are smaller and, like most animals from desert areas, are rather light in colour. Those from Alaska are huge and may weigh up to three-quarters of a ton. Grizzly and Kodiak Bears are now thought of as no more than giant races of the Brown Bear. The Kodiak form is the largest of all living land carnivores.

Brown Bears are omnivorous, eating all kinds of vegetable matter, honey from wild bees' nests, fish, carrion, or flesh from animals which they kill for themselves. When out hunting, Brown Bears are unexpectedly agile and kill, not by hugging, but with powerful blows of the fore-limbs which are armed with impressive claws. They can be dangerous to man, more especially because they are poker-faced, giving no warning of impending attack. They have few natural enemies, but are occasionally attacked by Wolves and, in Siberia, by Tigers.

Brown Bears are solitary, each occupying a territory of its own, about 10 square miles in extent, marked out with the occupant's regular paths, and containing the den in which the bear spends the worst of the winter.

In captivity they breed more freely than any other bear species.

269

AMERICAN BLACK BEAR

Ursus americanus

(Forests of North America)

All bears are adaptable and able to eat a wide variety of food, and it is therefore not so surprising that the Black Bears of North America are still reasonably numerous despite the dramatic changes that have occurred in that Continent during the last few hundred years.

Despite their name, occasional members of this species are brown in colour. American Black Bears are distinguished from the true Brown Bears, which are also found in North America, by their smaller size and their more rounded shape. Partly because they are smaller and partly because of their temperament, Black Bears are less dangerous than Brown Bears and are also better climbers.

Black Bears rob wasps' and bees' nests, hunt for small mammals, and also eat pine cones, grasses, bulbs, roots, briars and acorns, and strip the berries from blueberry and mountain holly bushes with their teeth. Using their weight they sometimes force young cherry trees to the ground and then proceed to gather the fruit with ease.

In winter, when food becomes scarce, they spend a great deal of time sleeping in caves or sheltered dens under fallen trees. In such a den the cubs, usually two in number, are born towards the end of the winter. At birth, each cub weighs less than 1 lb., and is blind and toothless. For two months the mother remains in the den with her young, suckling them there until they are about 4 to 5 lb. in weight.

Black Bears are sometimes hunted for their fur. It is from this species that the raw material for the "bearskin" hats worn by British guardsmen is obtained.

270

POLAR BEAR

Thalarctos maritimus

(Polar regions of the Northern Hemisphere)

The Polar Bear lives on the inhospitable shores of the Arctic Ocean, spending much of its time on the pack-ice, and it is therefore scarcely surprising that this is the most carnivorous of all bears. In the Arctic summer a Polar Bear may sometimes eat a little lichen or moss, but normally, and from preference, it eats the meat of the Ringed Seal. Seals are caught either after being stalked across the ice, an operation during which the white camouflage of the bear is extremely useful, or else are ambushed by a bear which is lying in wait when they come up to breathe.

Polar Bears vary this diet with occasional fish, and in the summer eat sea birds and their eggs. When, as frequently happens, food is scarce, they will scavenge, often eating the remains of Walruses left by hunters, or the carcasses of stranded whales.

Most carnivores live within a more or less restricted territory, but in the changing icy landscape of the north, Polar Bears wander constantly. Males even travel during the winter, moving southward, but the females at this stage construct a den beneath the snow, and spend much time sleeping.

Here, in late November or early December, the mother gives birth to her young, usually two in number. Like all young bears they are tiny at birth, and she cares for them assiduously, not leaving them for weeks on end, even to obtain food for herself.

During their first summer the young are extremely playful, often romping with their mother in the water. When they are alarmed they seize her by the ear or tail, and are towed to safety.

271

L 43

SUN BEAR

Helarctos malayanus

(Forests of South-east Asia, Sumatra and Borneo)

Typically bears inhabit temperate and northern forests, but the Sun Bear, which is only 4 feet long from the tip of its nose to the root of its stumpy 2-inch tail, lives in the hot tropical forests of southern Asia. It is found in Assam in the foothills of the Himalayas, and in Burma, Malaya, Sumatra and Borneo. It is not only the shortest, but also the most lightly built of all bears, weighing only 100 lb.

The coat of coarse, short hair is black except for a yellow crescent on the chest and the yellowish snout. In folklore, the yellow crescent is said to represent the rising sun and this is apparently the origin of the name Sun Bear.

This bandy-legged species is an expert climber, and spends a great deal of its time far above the ground searching the leafy crowns of the tall forest trees for food. It feeds on any small vertebrates that it can find, such as lizards or nestling birds. It also eats certain kinds of fruit. Above all, the Sun Bear is fond of honey and is, indeed, sometimes called the Honey Bear. Its mobile lips and long, extensible tongue are well adapted to extracting the honey and grubs from wild bees' nests, while the bear's coat protects it from the vengeance of the adult insects. Other local names by which it is sometimes known include Malay Bear and Bruang.

When young these bears are often sold as pets, but they inevitably become dangerous as they mature.

SLOTH BEAR

Melursus ursinus

(Forests of Southern India and Ceylon)

Like the Sun Bear and the Asiatic Black Bear, the Sloth Bear has a black coat with a yellowish snout patch and a yellow crescent on its chest. Unlike them, its hair is long and shaggy, giving the animal a permanently unkempt appearance.

The snout is elongated and the nostrils at its tip can be completely closed by muscular action. The teeth are small and the central upper incisors are missing. These features are connected with the development of efficient insect-eating. The Sloth Bear is expert at attacking the nests of social species, such as bees (especially *Apis indica* and *Apis dorsata*), and termites. Its huge, curved, front claws rip a hole in the nest and it can then shut its nostrils, insert the long nose and suck the occupants into its mouth. The absence of the incisors aids the flow of insects through the mouth aperture. The whole process is extremely noisy, with much huffing and snuffling.

Apart from social insects, it also devours a variety of small vertebrates, certain fruits and beetles. It is rather more nocturnal in its food-searching than other bears and usually spends most of the day asleep in caves or other retreats. Even when active it is normally a shambling, slow-moving creature, hence its popular name. However, when pursued, it can run at a remarkable speed and, despite its clumsy appearance and its weight (300 lb.), is an excellent climber.

The female produces a litter of from one to three cubs after a gestation period of 7 months. While these are still young they frequently ride on the mother's back, clinging to the long fur of her shoulders.

273

NORTH AMERICAN CACOMISTLE

Bassariscus astutus

(Southern North America)

The North American Cacomistle is a close relative of the Raccoon, but it is lighter in build, has more sharply cusped teeth, and is more active in its habits. It is sometimes called the Ring-tailed Cat or the Cunning Cat-Squirrel and looking at the photograph above it is easy to see how it came by these alternative names. The beautifully ringed, 15-inch tail is as long as the head and body combined. The face also has black and white markings and the body fur is a delicate yellowish-grey. In the southern States of North America where it is found, the Cacomistle inhabits many different types of country-side. It is sometimes found on hillsides or in rocky deserts, but is perhaps most at home in woodlands for it is primarily a climbing animal.

It is an able hunter, digging for insects, climbing after birds, and pouncing on small mammals such as wood rats, chipmunks, or ground squirrels. Some vegetable matter is also eaten, including green corn, dates, figs and the fruit of the prickly pear.

Cacomistles are solitary and shy and, as they are most active at night, they are seldom seen by man, even in areas where they are quite common. In the south-west of the United States, however, individual North American Cacomistles have sometimes come to tolerate man's presence, haunting isolated dwellings for the sake of the mice which are to be found there.

In Central America there is a second species known as Sumichrast's or the Central American Cacomistle (*B. sumichrasti*). It is larger and greyer than the North American form.

Family PROCYONIDAE

CRAB-EATING RACCOON
Procyon cancrivorus
(Central and South America)

Raccoons are famous as animals that "wash" their food, but they only do this in captivity, where they are unable to perform their instinctive riverbank hunting activities. They overcome this difficulty by carrying a food object to the water dish, dropping it into the water, "losing" it, and then searching for it with specialized movements of their sensitive hands. In this way they can express their fundamental urge to dabble for small aquatic prey. No true cleansing takes place and it is therefore true to say that the fastidious food-washing of this species is a myth.

An omnivorous creature, the raccoon not only eats aquatic animals such as crayfish, shrimps, frogs, water snails, crabs, mussels and small fish, but also land snails, earthworms, large insects, rodents, small birds and eggs. In addition, many plant foods are taken, including fruits, nuts, root vegetables and corn. Despite its rather stocky shape, it will climb with great agility when searching for certain of these foods, or when escaping from predators.

Modern American authorities claim that there are seven species of raccoons: five isolated on small islands, one on the mainland of North America and one on the mainland of Central and South America. The latter, illustrated above, has longer legs and a thinner coat than its northern relative. In particular, it lacks the bushiness of the tail.

North American Raccoon fur is used commercially in large quantities, over 1 million pelts a year being sold in the United States. Despite these depredations, this adaptable and resourceful animal continues to flourish and is still to be found wherever forests and rivers meet.

L 54

COATI

Nasua nasua

(Forests of Central and South America)

Coatis look like raccoons with elongated bodies and tails. Above all, the nose appears to have been stretched out to form a long, tapering, mobile snout. Most Coatis are brindled in colour, the tail being ringed with black, but those from certain South American regions are bright orange-red and were once thought to be a distinct species.

Bands of Coatis, numbering usually between five and twelve, and consisting only of females and their young, roam through the forests throughout the day. Some of them investigate the branches, while others move on the ground below, their tails curving stiffly upward. They comb their home range for food, seeking fruits, insects, sitting birds, or big lizards such as iguanas. When forced to take to water, Coatis swim strongly, paddling along with their snouts curled upwards like snorkels.

Adult males live apart from the group and must hunt on their own. These solitary animals are known as Coatimundis and this name has often been wrongly applied to the species as a whole in the mistaken belief that the word Coati is a slang abbreviation of it. There is a brief breeding season during which the solitary male is allowed to join the band. He is completely subordinate to the females, but will attack any other male that attempts to join his group.

The gestation period is 77 days. One week before the litter of four to five young are born, the pregnant female isolates herself from the band and builds a special tree-nest. There she gives birth, and cares for her offspring for a period of 5 weeks. Together they then re-join the group.

KINKAJOU

Potos flavus

(Forests of Central and South America)

"Kinkajou" is a native Indian name. The same animal also bears the tribal name "Potto", from which its Latin name, *Potos*, is derived. It is an intriguing fact that in the forests of Africa another mammal bears the same native name, and that the African Potto, although totally unrelated to the Kinkajou, has a remarkably similar appearance.

As the illustration shows, the Kinkajou has a blunt head, large eyes, rounded ears, short thick legs, a slender body, and a long curling tail. This tail is a powerful prehensile organ that can wrap around and grip branches, acting almost as a fifth limb when the animal climbs. The only other member of the Carnivora that has a prehensile tail is the unrelated Binturong (*Arctictis binturong*) which comes from south-east Asia.

Primarily a nocturnal forager, the Kinkajou spends almost all of its time above ground level. By day it sleeps in a hollow tree, waking at nightfall to climb in search of the fruit which forms the bulk of its diet. Because the tail is able to grip a branch in conjunction with the hind feet, the animal's arms and mouth are free to reach out farther for the wild figs and other delicacies on which it gorges. The surprisingly long tongue is then used to extract the pulpy centre of the fruit. Kinkajous appear to have a very "sweet tooth". They are particularly fond of honey, and are often called "Honey Bears". Tame ones have been known to frequent the local bars in tropical America, dropping from the ceiling from time to time to steal a startled customer's drink.

277

ALLEN'S OLINGO

Bassaricyon alleni

(Forests of South America)

Allen's Olingo bears a strong resemblance to the Kinkajou. Not only are these two species very similar in appearance and structure, but both come from the same region and appear to live in much the same way. The native Indians, in fact, make no distinction between the two animals, which are said to feed sometimes side by side in the same tree. For this reason the Olingo presents rather a problem.

Where the two species do differ, the Olingo is always the more primitive. It has, for example, a longer muzzle than the Kinkajou and teeth which are reminiscent of the Raccoon or Coati. Most important of all, the Olingo's tail is not prehensile. This being so, it is difficult to see why it survives at all. If the two species do compete for the same food in the same places one would expect that the more efficient Kinkajous would flourish while the Olingos died out.

This does not appear to be the case. Indeed, although we know little about the Olingo it appears to be quite a common, successful animal in the tropical American forests. It is far from easy to investigate the habits of an animal that is active only at night, high in the tree-tops, but when the Olingo is eventually studied more closely, we shall no doubt find that it has at least some advantages which the Kinkajou lacks. Possibly, for example, it is able to move a little faster, and thus include a greater proportion of animal food in its diet.

There are three closely related species of olingos, one of which (*B. gabbii*) extends up into Central America.

278

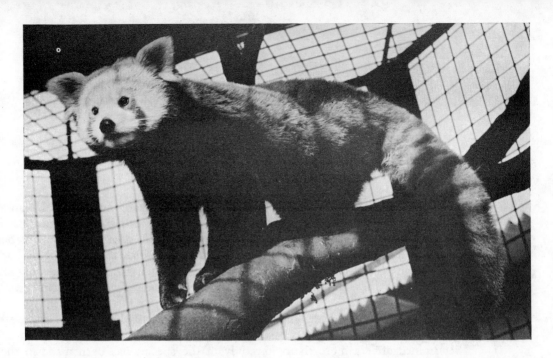

RED PANDA

Ailurus fulgens

(Forests of Western China and Eastern Himalayas)

Along with its close relative the Giant Panda, the Red Panda is generally accepted today as a member of the raccoon family, but whereas all other members of this group are found in the New World, the pandas live in Asia. The Red Panda itself inhabits the forested slopes of the Himalayas and the mountains of western China, at 7,000 to 12,000 feet. Its dense woolly coat is bright chestnut-red, and the bands on its tail are of alternating lighter and darker shades of red-brown. The edges of the ears are white and the face is white with black markings. The legs, the underside of the body and the tip of the tail are black.

Like the Giant Panda, the Red Panda has rather pigeon-toed front legs and an easily recognizable, waddling walk. Its overall length is about $3\frac{1}{2}$ feet. Much of its apparent bulk is accounted for by the thickness of its fur and, although it appears to be stockily built, it is in reality a comparatively light-weight species, weighing only 10 to 12 lb.

It sleeps in a hollow tree, or in the fork between two branches. When it wakes, usually at dusk and again at dawn, it descends to the ground where it feeds upon fallen acorns, roots, the long lichens which festoon the rocks, and bamboo shoots. Should danger threaten, it immediately takes refuge in a tree. If cornered, it strikes out, bear-like, with its paws, the claws of which are semi-retractile, and rather similar to those of a cat. It is, in fact, sometimes known by the name of "Cat-bear".

GIANT PANDA

Ailuropoda melanoleuca

(Bamboo forests of China)

Despite the fact that it is familiar to every child, remarkably little is known about the natural behaviour of the Giant Panda. Its specialization as a bamboo feeder has led to its confinement in the comparatively small areas of cold, damp, mountainous bamboo forests of Central China. This has resulted in its becoming today one of the rarest of all large animals. Not only is it rare in the wild, but it has been bred only once in captivity and the total number of individuals studied alive is probably less than twenty.

It is a bulky animal, weighing 2-300 lb. and superficially bear-like in shape. Its bold black and white markings remain a mystery. Their value to the Panda can only be determined after a more thorough study of the species has been made in the wild state. It has been suggested that they may render it cryptic against a broken snow line, but at present this is no more than a wild guess.

The Panda's diet has become almost entirely restricted to tender young shoots of bamboo, and its front feet have become specially modified in connection with this trend. The thin sticks of bamboo require delicate manipulation and the Panda, with its large, flat feet, does not at first sight appear to be capable of this. That it does in fact solve the problem extremely deftly is due to the development of an elongated wrist-bone that acts as a kind of sixth claw. It functions like a "thumb", opposing the digits with sufficient precision to enable the animal to clasp firmly even the most slender length of bamboo.

STOAT

Mustela erminea

(Europe, Asia and North America)

The Stoat is found in western Europe as far south as the Pyrenees and the Alps; also in central Europe, a large part of Asia and in the northern areas of North America. It occurs as far north as the shores of the Arctic Ocean, although it does not actually venture on to the pack-ice. It is also found in Greenland. A larger animal than the Weasel, it measures about 15 inches overall, and has a proportionately longer tail with a distinctive black tip.

In the more northerly parts of its range the Stoat grows a white coat in the autumn, underneath its brown one. With the onset of cold weather, the brown coat is quickly moulted in a matter of days, leaving the white coat exposed, and thus providing much better camouflage under snowy conditions. The tip of the tail, however, remains black. This winter coat provides the valuable fur known as ermine, upon which the black spots formed by the tail are clearly to be seen.

Stoats have abundant energy and, although they usually hunt on their own, they sometimes collect in what appear to be play-groups, when they leap, wrestle, and tumble with great vigour and abandon. A rather similar technique is occasionally used in hunting, when a Stoat will put on an exhibition of acrobatics with the apparent effect of lulling the suspicions of a wary bird. Stoats prey upon many small mammals and birds, but above all they hunt rabbits. The way in which a hunted rabbit squats, frozen like a statue, awaiting the Stoat's onslaught, is proverbial.

L 67   Family MUSTELIDAE

AMERICAN MINK

Mustela vison

(Forests of North America)

Many members of the order Carnivora have valuable coats, but few today command a higher price in the fashion centres of the world than those of the American Mink. This was not always the case. At one time, fur-trappers regarded them as being of little interest. Now, however, American Mink are farmed extensively for their lustrous, rich-brown pelts, and these animals have been deliberately introduced into other parts of the world because of their economic importance. In Russia, both the smaller European Mink (*M. lutreola*) and the Siberian Mink (*M. sibirica*), which is found east of the Urals, are today being displaced by the introduced American species. In Britain, specimens which have escaped from fur farms have set up breeding colonies that are causing some concern.

The American Mink resembles a Polecat in appearance, but has thicker fur and only a small white patch on the chin. In its habits it is not unlike the Polecat, but is more often found close to water. The hind feet are slightly webbed and, in addition to the rodents to be found at the waterside, such as the Muskrat, it often preys on crayfish, frogs, and even fish, hunting mainly at twilight or during the night. One animal may quarter an area of 100 acres for food in the course of a single night.

The female, which is considerably smaller than the male, gives birth to one litter each year, usually in March or April, after a gestation period of 50 days. The eyes are open at about 35 days and the young are weaned shortly after that. They are mature the following season.

282

WEASEL

Mustela nivalis

(Europe, Asia and North Africa)

Small, long-bodied, short-legged predators belonging to the weasel family are to be found in all parts of the world except Australia. Originally there were none in New Zealand, but the European Weasel has been introduced there in recent times and now thrives.

In Europe, many of the larger carnivores have been drastically reduced in numbers, or completely exterminated by man, but the Weasel has managed to survive remarkably well. This is primarily because of its size. The male is only about 11 inches long, including 2½ inches of tail, and weighs about 8 ounces, while the female is smaller still. This means that a Weasel can easily hide and escape detection, and that in its hunting it tends to prey upon the smaller mammals, such as rats, mice and voles. This renders it tolerable to man, who is apt to resent the attentions paid to bigger mammals and to game birds by the larger predators.

Weasels hunt through hedges and ditches, combing the crevices in dry stone walls, and entering rats' burrows. Apart from rodents, they also kill and eat some reptiles, frogs, and small birds. They can swim well should the occasion arise, but rarely climb.

From four to six young are born after a gestation period of 35 days. The nest is usually placed in a rabbit burrow, a hollow tree, or a hole in a wall, and is lined with leaves and dry grass.

Weasels are bright reddish-brown above and white below. They lack the black tip to the tail that is characteristic of the Stoat.

283

EUROPEAN POLECAT

Mustela putorius

(Woodlands of Europe, Asia and North Africa)

Polecats are much larger than Weasels, being almost 2 feet long including a tail of up to 6 inches, but bear a strong family resemblance to them. They are found all over Europe except Ireland and northern Scandinavia, and also occur in Asia and North Africa. The coat is blackish-brown in colour with lighter underfur showing through. There are yellowish patches on the ears, face and nose. The belly, feet and tail are very dark, being almost black.

The Polecat is almost certainly the animal from which the domestic Ferret was developed. Ferrets differ from the wild-type in colour and in the shape of the skull. They are albino mutants, specially bred so that their coats show up clearly when they are taken out hunting. They are of ancient origin and we know that they had been domesticated at least as early as the fourth century B.C.

Like other members of the weasel family, Polecats have large anal glands that are used to mark out the home range with the personal scent of its owner. The Polecat's den reeks of its occupant, which in England was once known as the Foul Marten because of its potent smell.

Polecats inhabit woods and hilly thickets. They are largely nocturnal and feed on small mammals, birds, eggs, and insects. In the past, Polecats frequently raided roosting poultry, and for this reason they have been ruthlessly persecuted in many areas. At one time it appeared that they would become extinct in whole countries but they still occur in some numbers in the wilder districts of most parts of their geographical range.

AMERICAN MARTEN

Martes americana

(Forests of North America)

The American Marten has a luxuriant brown pelt, known as American Sable, which is highly prized in the fur trade. It is also known as Hudson Bay Sable. It should not, however, be confused with the even more valuable Siberian, or true Sable (*M. zibellina*).

Like all martens this species has become specially adapted to obtain its food by preying upon animals which live in trees. The feet have long, flexible toes armed with strong claws that enable the Marten to obtain a firm foothold on the branches. The bushy tail is an indispensable balancing organ. With its supple body the Marten is easily capable of overtaking all but the fastest of arboreal prey.

In the coniferous forests of Canada the range of the species largely coincides with that of the American Red Squirrel. Should the prey prove too elusive by day, then the Marten becomes a night-time hunter, catching the sleeping squirrels in their dreys. In addition to its tree-top pursuits, the American Marten hunts for partridges, rabbits, chipmunks, various other small animals and even carrion.

The gestation period is 267 days, a long time for a mammal that weighs only 2 to 3 lb. as an adult. The explanation is that the American Marten, in common with some other members of its family, exhibits delayed implantation. This means that the egg-cell does not start to develop as soon as it is fertilized, but remains inactive inside the female for some months before the embryo starts to grow. As a result of this, although mating occurs in the summer, the three or four young are not born until the following spring.

285

TAYRA

Eira barbara

(Forests of Central and South America)

Martens of various species are the arboreal hunters of Europe, Asia and North America, but in Central and South America they are replaced by the Tayra.

This animal is larger than the martens, being up to 3 feet 6 inches long, including a tail of 18 inches, and has legs which are proportionately slightly longer. The fur is dark brown to black, except on the head and neck, where it is lighter, and on the throat, where there is a patch of orange.

In parts of tropical America the Tayra is a comparatively common sight, for these animals are quite abundant, and move boldly by day. They can run swiftly through the branches, but quite frequently descend to the ground, and are sometimes found in open country. Tayras are more sociable than many of their relatives and live in pairs or family groups. During the breeding season large numbers have sometimes been seen to congregate in one area. The nest is built in a hollow tree, a burrow, or occasionally in the open under overhanging grasses. The litter consists of three or four young.

Their diet is something of a mystery. There is no doubt that they eat meat. They are known to hunt small birds and tree squirrels, and to search for various rodents and insects beneath fallen logs. This is not surprising as their close relatives are amongst the most exclusively predatory of all mammals. However, the stomachs of healthy and well-nourished specimens have been found, upon examination, to contain fruit pulp. It may well be the case, therefore, that the diet of the Tayra varies dramatically from one time of the year to another.

286

LESSER GRISON

Galictis cuja

(South America)

The Grison has a head and body about 18 inches long, a 6-inch tail and short legs. The claws are blunt and non-retractile, and the soles of the feet are hairy. It is not such a good climber as its relative the Tayra and hunts almost entirely at ground level. The face, flanks, and the underside of the body are blackish, whilst the top of the head and the back are grey. There is a distinct borderline that separates these two colours on the head, passing above the eye and through the ear. It is usually a much more conspicuous division than is seen in the photograph above. On the neck and shoulders this demarcation becomes blurred and fades out.

The two species of Grisons are found from southern Mexico to Argentina and Chile, and within this vast area they inhabit many different types of country. Some live in the tropical forests of Panama and the Amazon. Others are found in the less luxuriant woodlands of cooler climates, or inhabit the open grasslands high in the Andes of Peru.

Grisons are normally active during the day. Their food consists of any small vertebrates they can catch. In the forests they search assiduously through the undergrowth, giving loud squeals when they become agitated or excited. In less overgrown surroundings they frequently follow their prey through underground burrows. In Peru they prey upon the numerous wild Guinea-pigs, and were at one time domesticated so that they could be used, Ferret-like, to drive Chinchillas from their burrows. The diet is not purely carnivorous, and Grisons have occasionally been known to eat certain fruits.

287

ZORILLA
Ictonyx striatus
(Africa)

The Zorilla, or Striped Weasel is the African equivalent of the American skunks. As the illustration shows, its markings are highly conspicuous. The lower surface of the body and legs are black, but along the back run broad white stripes which unite behind the head. The three large spots on the face are also pure white, as is the bushy hair of the long tail. This animal bears a strong resemblance to the slightly larger and stockier Striped Skunk of North America and, like the skunk, it has well developed anal glands. These are capable of ejecting a fluid with a highly offensive odour as a self-defence reaction when the animal is strongly provoked.

Again like the Skunk, the Zorilla gives its adversaries due warning by first erecting the hair on its body and stiffly raising the tail, with all the tail-hairs fully spread out. This is a striking case of convergent evolution, with two kinds of animals independently evolving, not only the same sort of defence glands, but also the same accompanying markings and behaviour.

Zorillas are weasel-like in their general behaviour, usually hiding by day in crevices round rocky outcrops, and hunting at night. They feed on small reptiles and birds, and follow the burrowing Mole Rats underground. The Libyan Striped Weasel (*Poecilictis*) and the White-naped Weasel (*Poecilogale*) are close relatives, with similar black and white markings. The former comes from North Africa and the latter from Central and South Africa. They are both known as Snake-weasels, partly because of their slender, serpentine bodies, and partly because they kill and devour snakes. The larger Zorilla is also known by the name of Striped Polecat.

Family MUSTELIDAE

WOLVERINE

Gulo gulo

(Coniferous forests of Northern Europe, Asia and America)

The Wolverine is the giant of the weasel family, being 40 inches long and weighing about 40 lb. It comes from the cold pine forests of all of the northern Continents, and in summer ventures even farther north into the treeless tundra. It is therefore not surprising that the fur is immensely thick. Its hairs are rather coarse and shiny and are remarkable in that they do not collect and hold moisture. For this reason Wolverine fur is prized above all others for providing the trimming round the openings of Eskimo clothing which would otherwise rapidly become uncomfortable with frozen, condensed moisture.

The animal's legs, lower surface, and the tip of the tail are dark brown, the back is a little lighter, and the sides are almost fawn in colour. This last feature is variable, however, and is absent in the individual shown above. The Wolverine is sometimes called the Glutton because it has been known to uncover human food stored in snow-banks, eat some of it, and render the rest uneatable by smearing it with smelly glandular secretions. In a sense this really is "greedy" behaviour, for in doing it the animal is marking the food as its own property, treating it as part of its territory.

It is a solitary animal and normally feeds on lemmings and hares which it catches by lying in ambush. Sometimes it lies along a branch or overhanging rock to wait for larger prey. The Wolverine is reputed to be powerful enough to overcome a Reindeer and occasionally even a Moose, but in these instances the prey are probably sick or weak individuals.

K

Family MUSTELIDAE

RATEL

Mellivora capensis

(Africa and Southern Asia)

Although it is a member of the weasel family, the Ratel, or Honey Badger, has no very close relatives. The sole member of its subfamily, it is found over a very wide area from India, through south-west Asia, to most of Africa, as far south as the Cape. It is a thick-set, squat animal with small eyes and ears. The coat is black on the lower half of the body, but pale grey above. The contrast between the two colours is heightened at the sharp line where they meet, the grey becoming paler at the point where it joins the black. Immature animals have a rusty brown back and lack this strong contrast line. The skin is remarkably tough, forming a useful armour against bee stings, or the fangs of snakes.

Typically, the ratel lives in overgrown and forested country. It is a solitary creature, feeding on ants, beetles and reptiles, including the deadly mamba. It also eats small mammals and young antelopes which it overcomes, using aggressive, bulldog tactics. The favourite food, however, is honey.

The species is most remarkable for the association it forms with the Indicator Bird or Honey Guide (*Indicator indicator*). When this bird encounters a Ratel it chatters loudly and persistently. Attracted by the noise, the Ratel jog-trots towards its source making strange hissing and chuckling sounds in reply. The bird keeps moving and calling until it locates a bee's nest. With its powerful claws the Ratel then rips the nest open and, ignoring the stings, gorges itself on the contents. Its partner, the Indicator Bird, unable to break into the nest by itself, is then able to obtain a share in the feast.

Family MUSTELIDAE

EURASIAN BADGER

Meles meles

(Forests of Europe and Asia)

The common Eurasian Badger, which measures up to 3 feet in length and weighs 28 lb., is a very large carnivore to have survived so well in densely populated western Europe. It owes its survival not so much to protection for sporting purposes, as does the Fox, but because it is secretive in its habits and because its favourite foods are not also sought after by man.

With its thick-set body and broad, strongly clawed forepaws, the Badger is well adapted to dig the extensive burrows or "sets" in which it hides by day. These usually open on to dry, sandy slopes in woods and copses. The occupants, which often live in pairs, emerge at night to feed or to collect bracken and leaves for use as bedding. Badgers eat many things, but the most common items of diet are young rabbits, rats, mice, slugs, worms, beetles, wasps and bees and their larvae, berries, roots and acorns. They are active throughout the winter although, with the scarcity of food, they tend to lose a considerable amount of weight.

The young, usually two or three in number, are born in February or March after a long gestation period of 7 months. Implantation of the ova is known to be delayed in this species, as it is in the Marten. At the age of 6 weeks the young begin to emerge from the set, but it may be two years before they are fully grown.

The Badger's range covers much of Europe and Asia, including Japan. The New World equivalent of the Eurasian species, the American Badger (*Taxidea taxus*), is slightly smaller and tends to live on open sandy plains.

L 97

HOG BADGER

Arctonyx collaris

(South-eastern Asia and Sumatra)

The Hog Badger, or Sand Badger, replaces the common Eurasian Badger (*Meles meles*) in the eastern Himalayas, southern China and Sumatra. According to some authorities, three species of Hog Badgers exist in this region, but they are all very similar, and best regarded as three races of a single species. They have a body length of 26 to 30 inches.

Hog Badgers differ from typical Badgers in having a rather pig-like, mobile snout with the nostrils on its square truncated tip. They also have slightly longer legs, and a longer, 6 to 9 inch tail. For some reason, the claws are pale instead of dark. The body fur is greyish except for a white patch on the throat; the tail is also white. They are nocturnal animals, spending the day in burrows or deep fissures amongst rocks. Their teeth are very much like those of other badgers, and their diet is similarly varied.

A related form is the Teledu or Malay Badger (*Mydaus javanensis*) found in Malaya, Java, Sumatra and Borneo. It is a smaller animal, and has rather long brown fur, except for a broad band of white along the back, from the top of the head to the root of the tail. This is, no doubt, warning coloration like that of the skunks, for the Teledu is well able to defend itself by means of the offensive secretions of its large anal glands. It is sometimes aptly known as the Stinking Badger. The toes of its fore-limbs are joined by a web of muscle as far as the roots of the long sharp claws. This is an adaptation for digging, the Teledu being an expert burrower.

CHINESE FERRET BADGER

Melogale moschata

(Forests of Southern and Central China)

As its name suggests, the Ferret Badger is a true Badger that looks like a Ferret. It is about 18 inches long including the tail, which measures 5 inches. It has a pointed muzzle with a pink nose at the tip, and smells remarkably like a Ferret.

The soft fur is orange on the lower surface of the body and a darker shade of brown on the back. The face is still darker, except for whitish spots above each eye and on the bridge of the nose. There is also a white streak on top of the head. The pelt is of some importance commercially, being used to make fur collars and for trimming.

Very little is known of the habits of this animal, but it appears to be partly arboreal and is sometimes referred to as the Tree Badger. Despite this name it is less nimble in the trees than the martens. It is active at night, and nocturnal species are rarely rapid climbers, clear vision being vital to animals that have to leap from branch to branch. The Ferret Badger is omnivorous, eating small mammals and birds and some fruit.

Closely related species which differ slightly skeletally and in their colouring are the Burmese Ferret Badger (*Melogale personata*) from Burma, Viet-Nam, Nepal and Assam, and the Javan Ferret Badger (*Melogale orientalis*) which comes from Java and Borneo. The genus *Melogale* used to be widely known as *Helictis*, and is still frequently referred to by this name, despite the fact that it is invalid and has been officially discarded.

293

Family MUSTELIDAE

STRIPED SKUNK

Mephitis mephitis

(North America)

The bold black and white markings on the skunk's coat render it highly conspicuous and act as a serious warning to any would-be attackers. If an enemy ignores this signal, the skunk reinforces it by erecting its bushy tail and stamping with its front feet. After this last warning it turns its back on the enemy and squirts it with the contents of its large anal glands. This secretion not only smells exceedingly unpleasant, but also causes copious watering of the eyes. Needless to say, most predators give skunks a very wide berth, although Pumas and Bobcats have been known to kill and eat them occasionally.

Skunks do not hibernate fully in winter, although they become very sluggish, sleeping for days on end during cold spells. The young, sometimes as many as ten in number, are born in May.

Skunks consume a wide variety of foods. In particular, they eat beetles, crickets and grasshoppers, and are attracted to areas infested with caterpillars. In summer they also eat some fruit, rodents, and eggs. As winter approaches, leaves, grain, nuts and carrion are added to the diet.

The Striped Skunk is the most common species, but in Central America it is replaced by the Hooded Skunk, which lacks the bold white V on the back. The smaller Spotted Skunk is easy to identify, as its name suggests. The Hog-nosed Skunk of Central and South America can be distinguished by its naked, pig-like snout. It has five close relatives in South America, bringing the total number of existing skunk species up to nine.

294

GIANT OTTER

Pteronura brasiliensis

(Rivers of South America)

The Giant Otter or Saro, is found in the slow moving rivers of South America, such as the Essequibo of the Guianas, the Amazon and its tributaries in Brazil, the Parana in north-eastern Argentina, and the Rio Negro in Paraguay. It is the largest of all the otters, averaging 5 to 6 feet long, with big specimens measuring up to 7 feet 2 inches.

The tip of the Giant Otter's nose is hairy and the small, rounded ears are situated far back on the flat, wide head. The muzzle is short, and the mouth is set well behind it. The legs are extremely short and thick and are of little use out of water. When on dry land, the animal often humps itself along on its belly like a seal. The feet are strongly webbed, and the lower surface of the tail bears a curious keel, apparently connected with more efficient aquatic locomotion. The fur on the back is sepia in colour, that on the lower surface being lighter.

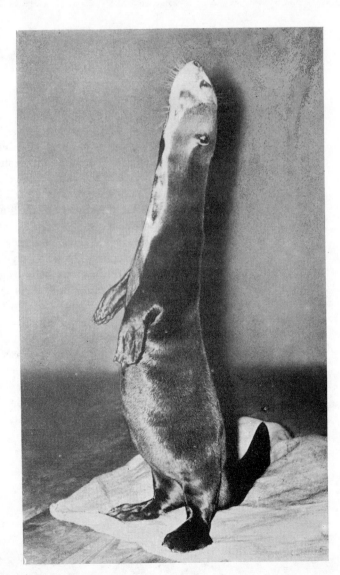

Giant Otters are active by day, when they hunt for food, often in small groups. They are by no means rare, being quite abundant in some localities, but are difficult to observe because they are shy and submerge rapidly at the slightest sign of danger. Their diet consists of fish, molluscs and crustaceans. Small mammals and birds may also be caught whilst they are swimming.

These otters can be tamed comparatively easily despite their size, and are sometimes obtained as cubs and raised as pets by the primitive tribesmen along the Xingu River in Brazil.

Family MUSTELIDAE

CAPE CLAWLESS OTTER

Aonyx capensis

(Lakes and rivers of Central and South Africa)

The Cape Clawless Otter is the largest otter from the Old World, and may measure well over 4 feet in length. The tail is horizontally flattened and, as shown above, tapers considerably. The head is flat and wide, the eyes are small, and the nostrils can be closed when the animal swims under water. The front digits lack claws and are webbed at their bases only, but the digits of the hind feet are more fully webbed and two of them on each foot do bear tiny claws. The coat is thick, consisting of long, stiff, brown guard hairs and a waterproof fawn undercoat which traps air and keeps the otter's skin dry. The patch on the chin and throat is yellowish-white.

The Clawless Otter feeds upon fish, frogs, shellfish and water-fowl. It is a wary animal, as indeed it must be, for crocodiles teem in the waters in which it swims. When it has fed, it lies up in dense bush close to the river. Occasionally Clawless Otters are known to make long journeys overland.

Otters of various species are to be found living near fresh water in most parts of the world. For example, the common Eurasian Otter (*Lutra lutra*) has a range which extends as far as North Africa, Java and Japan. Like most otters, it has feet with strong non-retractile claws. It feeds on fish, frogs and crayfish, and has been known to raid lobster-pots on the sea coast. Very similar species occur in other parts of Asia, in Africa and in the Americas. In total, there are seventeen species of fresh-water otters recognized today.

Family MUSTELIDAE

SEA OTTER

Enhydra lutris

(North Pacific Coasts)

Various species of otters enter the sea at times, but only one species, the Sea Otter, is entirely marine. This large animal, 4 feet long and weighing up to 85 lb., is rare today and receives rigorous protection from both the United States and Russian Governments. In the past it was hunted ruthlessly for its thick, dark brown fur. For example, in the first 50 years after the discovery of the Commander Islands 120,000 pelts were taken from there alone. Protection came only just in time to save the species from extinction. Today the Killer Whale is the Sea Otter's most dangerous enemy.

Sea Otters live in herds, and never go far from the shore. They frequently swim on their backs, propelling themselves by means of leisurely movements of the short, thick tail, the limbs being folded limply against the body. They rarely emerge from the water and move only with some difficulty on dry land. At night they sleep in the kelp beds, anchoring themselves to fronds of seaweed. The female even gives birth to her single cub in the sea, afterwards hugging the young one to her chest.

The food consists of sea urchins, molluscs, crabs, fish and seaweed. The Sea Otter dives, tucks the food objects into loose folds of skin, picks up a flat pebble or small rock and swims to the surface. There, it lies on its back, places the rock on its chest and, one by one, takes the food objects and cracks them open on the hard surface. The photograph above shows this extraordinary pattern of behaviour in progress.

297

BLOTCHED GENET

Genetta tigrina

(South and East Africa)

The Blotched Genet has an elongated head rather like that of a fox, the body of a weasel, and the legs, feet, retractile claws and tail of a cat. It is, in fact, closely related to none of these, but belongs to the same family as the civets and mongooses.

It is a solitary, nocturnal animal and spends the day either inside a hollow tree, or stretched along a branch with its spotted coat blending with the shadows of the leaves, or, less often, lying concealed in long grass. By night it is a lithe, agile hunter searching both the trees and the ground for roosting birds, such as Guinea-fowl and Francolins, and mammals, such as rats, mice, tree and ground squirrels, and hares. The individual shown below was capable of jumping a distance of 7 feet from a standing start.

There is no particular breeding season and the two or three young are born in a hollow tree or a hole in the ground at any time of the year. Members of this species have been known to live as long as 15 years.

There are nine species of genets in all and eight of these are found only in Africa. The ninth is the Common, or Small-spotted Genet (*G. genetta*), the range of which extends from South Africa to Palestine and southern Europe. In general appearance it differs little from the Blotched Genet shown below. In south-western Europe it is seldom seen, being shy and rather rare.

Two new species of genets (*Genetta deorum* and *lehmanni*) have been described only recently (1960; from Somalia and Liberia respectively).

298

AFRICAN CIVET

Viverra civetta

(Africa South of the Sahara)

Civets are taller animals than genets, and are less arboreal in their habits.

The African Civet lives in overgrown country often quite near rivers and swamps. It is about 4 feet long and in appearance rather like a large, ungainly tabby cat with an elongated face. Along the back runs an erectile crest of black hair, and the limbs, cheeks and throat are also black.

African Civets are nocturnal animals, lying up during the day in old Aardvark burrows or other similar retreats, and emerging to prowl stealthily at night. They are mainly carnivorous, eating Francolins, hares, reptiles, insects and some carrion, but also take some wild fruits and tubers. From time to time they utter a high-pitched coughing cry. The litter, numbering two or three young, is born in a burrow.

Like many members of the Carnivora, the Civet has well developed anal glands, the secretion of which plays an important role in the animal's social communication. Although in its natural condition this secretion does not smell very attractive by human standards, it is of considerable commercial value. It is used in the manufacture of expensive perfumes, not so much for the sake of its odour, but because it acts as a fixative, giving other scents improved and lasting qualities.

There are a number of related species. In the forests of the Congo lives the rare Water Civet (*Osbornictis*) that has never been seen alive. Three kinds of Asiatic civet are found from India to southern China and as far as Celebes. The Rasse, or Small Indian Civet, lives in the same general region and is a smaller more genet-like animal.

L 154   Family VIVERRIDAE

MASKED PALM CIVET

Paguma larvata

(Forests of South-east Asia, Sumatra and Borneo)

The palm civets are smaller than the true civets, and differ from the genets in being more omnivorous in diet. Whereas the genets are predominantly African, the palm civets almost all come from Asia. They usually have some degree of spotting or striping on the body, but this is not the case in the species illustrated here.

The Masked Palm Civet has a very wide distribution, being found from south China and through the Malay Peninsula to Sumatra and Borneo. Apart from the black mask and the white stripe down the top of the head, it is a uniform grey-brown. The tail is almost as long as the head and body combined. It is an excellent climber and is nocturnal in its habits. The food consists of fruit, insects, and small vertebrates. It digs in the ground for worms and grubs, and can catch fish with some skill. The three to four young are usually born in a hollow tree.

Closely related is the Common Palm Civet, or Musang, also known as the Toddy Cat (*Paradoxurus hermaphroditus*). It differs from the Masked Palm Civet in that the face is less boldly marked and the body is patterned with dark spots. The Small-toothed Palm Civet (*Arctogalidia trivirgata*) of south-east Asia has a softer, tawny-coloured coat, marked with two or three rows of weak spots on either side of the back.

The only African species, the Two-spotted Palm Civet (*Nandinia binotata*) inhabits the forests in the west of that Continent. It is easy to identify, having two pale blotches on the shoulders, in addition to numerous black spots on the body.

300

BINTURONG

Arctictis binturong

(South-east Asia, Java, Borneo, Sumatra and the Philippines)

The tree-dwelling Binturong has the same build as its close relatives, the palm civets, but is larger and looks very different because it is covered with immensely long, shaggy, black hair. Tufts of long fur even grow on the backs of the short, rounded ears. Whitish hairs are scattered through the coat, giving it a generally grizzled, dark grey appearance. The long whiskers and the edges of the ears are white. The feet have partly retractile claws. The bushy tail, which is 2 feet long and equals the combined lengths of the head and body, is prehensile and is always held in readiness to act as a safety hook should its owner slip as it moves along a branch. When the Binturong climbs head-first down to the ground, the tail is used as a brake. It is the only Old World placental mammal with a fully developed prehensile tail.

The Binturong is the largest member of the civet family to be found in Asia, measuring nearly 5 feet in length. It inhabits the dense forests of southern Asia, including Assam, Burma, Malaya, Java, Borneo, Sumatra and the Philippines. The teeth are less sharply cusped than those of the palm civets, being adapted to deal with a predominantly vegetarian diet, although some meat is also eaten. The Binturong is less likely than other members of its family to catch small animals, because it does not leap, but moves with deliberation. It is reputed to be the most vocal of the civets, howling and growling regularly during the night. In some regions it is referred to as the Bear-cat.

L 161   Family VIVERRIDAE

OTTER CIVET

Cynogale bennetti

(Rivers of South-east Asia, Sumatra and Borneo)

The Otter Civet is a true civet that has come to look superficially like an otter because it has become adapted to a similar way of life. Like the otter, it is a fish-eating, river-hunter.

The head and body are about 2 feet long, while the tail measures 6 inches. In shape the head is rather broad and flat and, as is usual in amphibious species, the nostrils can be closed by muscular action whilst the animal is submerged, and are on the upper surface of the snout. The enormous, stiff, constantly moving whiskers are important tactile sense organs that are invaluable to a nocturnal aquatic hunter such as this. The sharp cusps of the teeth are well adapted for gripping slippery fish, while the feet are partly webbed. The thick, soft fur of the back is greyish-brown, becoming darker on the lower surface. The snout and the tip of the tail are white.

The Otter Civet, or Mampalon as it is sometimes called, lives in the rivers of Malaya, Borneo and Sumatra. A distinctive race has also been found in Viet-Nam. This can easily be distinguished by its almost white underside. It was originally described as a distinct species (*C. lowei*), but there is too little evidence to support this view.

Apart from fish, the Otter Civet also eats frogs, crustaceans and a certain amount of fruit. It is occasionally seen in trees, but is not a good climber and cannot ascend vertical trunks. It is believed to reach the branches by walking up those trunks that have a gradual slope.

302

SLENDER-TAILED MEERKAT

Suricata suricatta

(Grasslands of South Africa)

The Suricate, or Slender-tailed Meerkat is the most atypical of the mongooses, having only four toes on each foot and a pointed face almost like that of a lemur. Except for its dark eye-patches, it is yellowish-brown in colour and just under 2 feet long to the tip of its tail.

It is a characteristic inhabitant of the dry, open grasslands, avoiding forests and thick vegetation. Arid climates do not seem to trouble it, even though it can rarely have the chance to drink water. Meerkats are sociable animals, living in large colonies. They are good at digging, and excavate for themselves shallow communicating burrows, 4 or 5 inches in diameter, in which they spend the night. In the early morning they emerge, and sun themselves at the mouths of the burrows.

In doing this they adopt the posture shown in the photograph. When alarmed, they crane their necks and stand on the toes of the hind feet, using the tail to give additional support, before diving into the burrow for safety. It is easy to understand why the first Dutch settlers in South Africa compared the Meerkats to ninepins.

During the day they do not roam far from the burrows, but wander restlessly about making low, grunting noises as they scratch in the loose soil in search of food. They eat a few small vertebrates and birds' eggs, but mainly live on insects and their larvae, centipedes, and spiders. They may also supplement their diet with succulent bulbs.

The young, usually two, but sometimes more, are reared in a nest at the end of the burrow.

MARSH MONGOOSE

Atilax paludinosus

(Central and Southern Africa)

The Marsh Mongoose makes its home in reeds or long grass in the vicinity of rivers and swamps. A large, dark, long-legged species, it is a good swimmer. The diet includes young waterfowl, small mammals, fish, and insects. It shares with the Monitor Lizard the habit of digging up and devouring the eggs of crocodiles. As a defence the female crocodile keeps vigil over the eggs whenever possible.

The Marsh Mongoose is also very fond of birds' eggs. The photograph shows the way in which it picks up an egg between the fore-paws before dashing it to the ground and lapping up the contents. This behaviour can readily be demonstrated with captive specimens, and it appears to be inborn. Different species perform the action in a slightly different way. Some, like the Marsh Mongoose, throw the egg almost straight downward, others throw it horizontally backwards between the hind legs at a hard, vertical surface, while others throw it backwards diagonally.

There are thirty-nine species of typical mongooses. They are restricted to the warmer regions of the Old World, ranging from Africa and the Mediterranean to south-east Asia. In this vast area they partly replace the weasels as the principal small predators, hunting through the undergrowth and sometimes in burrows below the ground. They are extremely agile and some can climb reasonably well, even though the five claws on each foot are not retractile.

The Indian Mongoose's ability to grapple with, kill, and eat even the largest cobra is well known, and is a good illustration of the hunting ability of the mongooses as a whole.

304

FOSSA

Cryptoprocta ferox

(Forests of Madagascar)

The island of Madagascar has been separated from the African continent by a channel 250 miles wide for millions of years, and for this reason many unique species of mammals are to be found there. One of the most remarkable of these is the Fossa, which is the largest, and in many ways the most primitive member of the civet family alive today.

No true cats occur naturally in Madagascar, but the Fossa to a certain extent replaces them as the principal large carnivore of the island, and has evolved many cat-like characteristics. It is about 5 feet long in all, with short legs. The feet are armed with sharp, retractile claws. The thick, short fur is orange-brown. It is a solitary and nocturnal creature, equally at home in the trees and on the ground, in both the dry forests in the west of the island and the rain forests farther to the east.

It has been known to prey upon poultry and other birds, but there can be little doubt that its main items of diet are the equally unique lemurs for which the island is famous. If surprised by man, the Fossa defends itself by producing a glandular secretion which rather resembles that of the skunks.

Apart from man, the Fossa appears to have virtually no enemies, being well able to look after itself. However, the persistent belief that this animal is as fierce as a lion, and normally preys upon cattle and other large mammals is considerably exaggerated.

This species should not be confused with the Malagasy Civet which unfortunately has the scientific name of *Fossa fossa*.

305

AARDWOLF

Proteles cristatus

(Plains of Southern Africa)

The Aardwolf's name means "earth wolf", but this is misleading. It is true that the animal lives in burrows, which it either digs for itself or takes over from other species, but the Aardwolf is no wolf. It is in fact a specialized, insect-eating member of the hyaena family. It has the general appearance of a hyaena, but it is a much smaller animal measuring only 20 inches at the shoulder. The fur is yellow-grey with dark stripes, and is rather long, especially on the back, where there is an erectile crest.

The teeth, however, are the animal's most remarkable feature. The other members of the family have powerful jaws and strong teeth, but the teeth of the Aardwolf are small, simple in shape, and widely spaced. This dentition would be ill-adapted to deal with a hyaena's diet of carrion, but is adequate for the insectivorous diet of this species.

Aardwolves often live singly or in pairs, but sometimes several combine to form a pack of about half a dozen. During the day they lie up in their burrows, emerging at night to prowl with a slow and deliberate gait. They cannot run fast and in self-defence would give a poor account of themselves were it not for the anal glands, which can emit a smell said to be even more offensive than that of the Striped Weasel.

The food consists almost entirely of termites, although they also eat beetles and may sometimes dig up and eat gerbils. There are usually about three young in a litter, and they are reared in one of the burrows.

306

Family HYAENIDAE

SPOTTED HYAENA

Crocuta crocuta

(Africa South of the Sahara)

The Spotted Hyaena can easily be distinguished from the Striped Hyaena, not only by the spots, but also because it is a larger animal, with a shoulder height of 31 inches, and has rounded instead of pointed tips to its ears. Like the striped form, it feeds mainly on carrion, but it is a powerful animal and has been known to kill and eat injured human beings, and even old and crippled Lions.

It is quite often active during the daytime as well as at night, but dislikes intense heat and has been observed to immerse itself in water when the sun is at its height. When hungry, the Spotted Hyaena usually relies on its keen sense of smell to find food, but is sometimes guided by the sight of gathering vultures. Hyaenas are solitary animals, but it frequently happens that several may congregate at the discarded kill of a pride of Lions. It is because of the Spotted Hyaena's prodigious appetite that the Leopard is frequently forced to lodge its kill in the fork of a tree. With its powerful jaws, there are virtually no marrow bones that the Hyaena cannot crack. If all else fails it can feed on insects, or the catfish which it can catch by straddling shallow pools.

It is very difficult to distinguish the sexes of this species, the female having sexual organs that closely resemble those of the male in external appearance. As a result of this, a myth has grown up that each Hyaena can act as both male and female, and this, according to native legend, is why they are always laughing.

L 216

STRIPED HYAENA

Hyaena hyaena

(Southern Asia and North-eastern Africa)

The hyaenas superficially resemble big dogs, but they are placed in a family of their own and are, in fact, more closely related to the cats. They have a reputation for cowardice which is only partly deserved.

The Striped Hyaena typically feeds upon carrion, being ill adapted to kill prey for itself. Although it stands 28 inches high at the shoulder and may weigh 100 lb., the back slopes down to poorly muscled hindquarters and it is incapable of running at high speeds. However, the fore-paws are strong and well adapted for digging up meat from caches made by other carnivores, and the animal has strong jaws and a good digestive system which make short work of even the toughest gristle. It has become extremely unpopular in many areas because of its tendency to raid human graves and dig up and consume recently buried bodies.

It is a solitary animal and is most active by night when it disturbs the silence with the eerie, chattering call that is often compared with a cackling human laugh. By day it hides in caves, burrows, or among clefts in rocks.

After a period of 3 months gestation three young are born, usually at the hottest time of the year. Striped Hyaenas have been known to live for as long as 23 years.

In colour the Striped Hyaena is grey-brown with darker stripes. The Brown Hyaena (*Hyaena brunnea*), a closely related form from South Africa, is dark brown all over except for a lighter area on the neck. The coat is exceptionally long and heavy.

308

Family FELIDAE   L 217

EUROPEAN WILD CAT

Felis silvestris

(Forests of Europe and Western Asia)

The Wild Cat looks very much like a large domestic tabby, but can be distinguished by the heavy tail with a broadly rounded tip. The Domestic Cat can, and often does, interbreed with the wild species, but there are certain physiological differences. For example, Domestic Cats reproduce two or more times a year, while Wild Cats normally breed only once. Many of those living in Scotland now resemble the Domestic Cat in this respect, however, showing the effects of repeated cross-breeding.

Wild Cats inhabit the most remote wooded areas, especially deciduous forests, in Scotland, France, central Europe, Italy, Greece and a large part of Russia. The den, which is often flea-infested, is usually inside a hollow log or a hollow standing tree. Here, from three to six kittens are born in spring after a period of 68 days gestation. Like all kittens, they are immensely playful, but they grow rapidly and by the autumn they are almost full sized and able to fend for themselves. They are sexually mature in less than 12 months from birth.

Hunting occurs either by day or by night. The methods used are those typical of the cat family—ambush after a long, patient wait, or stealthy stalking followed by a swift, silent pounce. The Wild Cat can climb well but usually hunts on the ground. Company would be a disadvantage, making it more difficult to surprise the prey, and the Wild Cat, like most other members of its family hunts on its own. The prey consists largely of birds and rodents. Twenty-six Wood Mice were once found in the stomach of a single Wild Cat.

309

L 229   Family FELIDAE

NORTHERN LYNX

Felis lynx

(Northern forests of Europe, Asia and North America)

The Canadian Lynx is sometimes considered to belong to a separate species from the Eurasian Lynx, but it is more correct to regard them both as races of a single species. Lynxes have slightly spotted yellow-brown fur and are of medium size, measuring just over 3 feet from the tip of the nose to the end of the short, 5-inch tail.

Most cats use the tail as a signal to others of their kind, waving it, for example, when they are angry. In this respect the Lynx is at a slight disadvantage. However, cats also signal by moving their ears, different ear positions denoting different moods, and here the Lynx is better equipped, having long black ear-tufts which greatly add to the conspicuousness of these movements. In addition, there are two throat tassels that move outwards when the animal hisses.

The Lynx usually hunts at night, the prey consisting of chipmunks, lemmings, rats, mice, rabbits, hares and small ungulates such as Roe Deer. In deep snow the Lynx can move more easily than heavily-built animals, and it is then sometimes able to attack and kill a floundering Moose or Reindeer.

There is a distinctive race of this species in Spain. It is more vividly spotted and is becoming extremely rare. Farther to the south, other related species occur. In the New World there is the well known Bobcat of North America and in the Old World there is the sandy-coloured Caracal Lynx of Africa and south-western Asia. The Caracal is only 18 inches tall, but very powerful for its size, hunting at night for hares, birds and small antelopes.

BOBCAT

Felis rufa

(North America)

In southern Canada, the United States and parts of Mexico, the Bobcat replaces the Lynx which is found in the coniferous forests of the north. Like the Lynx, it is a short-tailed cat with tufted ears, but it is smaller in size. The average weight of a fully grown male Bobcat is about 17 lb., although exceptional specimens may be three times this weight. The legs are shorter than those of the lynx and the feet, not being adapted for snowy conditions, are much smaller. The ear tufts are a little less prominent, but the tail is relatively longer.

The Bobcat haunts rocky screes, rough ground, thickets and swamps, often making its den in the cavity left by the roots of a fallen tree. Hunting mainly takes place at night, when the large eyes are able to take advantage of every glimmer of light. The prey consists chiefly of rodents, such as voles and squirrels, but the White-tailed Deer also forms a substantial part of the diet, as do large birds like the Wild Turkey. When food is abundant the Bobcat remains close to the den, but in times of hardship it may patrol areas 50 miles apart.

Breeding occurs at any time of the year, but is most frequent in the spring. Some females may have two litters in a year. The gestation period is 7 weeks. There are usually two young in the litter although quite commonly there are more. Bobcats probably live for up to 15 years in the wild. In captivity, where life is easier, they have been known to live even longer.

SERVAL

Felis serval

(Africa South of the Sahara)

The Serval is a cat of medium size, the head and body being 3 feet in length and the tail another 12 inches. It is a slender, lightly built creature, having long legs and a small head set at the end of a rather elongated neck. The ears are relatively very large. In colour it is orange-brown and is marked with black spots.

It is found in the African bush, and is never very far from water. Occasionally it may venture into forests, but always avoids arid, open plains. It is capable of climbing, but usually only does so in order to escape from such enemies as dogs. It seldom moves by day, lying concealed in thick bush, or in the discarded burrow of a porcupine or Aardvark.

The Serval hunts a wide variety of prey. It eats birds like the Francolins and Guinea-fowl, and rodents like the Cane Rats, and has even been seen digging Mole Rats from their burrows. However, the long limbs and slender body suggest that it is primarily a sprinter, and hunts in a similar manner to the Cheetah, but on a smaller scale, pursuing prey such as hares and duikers.

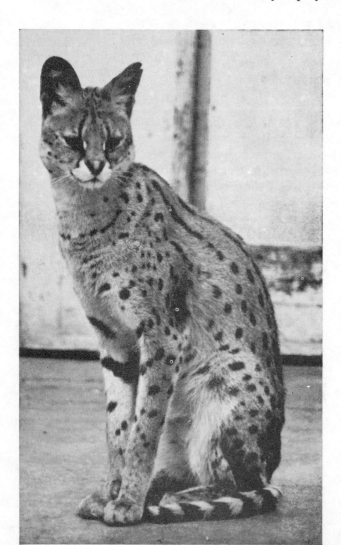

The young are born in a burrow, or a hollow in a grass clump after a gestation period of approximately two and a half months.

It was thought at one time that there were two species of Servals: the Large-spotted and the Small-spotted. The former was called the typical Serval, while the latter was described as the Servaline Cat (*F. servalina*). It is now known that they are merely two forms of the same species.

312

TEMMINCK'S GOLDEN CAT

Felis temmincki

(South-east Asia and Sumatra)

This is one of the few species of cats to have an elaborately patterned face combined with an almost completely plain-coloured body. The Golden Cat's head is marked with white, black and grey stripes. The ground colour, which is unrelieved over most of the rest of the body, is a rich golden-brown, giving the species its common name. The underside is paler, with black markings. In length, the head and body measure 32 inches and the tail another 18 inches.

As in all the cats, the external ears are extremely mobile, and the sense of hearing is good. The sense of smell is less well developed than that of the dogs, but is far better than that of man. The eyes are large and efficient. Cats can see more clearly than almost any other mammals except man and his closest relations, and hunt mainly by sight.

Golden Cats are found from the foothills of the Himalayas in Nepal and Assam, to western China and through the Malay Peninsula to Sumatra. They are retiring in their habits, living amongst rocks and preying upon rodents, pheasants and small deer. Little is known of the breeding habits, but it is said that the young, about two in number, are born in a hollow tree.

In West Africa lives a closely related species, *Felis aurata*, the African Golden Cat, which is very similar in appearance. This makes a den below ground and hunts among the secondary growth at the forest fringes. The two species are sometimes placed in a separate genus, *Profelis*.

313

OCELOT

Felis pardalis

(Forests of Central and South America)

Next to the Jaguar and the Puma, the Ocelot is the largest of the South American cats. In Mexico it is called the "tigrillo", or "little tiger", although the buff-brown coat is more spotted than striped. This pattern makes the Ocelot very inconspicuous in the forests where it lives and must assist the animal considerably in its hunting. Ironically, however, this coat is not without its disadvantages, for man finds it attractive and hunts the Ocelot for it, the pelt being made into fur coats and collars.

Where it is left undisturbed the Ocelot is diurnal, but it is a shy animal and becomes nocturnal in areas where it is hunted. Although it can climb, and often conceals itself in the branches of a tree, it normally hunts on the forest floor, making good use of its acute hearing and eyes. Like most cats it can see well in very dim light, having vertical slit-like pupils which can expand greatly at night.

The prey consists of agoutis, pacas, spiny rats, peccaries, brocket deer, birds and some reptiles. The Ocelot has been known to kill a boa 7 feet in length. Like the majority of carnivores, it confines its hunting to a more or less fixed territory which it defends against others of its own kind. It marks out this territory with its personal scent by erecting mounds of its own excrement.

The breeding season commences in December and January and is accompanied by vocalizations similar to the caterwauling of the Domestic Cat, except that they are louder. There are usually two young ones in the litter.

314

JAGUARONDI

Felis yagouaroundi

(Central and South America)

Of all the families of the order Carnivora, the cat group is the most exclusively carnivorous, but even here some members eat a certain amount of fruit. In Panama, Jaguarondis have been seen in the branches of trees feeding on green figs in the company of Howler Monkeys, and in zoos these unusual felines sometimes show a liking for grapes and bananas in addition to their meat.

The Jaguarondi is the most weasel-like of the cats, with a strange, sloping profile and small ears. The body is elongated and the coat is virtually plain coloured, having few distinct blotches or stripes. The legs are remarkably short and from this character alone it can easily be distinguished from the other cats in America.

Jaguarondis are found from the southern borders of the United States, south to Paraguay, and throughout this extensive range there appears to be only one species. Confusingly, however, it exists in two colour phases: red and grey. The red phase used to be thought of as a distinct species and was then called the Eyra Cat (*Felis eyra*), but this is no longer accepted.

They are found at the edges of forests and in savannah grasslands, usually preying upon birds. In Mexico, for example, they are known to catch Tinamous, ground-dwelling birds with poorly developed powers of flight, and farther south it seems likely they prey upon Trumpeters, which are also weak flyers.

The method of hunting is unusual, for, despite its short legs, the Jaguarondi is an excellent runner, being able to sprint after its prey either in the open, or in thin undergrowth, for over 1 mile if necessary.

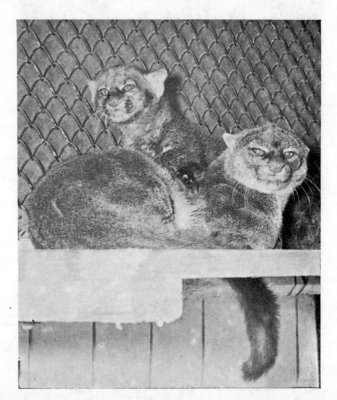

PUMA

Felis concolor

(North and South America)

The Puma's range extends from British Columbia in the north to Tierra del Fuego in the south, and includes pine, deciduous, and tropical forests, grasslands, and dry, cactus-studded deserts. Within this vast area there is only a single species, although as might be expected it shows considerable variation in different parts of the range. For example, the Pumas of the tropics are relatively small, but those from cooler climates are almost as big as the Leopard.

The Cougar, or Mountain Lion as it is also known, is a formidable hunter, feeding on anything from small rodents to fully grown deer. On the average each North American Puma kills one ungulate, such as a White-tailed Deer or Mule Deer, every week. Having made the kill, usually from an ambush after dark, the cat feeds well before dragging the remains of the carcass to a hiding-place, where it is covered with sticks and leaves.

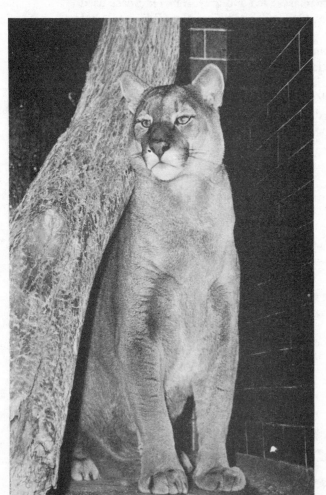

The Puma is reputed to stay in the vicinity of the kill and to return to feed again and again until all the meat has gone, but the evidence for this is scanty and some experts will not accept it.

Every Puma has an extensive territory, through which it roams on a roughly circular path which may be 100 miles in circumference, thus leaving each hunting ground undisturbed for days at a time.

The gestation period is 3 months and there are normally two or three young ones in the litter. The cubs are at first heavily marked with black spots, but these fade as the animals grow older, so that adult Pumas are plain greyish-brown over the whole body.

316

CLOUDED LEOPARD

Neofelis nebulosa

(Forests of South-east Asia, Borneo, Sumatra and Java)

This is perhaps the most strikingly marked of all the cats. There are dashes and spots on the limbs and the head, broken rings on the tail and large pale-centred black-edged blotches on the yellow-brown flanks. Despite its name, the Clouded Leopard is not very closely related to the true Leopard, which is slightly larger in size.

Like most cats which are marked with spots or blotches, the Clouded Leopard is a forest-dweller. It inhabits dense, wooded country from Nepal to south-east China, Malaya and the islands of Hainan, Formosa, Sumatra, Borneo and Java. It is an expert climber, using the incredibly long and heavy tail to help maintain its balance on the branches.

Being nocturnal and shy the Clouded Leopard is rarely seen in the wild and we know all too little about its habits. It haunts the thickest jungles close to river banks, sleeping in trees during the day. It feeds partly on birds but also kills mammals. In Formosa, for example, it is known to prey upon the Sika Deer.

It is nowadays customary to divide all cats other than the aberrant Cheetah into two groups—the "big cats", in the genus *Panthera*, and the more numerous "small cats", in the genus *Felis*. The Clouded Leopard is the most difficult species to fit into this classification, as it is to a large extent intermediate between the two categories in both structure and behaviour. It is therefore put into a separate genus, *Neofelis*.

The animal shown in the photograph was obtained from a Chinese market, where it was being offered for sale as food.

317

L 247   Family FELIDAE

LION

Panthera leo

(Africa and India)

Until recent times the Lion was common throughout much of the Old World. It was exterminated in Europe between A.D. 80 and 100. In North and South Africa and southern Asia it was brought to the verge of extinction by the beginning of the present century. In 1908 there were only thirteen wild Lions left in India. These were protected as a tourist attraction in the Gir Forest in north-west India where, by 1950, they had increased in number to 250. The species flourishes today only in the central region of Africa.

A full-grown male Lion measures about 9 feet from nose to tail-tip, has a shoulder height of approximately 3 feet, and weighs up to 400 lb. Lionesses are smaller and lack the mane which, as shown above, grows not only from the head and neck, but also from the shoulders and even sometimes the belly of the male.

Lions are the only truly social cats, and normally live in prides. These groups are very variable in composition, but usually consist of one or more adult males and a larger number of females and immature individuals. As many as thirty Lions have been seen in an exceptionally large pride. While food is plentiful the group stays inside a communal territory, roaming the game paths when they are hungry, and preying on almost any large herbivorous animals except adult Elephants, Hippopotamuses and Rhinoceroses. They hunt in silence, and it is the Lionesses that most often kill the prey. When they have eaten, the Lions rest. It has been estimated that a pride of four Lions kill and feed, on the average, only once a week.

318

TIGER

Panthera tigris

(Forests of Asia, Sumatra and Java)

The Tiger is normally thought of as an inhabitant of the tropics but, in fact, its range includes not only the humid jungles from India and Burma to Java and Sumatra, but also the cold, rocky forests of northern China and Siberia. It is in reality a species of the temperate north, which has only invaded the warmer climates relatively recently. Although Tigers tire quickly in deep snow, they are quite indifferent to frost. In the tropics, on the other hand, they show distinct signs of discomfort in the heat, always seeking the shade at midday, and frequently taking to the water to cool off.

In size and build the typical Tiger is very similar to the Lion, but the Siberian Tiger, a giant race, can be much larger, measuring as much as 13 feet in length and weighing 650 lb. Although Tigers are maneless, the illustration above clearly shows the long ruff which grows around the sides of the head. The arrangement of the stripes is very variable, but there are always bold white spots ringed with black on the backs of the ears.

They are solitary creatures and usually hunt at night, when they are completely noiseless, stalking the prey with great stealth before bounding the last few yards. Tigers have been known to kill a wide variety of prey, ranging from Roe Deer to young Indian Elephants, but their basic quarry are large antelopes and wild cattle. In a year each adult Tiger kills on average thirty victims with a total weight of about 6,000 lb.

From two to four cubs are born after a gestation period of 108 days.

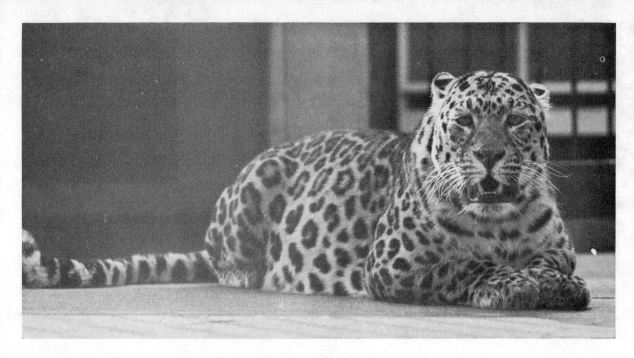

LEOPARD

Panthera pardus

(Africa and Asia)

The Leopard has a more extensive geographical distribution than any other member of the cat family, including even the Puma. It is found over most of Africa, and in Asia from the south-west to China, Korea and Java. It is not as massive as the Lion or Tiger, a large Leopard being about $7\frac{1}{2}$ feet in length, including a 3-foot long tail, but it is immensely powerful. A long-tailed species, it is an expert climber and is essentially a forest dweller.

Although the typical Leopard is famous for its spots, some members of this species have an excess of dark pigment in the fur which causes them to appear almost black. These dark individuals are most common in the humid forests of south-east Asia, and are often thought of as forming a separate species, usually called the Black Panther. They are, in fact, simply melanistic Leopards, and sometimes occur in the same litter as the spotted form. They even have the same spotted pattern, but it is difficult to see the dark spots against the almost jet black background, except in certain lights.

Leopards are solitary and nocturnal, cautiously stalking their prey, or lying in wait on a branch. A wide variety of prey species is eaten, ranging from antelopes and deer to monkeys and dogs. Towards morning the uneaten remains are often lodged in a tree, out of reach of the earth-bound scavengers such as jackals and hyaenas. Healthy Leopards always kill their own prey, but an old or sick individual may resort to eating carrion.

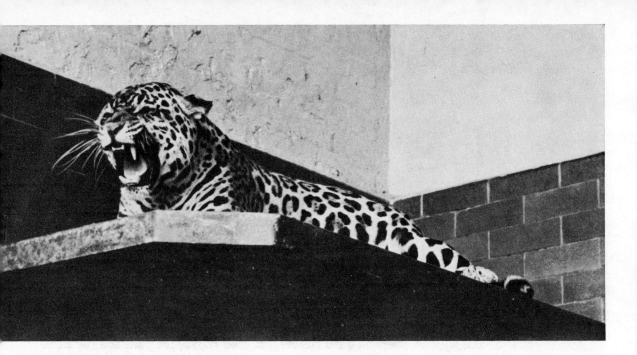

JAGUAR

Panthera onca

(Forests of Southern United States, Central and South America)

The Jaguar is the largest of the New World cats, being about the same size as the Leopard. Although both of these species are usually spotted in the same way, no confusion can arise between them in the wild because the Leopard is found only in Africa and Asia. Even in captivity the Jaguar can easily be distinguished by its shorter tail, by its thick-set, less graceful build, and by the size of its spots. The latter are usually bigger than those of the Leopard and have one highly characteristic feature, namely that some of them always have small black marks inside the rosette pattern. None of the Leopard's rosettes has any interior markings.

Jaguars are great wanderers, roaming even farther than Pumas. Sometimes they are seen on the pampas of the Argentine, but more usually they haunt forests where they hunt for deer and agoutis. Above all, they prey upon peccaries, following the herds and pouncing on any stragglers. They also attack the water-loving capybara.

All cats can swim, but most do so only with reluctance. The Jaguar, however, is often found beside rivers and frequently enters the water. It attacks the large Tapir as it comes down to drink and, if no other food is available, is a skilful fisherman, scooping fish from the water with its paws.

In Mexico the Jaguar is called *el tigre*—"the tiger"—to distinguish it from *el tigrillo*, "the little tiger", or Ocelot. It is able to breed at the age of 3 years, and does so at all times of the year. There are usually from two to four young.

SNOW LEOPARD

Panthera uncia

(Mountains of Central Asia)

The Snow Leopard, or Ounce, is closely related to the common Leopard, but is nevertheless a separate species, quite distinct in both its appearance and its way of life.

The head and body are about 3 feet 6 inches long, the heavy tail a further 3 feet. The fur, which is pale ashy-brown and marked with black rosettes, is exceptionally long, being 2 inches thick on the back, and up to twice that length on the under surface. This coat provides valuable protection from the cold in the Altai Mountains and the Himalayas where the Snow Leopard lives.

It is not, of course, a permanent resident among the snows of the highest peaks. As a large carnivore it must follow the Wild Goats, Wild Sheep, Bharal, Musk Deer, Persian Gazelle, Wild Boar and other smaller mammals such as the pikas and marmots. All of these are to be found feeding on the rocky grasslands between the tree line and the snow line. In the summer, when the ungulates migrate to the higher pastures, the Snow Leopard may be seen at heights of up to 13,000 feet above sea-level. It is a strong and agile hunter, usually preferring to stalk the prey while they are grazing or resting, although the technique of pouncing from ambush is also occasionally employed. Most of the hunting takes place at twilight or at night.

A particular den in a cleft among the rocks may be used regularly by the same animal for several years. Two or three young are born in April and by July they are strong enough to follow the mother, although they do not become fully independent until the following spring.

Family FELIDAE L 252

CHEETAH

Acinonyx jubatus

(Grasslands and semi-deserts of Africa and South-west Asia)

Although dogs are the typical running hunters, the fastest four-legged animal, the Cheetah, is a member of the cat family. Most cats have to bound up to their quarry once they have stalked it. The Cheetah too uses stealth to approach the prey initially, but because it lives in open country it cannot get very close in this way, and is compelled to make its final onslaught from a greater distance. Because of this, it has become specialized as a lanky, powerful sprinter, and has often been described as the most dog-like of the cats. The adult Cheetah is the only cat with permanently extended claws.

Over a distance of up to 400 yards it can reach speeds of about 60 miles an hour, but it lacks stamina and if the prey is not caught inside this distance it soon slows down to await a more favourable opportunity. Cheetahs often hunt in pairs or family groups, usually during the cooler parts of the day. The prey consists of gazelles, Impala, Waterbuck or Ostriches.

Man has used tame Cheetahs as hunting animals for hundreds of years and it is therefore remarkable that this was the last of the large cats to be bred successfully in captivity. Even today it has only been bred in zoos in a few instances, the first occasion apparently being as late as 1960, at Krefeld. Young Cheetahs have a characteristic silver mane that runs down the whole length of the back. This mane, or crest, disappears after the tenth week, at the same time that the cubs lose the ability to retract their claws.

M. SEALS

The thirty-two species of seals are virtually world-wide in distribution, being found along almost all coastal regions, including both the Arctic and the Antarctic.

The name Pinnipedia means literally "fin-footed" or "feather-footed" and refers to the aquatic modification of the limbs as swimming flippers. The seals have strikingly streamlined bodies, but are less intensely modified for marine life than the whales or sirenians. Unlike these two orders, they have retained their hind limbs and they return to the land each year to breed. Some species (the otariids, or eared seals) spend a considerable part of each year on dry land and, in these cases, the hind limbs can be rotated forward as an aid to terrestrial progression. In the typical (phocid) seals, this is not possible, the animals dragging themselves along by a kind of jump and wriggle, but these species spend far less time on shore each year.

The seals are all carnivorous and in the past have sometimes been considered as no more than a suborder of the Carnivora. This view is now generally rejected. Their food is basically fish, but other sea creatures such as molluscs, crustaceans, and even sea-birds, are also eaten.

Seals have large brains with many convolutions and are relatively intelligent creatures. They are active and exhibit a high degree of curiosity.

They are covered with a short, tough coat of fur. In some species the dense under-fur is more luxuriant than in others and intensive seal-hunting by fur traders has led to near extermination in certain cases.

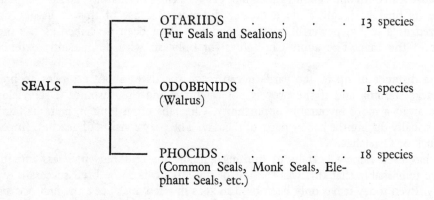

SEALS
- OTARIIDS . . . . 13 species
  (Fur Seals and Sealions)
- ODOBENIDS . . . . 1 species
  (Walrus)
- PHOCIDS . . . . . 18 species
  (Common Seals, Monk Seals, Elephant Seals, etc.)

M. Order PINNIPEDIA.   Seals.

    Family OTARIIDAE.   Eared Seals.

1	*Arctocephalus pusillus.*	**South African Fur Seal.** S. Africa. (EMH)
2	*Arctocephalus forsteri.*	**New Zealand Fur Seal.** New Zealand. (S)
3	*Arctocephalus doriferus.*	**Australian Fur Seal.** S. Australia. (S)
4	*Arctocephalus tasmanicus.*	**Tasmanian Fur Seal.** Tasmania. (SL)
5	*Arctocephalus tropicalis.*	**Kerguelen Fur Seal.** Subantarctic Islands. (S/K1)
6	*Arctocephalus australis.*	**South American Fur Seal** S. America, Falklands, Galapagos. (S)
7	*Arctocephalus philippii.*	**Guadalupe Fur Seal.** Guadalupe, off S.W. of N. America. (S)
8	*Callorhinus ursinus.*	**Northern Fur Seal.** Pribilof, Commander and Robben Islands, off N.E. Asia and N.W. of N. America. (EM)
9 ►	*Zalophus californianus.*	**Californian Sealion.** S.W. of N. America, Galapagos, and Sea of Japan. (EM)
10	*Eumetopias jubatus.*	**Steller's Sealion.** N.W. of N. America and N.E. Asia. (EM)
11	*Otaria byronia.*	**South American Sealion.** S. America and Falklands. (S)
12	*Neophoca cinerea.*	**Australian Sealion.** S. Australia and Japan. (EM)
13	*Phocarctos hookeri.*	**New Zealand Sealion.** New Zealand. (S/K2)

    Family ODOBENIDAE.   Walrus.

14 ►	*Odobenus rosmarus.*	**Walrus.** Arctic. (EM)

    Family PHOCIDAE.   Seals.

        Subfamily PHOCINAE.

15	*Phoca vitulina.*	**Common Seal.** N. America, N. Europe, N.E. Asia. (EM)
16	*Pusa hispida.*	**Ringed Seal.** Arctic, N. Atlantic, Baltic Seas. (S)
17 ►	*Pusa sibirica.*	**Baikal Seal.** Lake Baikal, Cen. Asia. (S)
18	*Pusa caspica.*	**Caspian Seal.** Caspian Sea. (S)
19	*Histriophoca fasciata.*	**Ribbon Seal.** N.W. of N. America and N.E. Asia. (S)
20	*Pagophilus groenlandicus.*	**Harp Seal.** Arctic and N. Atlantic. (S)
21 ►	*Halichoerus grypus.*	**Grey Seal.** N. Europe and N.E. of N. America. (EM)
22	*Erignathus barbatus.*	**Bearded Seal.** Arctic. (EM)

        Subfamily LOBODONTINAE.

23	*Lobodon carcinophagus.*	**Crabeater Seal.** Antarctic. (S)
24	*Ommatophoca rossi.*	**Ross Seal.** Antarctic. (S)
25 ►	*Hydrurga leptonyx.*	**Leopard Seal.** Antarctic. (EMH)
26	*Leptonychotes weddelli.*	**Weddell Seal.** Antarctic. (S)

        Subfamily MONACHINAE.   Monk Seals.

27	*Monachus monachus.*	**Mediterranean Monk Seal.** Mediterranean. (EM)
28	*Monachus tropicalis.*	**Caribbean Monk Seal.** Jamaica, W. Indies. (S)
29	*Monachus schauinslandi.*	**Hawaiian Monk Seal.** W. Hawaiian Islands. (S)

325

Subfamily CYSTOPHORINAE.

30	*Cystophora cristata.*	**Hooded Seal.** N.E. of N. America and Arctic. (EM)
31 ►	*Mirounga leonina.*	**Southern Elephant Seal.** Subantarctic Islands. (EMH)
32	*Mirounga angustirostris.*	**Northern Elephant Seal.** W. of N. America. (S)

CALIFORNIAN SEALION

Zalophus californianus

(Coasts of the Pacific Ocean)

The "performing seals" seen in circuses always belong to one particular species, the Californian Sealion, which is not a typical seal, but a member of the related otary or eared seal family. Typical seals have no external ear-flaps and have hind limbs that are important swimming organs in water, but are useless for locomotion on land. Eared seals like the Sealion, on the other hand, have small but distinct ear pinnae and can, as the illustration shows, rotate the hind feet forward beneath the body and in this way are able to gallop clumsily along on dry land. The Sealion swims mainly as a result of rowing movements of the fore-limbs, which may have an overall span of up to 6 feet when extended. At high speeds the hind feet also give some assistance.

In this way Sealions can attain speeds of up to 20 knots when they plane on the surface of the water. A fully grown male is 7 feet long and weighs up to 600 lb. A bull of this weight is too heavy to propel himself far out of the water, but one of the more lightly built females, like the one shown below, has been known to leap from the water to clear a hurdle over 7 feet high.

Captive Sealions usually feed exclusively on fish but in the wild they also eat squid, seabirds and shellfish. An adult male can easily eat 40 lb. of food in a day.

The young are born in May and June at which time the males fight and establish harems of up to forty females on the rocks.

Family ODOBENIDAE

WALRUS

Odobenus rosmarus

(North Atlantic and North Pacific Oceans)

There is only one species of Walrus and its members are divided almost equally between the Atlantic and Pacific Oceans. They live in the shallow waters at the edge of the polar ice, moving farther south during the winter.

They are large animals, reaching 10 or more feet in length when adult. They resemble the eared seals in being able to rotate the hind feet forward beneath the body, but have weaker fore-limbs than the Sealions and are not such powerful swimmers. Walruses are remarkable for the tremendous development of the upper canine teeth. In a big male, these tusks weigh 11 lb. each and may be over 3 feet long. The illustration shows a young specimen, the teeth of which have not yet grown.

Walruses have been known to eat the flesh of the Narwhal and the small White Whale, but there can be little doubt that they only do so when they come across a dead specimen. Normally they feed on shellfish, starfish and crustaceans on the sea bottom, at depths of up to 240 feet. The coarse white whiskers are useful as organs of touch in the murky water and, instead of having sharp, pointed teeth, like the fish-eating seals and sealions, the Walrus is equipped with flattened cusps well adapted for crushing the shells of molluscs. It has been calculated that to obtain sufficient food, a large Walrus must search nearly 50 square yards of the sea-bed each day. It is usually claimed that the huge tusks of this species have evolved as food-dredging organs, but it now seems more likely that their primary value is to act as ice-picks when their bulky owners are heaving themselves out of the water.

BAIKAL SEAL

Pusa sibirica

(Lake Baikal)

Almost all seals live in salt water. One species (*Pusa caspica*) is found in the brackish waters of the Caspian Sea, while in Canada some populations of the Common Seal (*Phoca vitulina*) are found in lakes of fresh water. However, in the latter case, Common Seals are also found in the sea close by, and the fresh water population has obviously not been isolated for many years. The only true species of exclusively fresh-water seal therefore, is the one found in Lake Baikal.

This lake is in central Siberia and is 400 miles long and up to a mile deep. It is 1,250 miles to the south of the Arctic Ocean, the nearest sea. In this inland water live between 40,000 and 100,000 small seals. Their closest relatives are the small Ringed Seals (*Pusa hispida*) which are common in the Arctic Ocean. Obviously at one time the Baikal Seals and the Ringed Seals formed a single species, but Lake Baikal has been cut off from the sea for many thousands of years and the two populations have been separated long enough for two distinct species to have emerged.

During the winter Baikal Seals are dispersed over the whole lake. The adult females haul themselves out on to the ice, but the males and immature individuals remain in the water, keeping their breathing holes in the ice clear by constant use. In summer the adults collect at the north end of the lake, where, on the rocks, the young are born and mating occurs.

They eat fish, being especially fond of gobies and eels. Several thousand Baikal Seals are killed annually for their valuable fur.

329

GREY SEAL

Halichoerus grypus

(North Atlantic Coasts)

There are eighteen species of true seals. One of the best known of these is the Atlantic Grey Seal, found on the coasts of northern Europe, Iceland and Greenland. Well over half the world population of this species assembles each autumn at breeding grounds or "rookeries" on the rocky coasts of the British Isles.

During August the massive bulls, like the one shown above, take up their territories. They may weigh up to a quarter of a ton. Later the females arrive, and shortly afterwards give birth to a single pup. The offspring is almost 3 feet long and weighs about 30 lb. at birth. It grows rapidly up to the time that it is weaned, at the age of 3 weeks. Shortly after this it moults its white juvenile coat, assuming a more adult, dark, spotted pattern. The bull then mates with his females before they all return to the sea. The gestation period is just over 11 months, and thus the females need come ashore only once a year. Delayed implantation of the ovum is normal in the seals, as it is among many of the weasels.

During the remainder of the year Grey Seals roam at sea in search of food. They are expert swimmers, propelling themselves mainly by means of the webbed hind feet. The nostrils are under powerful muscular control and are kept tightly closed whilst their owner is under water. Grey Seals can hold their breath for long periods, and have been known to stay below the surface for 20 minutes at a time searching for fish and squids.

LEOPARD SEAL

Hydrurga leptonyx

(Southern Ocean)

Second only in size to the Elephant Seal among the seals of the Antarctic seas, the Leopard Seal or Sea Leopard attains a length of up to 12 feet. The females are a little larger than the males, a size ratio that does not occur in any other seal species. In ferocity, the Leopard Seal is second to none, for, as the name implies, this is a voracious, spotted predator.

They are rather solitary creatures and are widely distributed around Antarctica, where they sometimes haul themselves out on to the ice floes. They are also occasionally seen off the southern shores of New Zealand, Australia, South America and South Africa, especially in the winter when they migrate northward to ice-free shores.

All seals have sharply cusped teeth which are well adapted to pierce and hold the flesh of live fish, but the teeth of the Leopard Seal are exceptionally long and sharp, and are set in long, powerfully muscled jaws. Despite their size these seals swim rapidly, and can leap clear of the water to come crashing down on the drift ice. These tactics are sometimes used against the penguins that form an important part of their food. The Leopard Seal is the chief predator of the Antarctic penguins, and often lurks in the water round the ice on which they are congregated. Penguins frequently show a marked reluctance to be the first of a group to enter the water in case Leopard Seals should be in the vicinity.

Other food eaten by this species includes fish, squids, sea-birds, and carrion, including that abandoned by whaling ships.

SOUTHERN ELEPHANT SEAL

Mirounga leonina

(Southern Ocean)

The Southern Elephant Seal, or Sea Elephant, is well named. A fully grown bull can be over 20 feet long and may weigh nearly 4 tons, which is only a little less than the weight of an ordinary elephant. Additionally adult males have a trunk-like snout which, when inflated is over 2 feet long. It curls round and into the mouth when the bull roars, acting as a resonating chamber.

This species is found throughout the Southern Ocean, where it breeds on the rocky shores of Gough Island, South Georgia, Kerguelen, and other islands. Another very similar, but rarer species, the Northern Elephant Seal (*Mirounga angustirostris*), differs slightly in profile and is found off the Pacific coast of North America.

Despite their great size, Elephant Seals are agile in the water, and the Northern species, at least, descends to great depths. The stomach of one animal was found to contain sharks, skates and squids that normally live at depths of between 300 and 720 feet. Both the Northern and the Southern species have large eyes that would be useful in the dim light at such depths.

Most animals have intestines six to eight times as long as their total body length and it is therefore remarkable that one 16-foot male Elephant Seal was found to have intestines with a total length of 662 feet, or forty-two times its body length. The reason for this is not clear.

During the breeding season they come ashore for 3 months. The young weigh 1 hundredweight at birth, and manage to double this in only 11 days, the mother's milk being extremely rich.

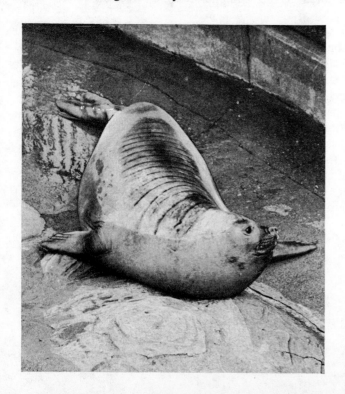

N. AARDVARK

The aardvark has the unique distinction of being the only mammalian species that is the sole representative of its order. This curious animal is confined to Africa and little is known about its ancestry, or its relationships to other living species. It used to be considered as a relative of the American anteaters (edentates), but this view is no longer held, the similarities being due to convergence rather than true affinity. From the slender clues that are available, it appears to be distantly related to early ungulates, but at the present stage of knowledge no detailed assessment can be made.

The name Tubulidentata refers to the strange tubule structure of its cheek teeth. There are no canines or incisors. The skull is slender and the gape of the mouth is small.

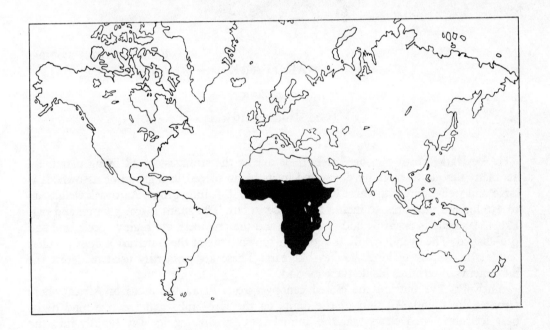

N. Order TUBULIDENTATA.   Aardvarks.

Family ORYCTEROPODIDAE.

1 ► *Orycteropus afer.*   **Aardvark.**   Africa. (EMH)

333

AARDVARK

Orycteropus afer

(Grasslands of Africa)

The Aardvark, Earth-pig, or Ant-bear, is one of the strangest of all living mammals. Its many unique features have resulted in its being placed in a group of its own. It is large and well-built, with short legs and a thick tail. A fully grown Aardvark weighs up to 150 lb. and measures 50 inches from nose to tail. The snout is exaggerated and pig-like, the tongue is extensile and elongated, and the few teeth are highly specialized and peg-shaped. The overall colour is a greyish-brown. One of the Aardvark's most peculiar features is its pair of long, donkey-like ears. These are reputedly used to detect the movements of termites inside their mound.

Aardvarks live outside the closed canopy forests in all the areas of Africa where termites are found. All four of the digits on the fore-limbs and the five hind digits bear well-developed claws that the animal uses for digging its way rapidly into the termite mounds. The termites are picked up by means of the 12-inch tongue which is covered with a sticky secretion.

The Aardvark is nocturnal and seldom seen by the Africans, who are very partial to its flesh. They hunt it by digging it out of its extensive burrows. Both the Lion and the Leopard will attack the Aardvark in the open at night, when it will defend itself by rolling over on its back and slashing with its claws.

Little is known of the breeding habits, but it appears that a single young is born in mid-summer.

O. ELEPHANTS

There are two species alive today, one in the African and the other in the southern Asiatic region. They represent the last remnants of a once extensive order of mammals. Several hundred extinct species are known from fossils and some of these—certain of the mammoths—survived long enough to co-exist with early man. The different species show varying degrees of specialization in the elongation of the nose and upper lip as a prehensile, food-gathering proboscis. In the two surviving forms, the trunk is well developed and both powerful and sensitive as a manipulating (or, more correctly, trombipulating) organ.

Canine teeth are absent. The premolars are functionless and are absent in the adult. There is a single pair of upper incisors that protrude from the mouth as powerful, ever-growing tusks. The huge, grinding molars are not present as a simultaneous set, but as a replaceable series. As each molar is worn down, it is substituted from behind by a new one. The Indian Elephant has a more complex molar design than the African Elephant. The great weight of the body is supported by thick pillar-like legs. With these an elephant can charge at high speed, but it is incapable of jumping even a low obstacle.

The large external ears are not only important as aids to hearing, but also function as valuable cooling surfaces. An over-heated elephant flaps its ears vigorously. The hair is sparse and coarse, the tough, thick skin being effectively naked.

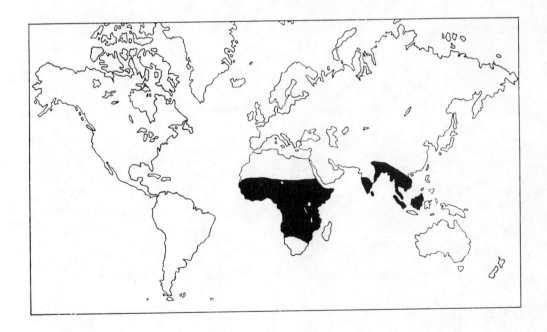

O. Order PROBOSCIDEA. Elephants.
  Suborder ELEPHANTOIDEA.
    Family ELEPHANTIDAE.

1 ►*Loxodonta africana.* **African Elephant.** Africa. (EMH)
2 ►*Elephas maximus.* **Indian Elephant.** S. Asia and Sumatra. (EM)

AFRICAN ELEPHANT

Loxodonta africana

(Tropical Africa)

The African Elephant is the largest living land mammal. Measuring as much as 11 feet at the shoulder, an adult bull may weigh more than 6 tons. The cow commonly weighs about 2 tons less. Unlike the Indian Elephant, the cow also bears tusks, but they are rather small compared with those of the bull which may be 8 feet in length. Other distinguishing characteristics of the African Elephant that can be seen in the photograph above are the very large ears, the ringed trunk, the flat forehead, the high position of the head on the body, and the concave curve of the back.

An Elephant herd, which usually numbers 20 or 30 individuals, consists of a mature bull, a few younger bulls, and a number of cows and calves. Older bulls lead a solitary existence.

The gestation period of the African Elephant is about 21 months. The single off-spring uses its mouth, not its trunk, when feeding from its mother. The nipples are situated between the fore-legs of the cow. The calf is only fully weaned when nearly 5 years old. The life span is very similar to man's—an Elephant reaching maturity at about 15 and living to the age of 60 or 70.

The African Elephant has few natural enemies and leads a peaceful existence in the company of other animals, often performing the useful service of digging holes in the dry river beds when searching for subterranean water.

It is generally considered that there are two types of African Elephant, a smaller Rain Forest form confined to the dense jungles of West Africa, and a larger Bush form which is more widely distributed.

337

INDIAN ELEPHANT

Elephas maximus

(Forests of Southern Asia and Sumatra)

Smaller than the African Elephant, the bull Indian Elephant rarely reaches 10 feet high at the shoulder. At this height its weight would be about 4 tons and its tusks would measure 5 or 6 feet in length. The cow is tuskless or has small tusks not visible from the exterior. The Indian Elephant is distinguishable from the African Elephant by its smaller ears, smoother trunk, domed forehead, and convex curvature of the back. Between the ear and eye (in both species) lies the opening to a "musth" gland which seems to have some sexual function.

The Elephant is entirely herbivorous, an adult consuming several hundred pounds of leaves, shoots, bamboo, reeds, grasses and fruit every day. The food is taken up by the sensitive trunk whose tip has one finger-like projection, in contrast to the two "fingers" in the African Elephant. Each animal drinks between 30 and 50 gallons of water a day, squirting it into the mouth from the trunk which has a capacity of $1\frac{1}{2}$ gallons. In spite of their thick skins, Elephants suffer from the attentions of flies and mosquitoes and must often take protective mud baths.

Elephants seem to sleep very seldom and then only for short periods, but, contrary to popular belief, they quite often lie down to do so. Their normal speed of walking is about 4 m.p.h., but their top speed can exceed 30 m.p.h.

Distinct races are recognized from Bengal, Ceylon, Sumatra and Malaya, in all of which areas they are extensively domesticated.

P. HYRAXES

There appear to be six species of hyraxes surviving today, all in the African region. One of these extends some way into south-west Asia, but the group does not appear to have spread its range farther at any point in its rather isolated history. Until recently, many more species were recognized, but as more and more specimens have been studied it has emerged that many of these have represented only local racial variations of true species. When further study is made of this fascinating order of mammals, it is probable that even some of the present six species may turn out to be no more than races.

Despite their rodent-like size and general shape, the hyraxes are, in fact, related to the ungulates. Although they have no close ties with other groups of mammals, their nearest living relatives are generally considered to be the elephants and the sirenians. Some early species of hyraxes were as large as pigs, but only the rabbit-sized forms have persisted to the present time. They are gregarious, rock or tree-dwelling, nimble and active. They have strange feet with three short, hoof-like toes on the hind feet and four on the front feet.

There is only one rootless upper incisor and two lower incisors, on each side of the jaw. The cheek teeth are high-crowned and similar in design to those of the rhinoceroses. There are no canines and a large gap exists between the incisors and the cheek teeth. The ears are small and the tail is reduced almost to nothing. Long, conspicuous guard-hairs project from the fur all over the body. The stomach is two-chambered. They are entirely herbivorous.

In personality, the hyraxes are an odd mixture of timidity and curiosity. They have a complex social life that has as yet not been the subject of intensive study.

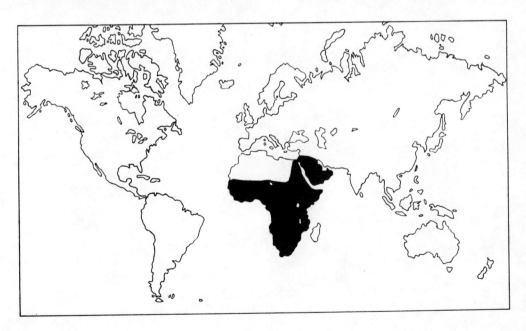

339

P. Order HYRACOIDEA.   Hyraxes.

Family PROCAVIIDAE.

1 ►*Procavia capensis.* **Rock Hyrax.**   Africa and S.W. Asia. (EMH)
2 *Procavia chapini.*   **Chapin's Hyrax.**   Cen. Africa. (A)
3 *Dendrohyrax brucei.*   **Yellow-spotted Hyrax.**   Africa. (EMH)
4 *Dendrohyrax arboreus.*   **Tree Hyrax.**   Africa. (EMH)
5 *Dendrohyrax dorsalis.*   **Beecroft's Hyrax.**   W. Africa. (A)
6 *Dendrohyrax validus.*   E. Africa. (A)

340

ROCK HYRAX

Procavia capensis

(Rocky outcrops in Africa and South-west Asia)

The Rock Hyrax, or Dassie, is found on rocky outcrops and mountain slopes throughout Africa, from sea-level to 15,000 feet. A Syrian race is undoubtedly the animal which is referred to in the Bible as a "cony". In general appearance the Hyrax resembles a Guinea-pig, but despite its shape it is capable of vigorous vertical leaps and delicate balancing manoeuvres. Males weigh about 8 lb.; the females are slightly smaller. The fur is coarse and there is a small, elongated glandular patch in the middle of the back, surrounded by a fringe of longer erectile hairs. When a Hyrax becomes agitated, these hairs stand on end, exposing the gland. This can clearly be seen when two animals are fighting and is presumably a form of scent signalling. The soles of the feet are thick and flat and always moist, providing an efficient gripping surface.

The Rock Hyrax is gregarious, living in colonies which vary from six to several dozen individuals. They make a wide variety of chattering, whistling calls, particularly when they are at their most active in the early morning and late evening. They are sharp-sighted, keen of hearing and very wary at all times. Hyraxes feed largely on grasses, leaves and bark. They have a characteristic habit of leaving all their droppings in one place.

They are preyed upon by Leopards, Caracals, mongooses and eagles, but the male can be a fierce adversary and has a savage bite. There are usually two or three young in a litter. They are born in the spring with their eyes open and their coats fully developed.

341

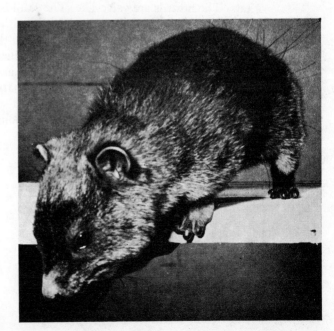

Q. SIRENIANS

There are four species of sirenians alive today. Two of these occur in the American region and two in the African. One of the latter extends into the Asiatic region. They are found in the shallow, tropical, coastal waters of the eastern side of the New World, West and East Africa, and southern Asia, through to Australia.

It is remarkable that these strange-looking creatures should have been confused with the sirens of ancient mythology; yet this is how they acquired their name. It is said that they reminded sailors of mermaids because of their humanoid method of nursing their young. All sirenians are completely aquatic. They have paddle-like front limbs, no hind limbs and a large fleshy tail that is flattened out horizontally. They never come out on to dry land, the young being born under water, as in the case of whales. Immediately after birth, the offspring is raised up out of the water by its mother and spends the first 45 minutes of its life on her back. During the following 2 hours she gradually submerges it until it is swimming with her. She suckles it in an anterior position, apparently by holding it in her flippers while it takes milk from the small mammary glands situated in the angle of the front limbs and the body. There is only a single offspring each year, the gestation period lasting as much as 11, or even 12, months.

Next to the cetaceans, the sirenians show the most extreme form of mammalian adaptation to aquatic life. These two groups are the only ones that are totally water-bound throughout life and that have lost their hind limbs. Despite these similarities they are not related, the ancestors of the whales having been carnivorous creatures, whilst those of the sirenians were plant-eating ungulates. The surviving species and the fossil sirenians that have been found in the African region reveal skeletal similarities to the early proboscideans—the ancestors of present-day elephants.

The sirenians are large mammals, typically measuring between 7 and 10 feet in length. The average weight of an adult is 450 to 500 lb. The young weigh about 40 lb. at birth. The skin is sparsely hairy. Beneath it is a thick layer of insulating blubber. The ribs are massive and heavy. There is a complex stomach, with three chambers. The eyes are weak, but the hearing is reputed to be good, despite the absence of external ears. The nostrils are valve-like. The skull is large, but the brain it houses is small and the animals are in general rather sluggish and unintelligent. They are defenceless creatures, surviving today simply because they live in regions that are unsuitable for their enemies, the sharks, crocodiles and killer whales. The waters the sirenians frequent are too shallow for the sharks and whales and too marine for most crocodiles. In some areas the sirenians do venture into the estuaries and larger rivers, but their basic habitat is the shallow, seaweed-laden coastal sea-water of the tropics. All four species are totally herbivorous, browsing hour after hour on a variety of marine vegetation.

Q. Order SIRENIA.   Sirenians.

Family DUGONGIDAE.   Dugongs.

1   *Dugong dugon*.   **Dugong.** E. Africa, Red Sea, Indian Ocean, S. Asia, Nicobars, Philippines, Formosa, N. Australia. (EM)

Family TRICHECHIDAE.   Manatees.

2 ►*Trichechus manatus*.   **North American Manatee.** N. America, W. Indies, N.E. of S. America. (HK)

3   *Trichechus inunguis*.   **South American Manatee.** S. America. (C2)
4   *Trichechus senegalensis*.   **West African Manatee.** W. Africa. (EMH)

NORTH AMERICAN MANATEE

Trichechus manatus

(South-east of North America, West Indies, North-east of South America)

This timid, aquatic mammal is found today along the coasts of the Caribbean in the warm, turbid shallows of salt-water bays and along the mud-bottomed estuaries of sluggish coastal rivers. There it browses on sea grasses, water hyacinths and lilies, gathering them by means of its powerful, prehensile upper lip. The latter is deeply divided into two lobes and is covered with short stiff bristles.

The teeth are unusual, there being no canines or premolars. The few, small incisors present in the young Manatee disappear in the adult leaving it with only its grinding molars. Only a few of these cheek teeth are present at any one time, old ones being replaced from behind, as in the elephants. There are no milk teeth.

An adult Manatee eats between 60 and 100 lb. of seaweed every day. The normal period of submergence when browsing is 10 minutes, the maximum 16.

The Dugong differs from the three species of Manatees in having a central notch in its tail that divides it into two pointed, lateral lobes. Also, the adult retains its incisors and, in the male, two of the upper incisors are enlarged as sharp, ever-growing tusks. This condition was even more extreme in the recently exterminated sirenian called Steller's Sea Cow (*Hydrodamalis*), where the males possessed a pair of huge tusks, but were otherwise toothless. This species was discovered by Bering in 1741 in the Bering Straits. Even then, there were only a few thousands of these vast, 3-ton, 30-foot long creatures surviving. By 1768 they had all been killed by Russian hunters.

R. ODD-TOED UNGULATES

Odd-toed Ungulates survive today in Central and South America (three species), in Africa (six species) and in Asia including Java, Sumatra and Borneo (six species). If the Domestic Horse is considered as a separate species that is extinct in the wild, there is then a total of sixteen species alive today. This is a mere remnant of the group, for there are 152 extinct genera of Odd-toed Ungulates known from fossils. When compared with the five existing genera, this gives the highest extermination ratio of any of the surviving orders of mammals.

Only three basic types have been able to hold their own—the horses (fast and sensitive), the tapirs (shy and retiring) and the rhinoceroses (large and armoured).

The Greek name Perissodactyla means literally "odd-fingered". The diagnostic feature of the group is that the axis of the foot passes through the middle digit. The legs are long and end in blunt hooves. The skull is elongated and there is a gap between the incisor teeth and the heavy, grinding cheek teeth.

Unlike the Even-toed Ungulates (see later), the stomach is simple and there are no bony outgrowths from the skull (the horns of the rhinos being dermal in origin).

Nearly all the living species of this group are rapidly approaching extinction. For example, recent surveys suggest that there are only 650 Great Indian Rhinoceroses, 150 Sumatran Rhinoceroses and 50 Javan Rhinoceroses alive at the present time.

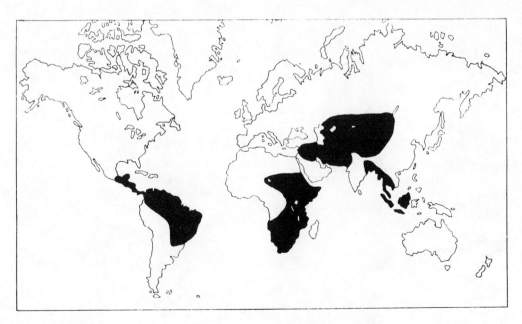

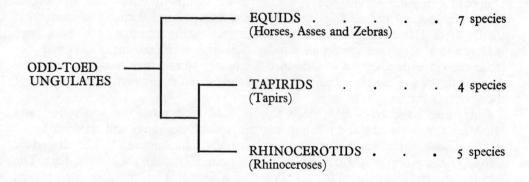

ODD-TOED
UNGULATES

EQUIDS . . . . . 7 species
(Horses, Asses and Zebras)

TAPIRIDS . . . . 4 species
(Tapirs)

RHINOCEROTIDS . . . 5 species
(Rhinoceroses)

R. Order PERISSODACTYLA.   Odd-toed Ungulates.

  Suborder HIPPOMORPHA.

  Superfamily EQUOIDEA.

  Family EQUIDAE.   Horses.

1 ►*Equus przewalskii.*   **Wild Horse.**   Cen. Asia. (EM)
2 *Equus caballus.*   **Horse.**   (Domestic)
3 ►*Equus hemionus.*   **Asiatic Wild Ass.**   Asia. (EM)
4 *Equus asinus.*   **African Wild Ass** (and Domestic Donkey).   E. Africa. (A)
5 ►*Equus zebra.*   **Mountain Zebra.**   S. Africa. (EMH)
6 ►*Equus burchelli.*   **Common Zebra.**   Africa. (EMH)
7 ►*Equus grevyi.*   **Grévy's Zebra.**   Cen. E. Africa. (A)

  Suborder CERATOMORPHA.

  Superfamily TAPIROIDEA.

  Family TAPIRIDAE.   Tapirs.

8 ►*Tapirus indicus.*   **Malayan Tapir.**   Sumatra and Malaya. (EM)
9 ►*Tapirus terrestris.*   **South American Tapir.**   S. America. (C2)
10 *Tapirus pinchaque.*   **Mountain Tapir.**   S. America. (C2)
11 *Tapirus bairdi.*   **Central American Tapir.**   Cen. and S. America. (C2)

  Superfamily RHINOCEROTOIDEA.

  Family RHINOCEROTIDAE.   Rhinoceroses.

  Subfamily RHINOCEROTINAE.   One-horned Rhinos.

12 ►*Rhinoceros unicornis.*   **Great Indian Rhinoceros.**   S. Asia. (EM)
13 *Rhinoceros sondaicus.*   **Javan Rhinoceros.**   S. Asia, Sumatra, Java. (EM)

  Subfamily DICERORHININAE.   Two-horned Rhinos.

14 *Didermocerus sumatrensis.*   **Sumatran Rhinoceros.**   S. Asia, Sumatra, Borneo. (EM)
15 ►*Diceros simus.*   **White Rhinoceros.**   Africa. (EM)
16 ►*Diceros bicornis.*   **Black Rhinoceros.**   Africa. (EM)

347

Family EQUIDAE

WILD HORSE

Equus przewalskii

(Central Asia)

In recent years the range of the Wild Horse has become limited, by human hunting, to the inhospitable plains of the Altai Mountain region and the extreme west of Mongolia. Not long ago herds of domestic cattle were moved into this area, and competed for the already scarce water. Wild Horses must drink at least once every two or three days, and so their numbers dwindled still further. In addition, Domestic Horses running loose in the area inter-bred with the wild specimens and diluted the stock. Today observers report that there are probably no more than twenty pure-bred Wild Horses in the natural habitat. There are a further 100, however, in various zoos and these are breeding regularly. All but two of these captive specimens are descendants of three pairs that were captured in 1901–2.

The Wild Horse differs from the Domestic Horse in having a short, stiff, erect mane, a heavy head, small ears, a low-slung tail and a shrill voice. The coat is a pale reddish-brown; in winter it is long and shaggy. The muzzle is white, the mane and tail black.

Another race of Wild Horse, *Equus przewalskii gmelini*, known as the Tarpan, became extinct in the wild in the nineteenth century. The last one in captivity died in 1919. Originally it inhabited the Steppes of eastern Europe and western Asia. It was mousy-grey in colour, had weaker back teeth, and a less sturdy build.

The exact form of Wild Horse that was involved in the ancestry of the Domestic Horse is unknown and it is therefore convenient to retain the name *Equus caballus* for domesticated specimens.

Family EQUIDAE

ASIATIC WILD ASS

Equus hemionus

(Asia)

The increasingly rare Wild Ass of Asia is known by a variety of names. In Mongolia, where it is now found only in the central regions, it is called the Kulan, or Chigetai (sometimes spelt Djiggetai of Dziggetai). In Tibet it goes by the name of Kiang, in Persia it is known as the Onager, and in India as the Ghor-khar. There are slight differences in races from the different regions, but they are variable and not particularly significant. The Kiang, for example, is larger than the others, the Onager (seen in above photograph) is smaller and generally more slender in build. The Ghor-khar is a particularly pale form.

The sandy-coloured coat of the Asiatic Wild Ass is paler below, with a short, erect black mane and a black tail tip. The tail-hairs are short except for those near the extremity, giving the tail a characteristic tufted appearance. There are callosities on the forelegs only (visible in the illustration). The ears are longer than those of the Horse, but smaller than those of the other species of Wild Ass—the African Wild Ass (*Equus asinus*). The latter is the ancestor of the Domestic Donkey. It is also becoming extremely rare but is still surviving in the bleak wastelands of north-east Africa. A generally larger creature, its braying is like that of the domesticated animals, but unlike the shrieking call of the Asiatic species.

The Onager itself was domesticated in Sumerian times, in the third millennium B.C., but by the second millennium it had been replaced by the stronger, more docile Horse. It does not appear to have been domesticated again since.

349

MOUNTAIN ZEBRA

Equus zebra

(Southern Africa)

The Mountain Zebra takes its name from its occurrence in the mountains of the Cape Province, as opposed to the plains inhabited by the other species. It was the first zebra species to be scientifically described and named (by Linnaeus).

The original Mountain Zebra (*Equus zebra zebra*), of which about 150 individuals remain, is now found only in protected areas in the western Cape. It was formerly abundant, extending as far east as the Drakensberg, but was in danger of extinction from ruthless hunting. A more recently described race, Hartmann's Mountain Zebra (*Equus zebra hartmannae*), is slightly larger and more numerous and still exists in small wild herds in the mountains of western South-west Africa and Angola.

The Mountain Zebra is more donkey-like than the Common Zebra and has the donkey's long ears, narrow hooves and heavy head. It is compactly built and moves with great agility across the rocky terrain. It has a more high-pitched voice than other zebras, and neighs more like a horse, although as a rule it is a rather silent species. Except for the belly, where markings are absent, the Mountain Zebra is covered with numerous stripes over the head, neck, body and legs down to the black hooves. The stripes are narrow and close-set, except on the hindquarters where they are broader and more widely spaced. The arrangement of the stripes is unique in having a grid-iron pattern on top of the rump. In Hartmann's Mountain Zebra (seen below) the stripes are more widely spaced, giving the appearance of a much lighter-coloured animal. The presence of a distinct dewlap on the throat distinguishes the Mountain Zebra from all other Equidae.

COMMON ZEBRA

Equus burchelli

(Africa South of the Sahara)

The Common Zebra is extremely variable in its markings. Some of its races have been considered as distinct species from time to time, but it is now known that there is a single continuous series—a cline—from north to south of its huge range. The farther north one moves, the more vivid and detailed is the striping. The races can be distinguished from one another as follows:

Burchell's Zebra (*Equus burchelli burchelli*), the original "type" race, is now extinct. It came from the Orange Free State and Bechuanaland, and had entirely unmarked legs. Shadow stripes were prominent.

The Damaraland or Chapman's Zebra (*Equus burchelli antiquorum*) extends from southern Angola to the Transvaal and Zululand. The legs have some striping, but it does not extend to the hoof. Shadow stripes are generally present, but rather narrow. This is the race illustrated above.

Selous's Zebra (*Equus burchelli selousi*) has legs completely striped to the hooves. The pasterns are striped on both sides and the lower portion is black owing to fusion of the stripes there. Shadow stripes are faint or absent. The neck stripes vary from ten to thirteen and the vertical body stripes from four to eight. Selous's Zebra is found from Southern Rhodesia to southern Nyasaland.

The fourth distinct race is Böhm's or Grant's Zebra (*Equus burchelli böhmi*). Here the legs are completely striped to the hooves and the markings on the pasterns are distinct. No shadow stripes are present, except occasionally and faintly, on the hindquarters only. The neck stripes are from seven to ten in number, and the vertical body stripes three to four. This Zebra ranges from Northern Rhodesia to the Sudan.

351

R 6a

QUAGGA

Equus quagga

(Southern Africa)

Although the Quagga is now extinct, it is included here because it survived long enough to be recorded photographically. The last Quagga, an old mare, died in the Amsterdam Zoo in 1883. The illustration above is one of the only four photographs of a living specimen in existence; all were taken from an animal kept at the London Zoo from 1851 to 1872.

The Quagga is so called from the barking noise it made, which sounded like "kwa-ha". Its name should not be confused with the word Bontequagga which is an alternative title for the Common Zebra.

Standing about 54 inches high at the shoulder, the Quagga measured nearly 9 feet in length. It has often been popularly described as having the front end of a zebra and the rear end of a horse.

The ground colour of the body was a sandy brown and only the head, neck and shoulders were striped. The legs and the flowing tail were almost white.

The Quagga was an animal of the open plains, similar in habits to the Common Zebra. It was found only in South Africa in the Central and South Orange Free State and in the south-western Karroo regions, where it was once very numerous. This distribution is of interest because the Common Zebra shows a tendency to become less and less conspicuously striped as one moves south over its range. It was once thought that the Quagga was no more than an extreme southern form of the Common Zebra, but it is now known that the two species inhabited the same region between the Vaal and the Orange River, but that the herds did not mix.

352

GRÉVY'S ZEBRA

Equus grevyi

(Southern Abyssinia, Somalia, East Africa)

Grévy's Zebra is the largest and most narrowly striped of the zebras. It was named after the President of the French Republic who received the first specimens known to science, although this species was probably the "Hippotigris" of the Roman Circus.

It stands over five feet at the shoulder and has a short, six-inch, erect mane. The nine-inch long ears are broad, well-rounded and thickly covered in hair. Unlike the Common Zebra, which has a barking call, Grévy's produces a deep baying noise like that of the African Wild Ass, perhaps betraying a closer relationship between these two than between Grévy's and the other species of *Equus*. It frequently trots and gallops, unlike the Common Zebra, which more typically canters.

The dense, fine striping extends from the long head and short neck, along the body, down to the mule-like hooves, with a broad stripe on the spine and ears. The belly is unmarked. The rump markings are unique, the stripes becoming smaller instead of larger, as in other species. The tail tuft is shorter than in other zebras, being only 9 inches long.

In their way of life, the species of zebras differ little from each other. Open plains near water are preferred, an old stallion leading the herd at dawn and dusk to the waterholes. All are sociable grazers, living in mixed herds with other big game. Depending on the area, Hartebeeste, Oryx, Eland, Gnu, Ostriches and other zebras are found together. The young, after a gestation period of 13 months, are born from May to August. The young Grévy's Zebra has a mane extending from shoulder to tail.

353   M

R 8

MALAYAN TAPIR

Tapirus indicus

(Forests of Malaya and Sumatra)

The Tapir of Malaya, Burma, Thailand and the island of Sumatra is a stockily-built survivor from a bygone age. Tapirs retain many of the primitive traits of their ancestors and are the only odd-toed ungulates which have four toes on the front feet. The hind feet, like those of the rhinoceros, are three-toed. The body is heavy; an adult standing only 3 feet tall may weigh 400 lb. The limbs are short and stout and the muzzle is lengthened to form a short, mobile trunk. The eyes are small and the tail is only a short stump. The head, neck, shoulders and legs are black, but the saddle-shaped area of the back and sides is pure white. This coloration may appear to be conspicuous, but in the shadowy moonlight it helps to disrupt the general body shape.

Malayan Tapirs live in the densest tropical forests, browsing during the night on shoots and twigs of trees and shrubs, and succulent water plants. Like the rhinoceros, they are reputed to deposit their droppings regularly in one spot. Tapirs often make nocturnal visits to the nearest available "salt-lick".

The sense of smell and hearing are acute, but the eyesight is rather weak. The Malayan Tapir spends much time in the water and swims well. It is reported that copulation typically takes place in the water. The gestation period is about 13 months and one, or sometimes two offspring are born at a time. The young Malayan Tapir, like the young of the American Tapirs, has longitudinal stripes and spots on the body and legs. These markings disappear when the animal is about half-grown.

354

Family TAPIRIDAE

SOUTH AMERICAN TAPIR
Tapirus terrestris
(Amazonian forests)

Very closely related to the Malayan Tapir (*Tapirus indicus*), and differing conspicuously only in adult colour and marking, are the tapirs which live in tropical America. The most common of these is the South American Tapir, which is a uniform dark brown in colour and measures 3 feet high and 6 feet in length.

The South American species, like the Malayan form, has four toes on the front feet and only three on the hind. It is a shy, nocturnal animal which confines itself to an intricate network of trails in the forests of the marshy lowlands of Brazil, the Guianas, Colombia, Venezuela, Ecuador, Peru, Bolivia and the north of Argentina. Water is essential for the survival of this species; it drinks a great deal and is an excellent swimmer. Like all the tapirs it is exclusively herbivorous, browsing on water plants and the leaves and twigs of most of the forest trees.

Its only enemies in South America are Jaguars and alligators, against which its only defence is to use its teeth.

After a gestation period of almost 400 days a single, striped and spotted offspring, such as the one shown above, is born in a secluded place in the forest. It is almost immediately able to accompany its mother.

The thick-coated Mountain Tapir (*Tapirus pinchaque*) is found at altitudes of 7,000 to 12,000 feet in the Andes of Colombia, Ecuador and Peru. It was first described by Roulin and is sometimes named after him. The Central American Tapir (*Tapirus bairdi*) has white patches on the head and chest, and is found up to 6,000 feet in Central America, Ecuador and Colombia.

355

R 12

GREAT INDIAN RHINOCEROS

Rhinoceros unicornis

(Nepal, Bengal and Assam)

There are five species of rhinoceros alive today, three in Asia and two in Africa. The largest of the Asiatic forms is the Great Indian Rhinoceros, which is confined to jungle and grassland areas of Nepal, Bengal and Assam. Like the African Black Rhinoceros (*Diceros bicornis*) it has a pointed, prehensile upper lip, but unlike the African forms, it has only one large horn. This is present in both sexes. The male may be 14 feet long, stand 6 feet high at the shoulder and weigh over 2 tons. The horn is rather short and blunt, but there is a pair of sharp-edged incisor tusks in the lower jaw. When attacking, this species slashes with these tusks, rather than charging with its horn.

The body of the Indian Rhinoceros is covered with a heavy, "studded" armour which is prominently folded in front of the shoulder, behind the shoulder, and in front of the thigh. The tail is set in a deep groove of this armour. Almost the only hair visible is a fringe on the end of the ears and the tip of the tail.

The Great Indian Rhinoceros is an inoffensive, retiring animal and usually solitary. It is strictly territorial, with tracks through the tall grasses, fixed dung-pile sites, and personal mud wallows. The food consists largely of grasses, shoots and reeds. A single offspring weighing over 100 lb. is born after a gestation period of about 18 months.

The other Asiatic rhinos are the Javan Rhinoceros (*Rhinoceros sondaicus*) which is smaller, horned usually only in the male, and practically extinct; and the Sumatran Rhinoceros (*Didermocerus sumatrensis*) which has two horns and a hairy coat.

356

WHITE RHINOCEROS

Diceros simus

(Central Africa and Zululand)

Amongst all the land mammals, the White Rhinoceros is second only to the elephant in size. An adult male measures 6 feet at the shoulder and may weigh more than 3 tons. Only slightly paler in colour than the Black Rhinoceros, the White species is believed to have acquired its name from the Afrikaans word *Weit*, meaning wide, which refers to the broad, square-lipped mouth that distinguishes it from the Black. Other diagnostic features are the prominent hump between the shoulders and the longer head.

The White Rhinoceros is confined today to two distinct and separate areas. In the more northerly of the two they are found in Uganda, the Congo, and the Sudan. Two thousand miles farther south, they occur in Zululand, where a recent count gave their number as approximately 600. In both areas they live in thorny savannah, but subsist almost entirely on grasses, using the trees only for cover. Water is essential both for daily drinking and for bathing.

A single offspring is born after a gestation period of 18 months, is only fully weaned at 12 months, and remains with the female for several years.

Rhinoceroses have weak vision, but the senses of smell and hearing are acute. The poor eyesight is compensated for by the presence of small birds, the Red-billed Oxpeckers (*Buphagus erythrorhynchus*), that travel on the Rhinoceros's back and sound an alarm in times of danger. Over most of the present distribution of the Rhinoceros there are few predators large enough to cause it any concern, but lions and crocodiles undoubtedly account for a number of wayward young.

The White Rhinoceros used to be considered as a separate genus (*Ceratotherium simum*) but this view is no longer held.

357

R 16

BLACK RHINOCEROS

Diceros bicornis

(Central and Southern Africa)

The Black Rhinoceros is the more common of the two African species. Unlike the White, or Square-lipped Rhinoceros, this species has an upper lip that is long and pointed, forming a prehensile organ—an adaptation to its life as a browser. It feeds usually on the leaves and shoots of shrubs and bushes.

Both sexes are horned, as with all species except the Javan Rhinoceros. The front horn averages about 18 inches long, and the rear 7 inches. They are composed of a solid mass of closely packed vertical fibres, with a slight hollow at the base resting upon a corresponding prominence on the bones of the skull.

The single offspring is born during the rainy season after a 16 to 18 months' gestation period, and is adult at 5 years. Its life expectancy in the wild has been estimated at about 25 years.

During the heat of the day the Black Rhinoceros lies up in the shade. It is partly diurnal, browsing during the late evening and early morning in its territory of about 10 square miles. At sunset it visits the near-by water-holes. Droppings are deposited in scooped-out hollows beside the territorial paths, and scattered with the forefeet.

The Black Rhinoceros is, like the White, becoming extremely scarce in the bushy country of its choice, and is now found mainly in game reserves. Its former range extended from the Cape, north to Egypt.

This species has a reputation for being "bad-tempered", but this has been wildly exaggerated. Usually it flees with its tail erect and avoids trouble, but if it is childishly baited by "Land-rover cowboys" it may well turn and charge.

358

S. EVEN-TOED UNGULATES

The 194 species of Even-toed Ungulates alive today are almost world-wide in distribution, only Australia, New Zealand and the Polar Regions being outside their range. Representatives of most of the major groups are found in both the Old World and the New World.

The Greek name Artiodactyla means literally "even-fingered". The diagnostic feature of the group is that the axis of the foot passes between the third and fourth digits. This distinguishes them from the superficially similar Odd-toed Ungulates. The similarity between the two groups, resulting from the fact that both have evolved long legs with blunt hooves and a reduced number of digits, originally led to their being grouped together under the general heading of "ungulates". It was later realized that they had arrived at this hooved condition independently and they were not, in reality, closely related. The group was then split into two separate natural orders, the Odd-toed and the Even-toed.

The Even-toed Ungulates have been much the more successful of the two and, despite intensive hunting by man, have held their own well in most parts of the world. Unlike the Odd-toed Ungulates, they have a complicated digestive system involving a two- to four-chambered stomach. In advanced ruminants (the vast majority of the order—172 out of 194 species—including the deer, giraffes, pronghorn, and all the bovids) there is always a four-chambered stomach and a special regurgitation system known as "chewing the cud". The food is torn up and swallowed quickly. It then passes into the first two chambers of the stomach (the rumen and the reticulum). Later, when the animals are resting safely, without fear of predators, this food, already worked on to some extent by bacteria, is brought back in small quantities to the mouth and thoroughly chewed. It is then swallowed a second time and passes now into the third and fourth stomach chambers (the omasum and abomasum). This process is repeated over and over again until all the food has been dealt with. This system enables the ruminant to gather a great deal of food rapidly and "consume" it in safety, and has probably been one of the main reasons why this group has been so much more successful than its other ungulate rivals. (The four species of chevrotains form an intermediate group that are included in the ruminants because they also chew the cud, but they have only three chambers to the stomach.)

Another way in which many of the Even-toed Ungulates differ from the Odd-toed Ungulates is in the possession of paired bony outgrowths from the top of the skull. These weapons are of four types. In the deer (as antlers) they are branched and seasonal. They are skin-covered as they grow each year, but the skin is later removed leaving a naked, bony structure. This is usually present only in the males. After the breeding season the antlers drop off, but new ones soon start to grow again. In the giraffe and okapi the bony outgrowths are permanent, short, simple and always skin-covered. In the pronghorn they are permanent and un-branching, but have a slightly forked, horny covering that is shed annually. In the bovids (antelope, cattle, sheep, goats, etc.) there are permanent outgrowths that are unforked and persistently horn-covered. They are usually present in both sexes.

359

The skull of Even-toed Ungulates is elongated and, as with the Odd-toed Ungulates, the front teeth are typically separated from the cheek teeth by a gap, or diastema. The upper incisors are often absent, being replaced by a horny pad. Against this the lower incisors bite when the animals are tearing off vegetation.

Nearly all man's important domesticated species come from this order of mammals, including pigs, camels, llamas, reindeer, yak, cattle, water-buffalo, goats and sheep. Throughout history they have supplied him with food, drink, clothing and transport. Earlier, during prehistoric times, they provided him with his most important prey species, enabling him to develop from a primitive food-grubber into an advanced, co-operative hunter.

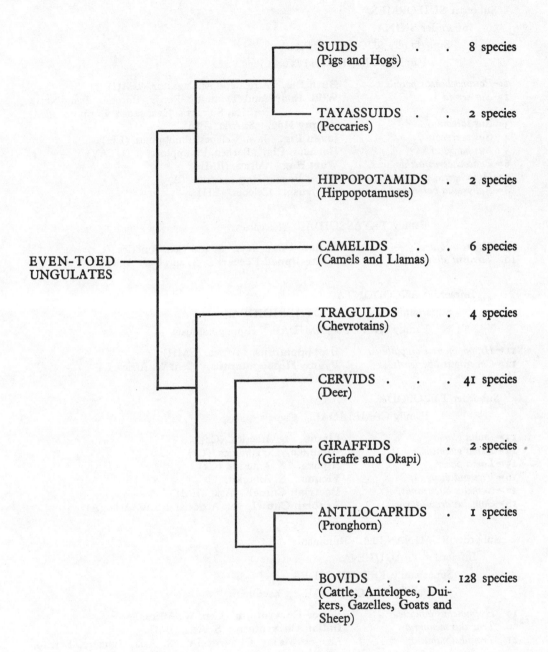

SUIDS   .   .   8 species
(Pigs and Hogs)

TAYASSUIDS .   2 species
(Peccaries)

HIPPOPOTAMIDS . 2 species
(Hippopotamuses)

CAMELIDS   .   . 6 species
(Camels and Llamas)

TRAGULIDS   .   . 4 species
(Chevrotains)

CERVIDS .   .   41 species
(Deer)

GIRAFFIDS   . 2 species
(Giraffe and Okapi)

ANTILOCAPRIDS . 1 species
(Pronghorn)

BOVIDS   .   . 128 species
(Cattle, Antelopes, Dui-
kers, Gazelles, Goats and
Sheep)

EVEN-TOED
UNGULATES

S. Order ARTIODACTYLA.   Even-toed Ungulates.

Suborder SUIFORMES.

Infraorder SUINA.

Superfamily SUOIDEA.   Pigs.

Family SUIDAE.   Old World Pigs.

1 ►*Potamochoerus porcus.* **Bush Pig.**   Africa and Madagascar. (EMH)
2 ► *Sus scrofa.* **Wild Boar** (and Domestic Pigs).   Europe, Asia, North Africa, Sumatra, Java, Japan, Formosa. (EM)

3   *Sus salvanius.* **Pygmy Hog.**   S. Asia. (EM)
4   *Sus verrucosus.* **Javan Pig.**   Java, Celebes, Philippines. (LH)
5   *Sus barbatus.* **Bornean Pig.**   Borneo, Philippines. (CH/TAY)
6 ►*Phacochoerus aethiopicus.* **Wart Hog.**   Africa. (EMH)
7 ►*Hylochoerus meinertzhageni.* **Giant Forest Hog.**   Africa. (A)
8 ►*Babyrousa babyrussa.* **Babirusa.**   Celebes. (LH)

Family TAYASSUIDAE.   Peccaries.

9 ► *Tayassu tajacu.* **Collared Peccary.**   S. and Cen. America. (C2)
10   *Tayassu albirostris.* **White-lipped Peccary.**   S. and Cen. America. (C2)

Infraorder ANCODONTA.

Superfamily ANTHRACOTHERIOIDEA.

Family HIPPOPOTAMIDAE.   Hippopotamuses.

11 ►*Hippopotamus amphibius.* **Hippopotamus.**   Africa. (EMH)
12 ►*Choeropsis liberiensis.* **Pygmy Hippopotamus.**   Cen. W. Africa. (A)

Suborder TYLOPODA.

Family CAMELIDAE.   Camels.

13 ►*Lama glama.* **Llama.**   S. America. (C2)
14 ►*Lama guanicoe.* **Guanaco.**   S. America. (C2)
15 ►*Lama pacos.* **Alpaca.**   S. America. (C2)
16 ►*Vicugna vicugna.* **Vicuna.**   S. America. (C2)
17 ►*Camelus bactrianus.* **Bactrian Camel.**   Asia. (EM)
18 ►*Camelus dromedarius.* **Arabian Camel.**   N. Africa and S.W. Asia. (A)

Suborder RUMINANTIA.   Ruminants.

Infraorder TRAGULINA.

Superfamily TRAGULOIDEA.

Family TRAGULIDAE.   Chevrotains.

19   *Hyemoschus aquaticus.* **Water Chevrotain.**   Cen. W. Africa. (A)
20   *Tragulus meminna.* **Indian Chevrotain.**   S. Asia. (EM)
21   *Tragulus napu.* **Larger Malay Chevrotain.**   S. Asia, Sumatra, Borneo. (EM)
22 ► *Tragulus javanicus.* **Lesser Malay Chevrotain.**   S. Asia, Sumatra, Borneo, Java. (EM)

362

Infraorder PECORA.
Superfamily CERVOIDEA.
Family CERVIDAE. Deer.
Subfamily MOSCHINAE. Musk Deer.

23 ►*Moschus moschiferus.*   **Musk Deer.** Asia. (EM)

Subfamily MUNTIACINAE. Muntjacs.

24 ►*Muntiacus muntjak.*	**Indian Muntjac.** S. Asia, Sumatra, Java, Borneo. (EM)
25 *Muntiacus rooseveltorum.*	**Roosevelt's Muntjac.** S. Asia. (EM)
26 *Muntiacus reevesi.*	**Reeves' Muntjac.** S. Asia. (EM)
27 *Muntiacus crinifrons.*	**Black Muntjac.** S.E. Asia. (EM)
28 *Muntiacus feae.*	**Fea's Muntjac.** S. Asia. (EM)
29 *Elaphodus cephalophus.*	**Tufted Deer.** S. Asia. (EM)

Subfamily CERVINAE. Eurasian Deer.

30 ►*Dama dama.*	**Fallow Deer.** S. Europe and S.W. Asia. (EM)
31 *Dama mesopotamica.*	**Persian Fallow Deer.** S.W. Asia. (EM)
32 *Axis axis.*	**Axis Deer.** S. Asia. (EM)
33 *Axis porcinus.*	**Hog Deer.** S. Asia. (EM)
34 *Axis kuhli.*	**Kuhl's Deer.** Bawean Islands (N. of Java). (CH/EM)
35 *Axis calamianensis.*	**Calamianes Deer.** Philippines (TAY/VB2/EM)
36 *Cervus unicolor.*	**Sambar.** S. Asia. (EM/VB1)
37 *Cervus equinus.*	**Malayan Sambar.** S. Asia, Borneo, Sumatra. (VB1)
38 *Cervus timorensis.*	**Timor Deer.** Timor, Celebes, Java, Borneo and near-by islands. (LH/VB1)
39 *Cervus nigricans.*	**Philippine Deer.** Philippines. (TAY/VB1)
40 *Cervus duvauceli.*	**Barasingha.** S. Asia. (EM)
41 *Cervus schomburgki.*	**Schomburgk's Deer.** S. Asia. (EM)
42 *Cervus eldi.*	**Eld's Deer.** S. Asia. (EM)
43 *Cervus nippon.*	**Sika Deer.** S. Asia, Japan, Formosa. (EM)
44 *Cervus albirostris.*	**Thorold's Deer.** Cen. Asia. (EM)
45 ►*Cervus elaphus.*	**Red Deer.** Europe and Asia. (EM)
46 *Cervus canadensis.*	**Wapiti.** N. America. (HK)
47 ►*Elaphurus davidianus.*	**Père David's Deer.** S.E. Asia. (EM)

Subfamily ODOCOILEINAE.
Tribe ODOCOILEINI. American Deer.

48 *Odocoileus hemionus.*	**Mule Deer.** W. of N. America. (HK)
49 *Odocoileus virginianus.*	**Whitetail Deer.** N. and S. America. (HK/C2)
50 *Mazama americana.*	**Red Brocket.** Cen. and S. America. (HK/C2)
51 *Mazama gouazoubira.*	**Brown Brocket.** Cen. and S. America. (HK/C2)
52 *Mazama rufina.*	S. America. (C2)
53 *Mazama chunyi.*	S. America. (C2)
54 *Hippocamelus antisensis.*	**Peruvian Guemal.** S. America. (C2)
55 *Hippocamelus bisulcus.*	**Chilean Guemal.** S. America. (C2)
56 *Blastocerus dichotomus.*	**Marsh Deer.** S. America. (C2)
57 *Ozotoceros bezoarticus.*	**Pampas Deer.** S. America. (C2)
58 *Pudu pudu.*	**Pudu.** S. America. (C2)
59 *Pudu mephistophiles.*	S. America. (C2)

Tribe ALCINI.

60 ►*Alces alces.*   **Moose.**   N. Europe, N. Asia, N. of N. America. (EM)

Tribe RANGIFERINI.

61 ►*Rangifer tarandus.*   **Reindeer.**   N. Europe, N. Asia, N. of N. America, Greenland. (EM)

Tribe HYDROPOTINI.

62 ►*Hydropotes inermis.*   **Chinese Water Deer.**   E. Asia. (EM)

Tribe CAPREOLINI.

63 ►*Capreolus capreolus.*   **Roe Deer.**   Europe and Asia. (EM)

Superfamily GIRAFFOIDEA.
Family GIRAFFIDAE.
Subfamily PALEOTRAGINAE.

64 ►*Okapia johnstoni.*   **Okapi.**   Cen. Africa. (A)

Subfamily GIRAFFINAE.

65 ►*Giraffa camelopardalis.*   **Giraffe.**   Africa. (EMH)

Superfamily BOVOIDEA.
Family ANTILOCAPRIDAE.
Subfamily ANTILOCAPRINAE.

66 ►*Antilocapra americana.*   **Pronghorn.**   N. America. (HK)

Family BOVIDAE.
Subfamily BOVINAE.
Tribe STREPSICEROTINI.   Spiral-horned Antelopes.

67	*Tragelaphus angasi.*	**Nyala.** S.E. Africa. (EMH)
68	*Tragelaphus buxtoni.*	**Mountain Nyala.** N.E. Africa. (A)
69	*Tragelaphus spekei.*	**Sitatunga.** Cen. Africa. (EMH)
70 ►	*Tragelaphus scriptus.*	**Bushbuck.** Africa. (EMH)
71	*Tragelaphus imberbis.*	**Lesser Kudu.** Cen. Africa. (A)
72 ►	*Tragelaphus strepsiceros.*	**Greater Kudu.** Africa. (EMH)
73 ►	*Taurotragus oryx.*	**Eland.** Africa. (EMH)
74	*Taurotragus derbianus.*	**Giant Eland.** Cen. Africa. (A)
75	*Taurotragus eurycerus.*	**Bongo.** Cen. Africa. (A/EMH)

Tribe BOSELAPHINI.

76 ►*Boselaphus tragocamelus.*   **Nilgai.**   S. Asia. (EM)
77   *Tetracerus quadricornis.*   **Four-horned Antelope.**   S. Asia. (EM)

364

Tribe BOVINI. Cattle.

78 ► *Bubalus bubalis.* — **Asiatic Buffalo** (and Domestic Buffalo). S. Asia and Borneo. (EM)

79   *Anoa mindorensis.* — **Tamarou.** Philippines. (TAY)
80 ► *Anoa depressicornis.* — **Anoa.** Celebes. (LH)
81   *Bos taurus.* — **Ox.** (Domestic)
82 ► *Bos gaurus.* — **Gaur.** S. Asia. (EM)
83   *Bos frontalis.* — **Gayal.** (Domestic)
84 ► *Bos banteng.* — **Banteng.** S. Asia, Java, Borneo. (EM)
85   *Bos indicus.* — **Zebu.** (Domestic)
86   *Bos sauveli.* — **Kouprey.** S. Asia. (EM)
87 ► *Bos grunniens.* — **Yak.** Cen. Asia. (EM)
88 ► *Syncerus caffer.* — **African Buffalo.** Africa. (EMH)
89 ► *Bison bonasus.* — **European Bison.** E. Europe. (EM)
90 ► *Bison bison.* — **American Bison.** N. America. (HK)

Subfamily CEPHALOPHINAE. Duikers.

91   *Cephalophus adersi.* — **Zanzibar Duiker.** Zanzibar. (A)
92   *Cephalophus callipygus.* — **Peter's Duiker.** Cen. W. Africa. (A)
93   *Cephalophus dorsalis.* — **Bay Duiker.** Cen. and W. Africa. (A)
94   *Cephalophus jentinki.* — **Jentink's Duiker.** Cen. W. Africa. (A)
95   *Cephalophus leucogaster.* — **Gaboon Duiker.** Cen. Africa. (A)
96   *Cephalophus natalensis.* — **Red Duiker.** Africa. (EMH)
97   *Cephalophus niger.* — **Black Duiker.** Cen. W. Africa. (A)
98   *Cephalophus nigrifrons.* — **Black-fronted Duiker.** Cen. Africa. (A)
99   *Cephalophus ogilbyi.* — **Ogilby's Duiker.** Cen. W. Africa. (A)
100   *Cephalophus rufilatus.* — **Red-flanked Duiker.** Cen. W. Africa. (A)
101   *Cephalophus silvicultor.* — **Yellow-backed Duiker.** Cen. Africa. (EMH)
102   *Cephalophus spadix.* — **Abbott's Duiker.** Cen. E. Africa. (A)
103   *Cephalophus zebra.* — **Zebra Antelope.** Cen. W. Africa. (A)
104   *Cephalophus monticola.* — **Blue Duiker.** Africa. (EMH)
105   *Cephalophus maxwelli.* — **Maxwell's Duiker.** Cen. W. Africa. (A)
106   *Cephalophus simpsoni.* — **Simpson's Duiker.** Cen. Africa. (A)
107 ► *Sylvicapra grimmia.* — **Grey Duiker.** Africa. (EMH)

Subfamily HIPPOTRAGINAE.
Tribe REDUNCINI.

108   *Kobus ellipsiprymnus.* — **Waterbuck.** Africa. (EMH)
109   *Kobus defassa.* — **Defassa Waterbuck.** Cen. Africa. (EMH)
110   *Kobus kob.* — **Buffon's Kob.** Africa. (A)
111   *Kobus vardoni.* — **Puku.** Africa. (EMH)
112   *Kobus leche.* — **Lechwe.** Africa. (EMH)
113   *Kobus megaceros.* — **Nile Lechwe.** Africa. (A)
114   *Redunca arundinum.* — **Reedbuck.** Africa. (EMH)
115   *Redunca fulvorufula.* — **Mountain Reedbuck.** Africa. (EMH)
116   *Redunca redunca.* — **Bohor Reedbuck.** Africa. (A)
117   *Pelea capreolus.* — **Vaal Rhebok.** S. Africa. (EMH)

365

Tribe HIPPOTRAGINI.

118	*Hippotragus equinus.*	**Roan Antelope.** Africa. (EMH)
119►	*Hippotragus niger.*	**Sable Antelope.** Africa. (EMH)
120►	*Oryx gazella.*	**Oryx** (includes Beisa and Gemsbok). S. and E. Africa. (EMH)
121	*Oryx leucoryx.*	**Arabian Oryx.** S.W. Asia. (EM)
122	*Oryx tao.*	**Scimitar-horned Oryx.** N. Africa. (EM)
123	*Addax nasomaculatus.*	**Addax.** N. Africa. (EM)

Tribe ALCELAPHINI.

124	*Damaliscus lunatus.*	**Sassaby.** Africa. (EMH)
125	*Damaliscus korrigum.*	**Topi.** Africa. (A)
126►	*Damaliscus dorcas.*	**Blesbok** (includes Bontebok). S. Africa. (EMH)
127	*Damaliscus hunteri.*	**Hunter's Hartebeest.** E. Africa. (EMH)
128►	*Alcelaphus buselaphus.*	**Hartebeest.** Africa. (EMH)
129	*Alcelaphus lichtensteini.*	**Lichtenstein's Hartebeest.** Africa. (EMH)
130	*Connochaetes gnou.*	**White-tailed Gnu.** S. Africa. (EMH)
131►	*Connochaetes taurinus.*	**Brindled Gnu.** Africa. (EMH)

Subfamily ANTILOPINAE.
Tribe NEOTRAGINI.

132	*Oreotragus oreotragus.*	**Klipspringer.** Africa. (EMH)
133►	*Ourebia ourebi.*	**Oribi.** Africa. (EMH)
134	*Ourebia haggardi.*	**Haggard's Oribi.** Africa. (A)
135	*Ourebia kenyae.*	**Kenya Oribi.** Africa. (A)
136	*Raphicerus melanotis.*	**Grysbok.** Africa. (EMH)
137	*Raphicerus campestris.*	**Steinbok.** Africa. (EMH)
138	*Raphicerus sharpei.*	**Sharpe's Grysbok.** Africa. (EMH)
139	*Nesotragus moschatus.*	**Suni.** E. Africa. (EMH)
140►	*Neotragus pygmaeus.*	**Royal Antelope.** W. Africa. (A)
141	*Neotragus batesi.*	**Bates' Dwarf Antelope.** Cen. Africa. (A)
142	*Madoqua cordeauxi.*	**Cordeaux' Dik-dik.** Africa. (A)
143	*Madoqua erlangeri.*	**Erlanger's Dik-dik.** Africa. (A)
144	*Madoqua phillipsi.*	**Phillips' Dik-dik.** Africa. (A)
145	*Madoqua saltiana.*	**Salt's Dik-dik.** Africa. (A)
146	*Madoqua swaynei.*	**Swayne's Dik-dik.** Africa. (A)
147	*Madoqua guentheri.*	**Guenther's Dik-dik.** Africa. (A/EMH)
148	*Madoqua kirki.*	**Damara Dik-dik.** Africa. (EMH)
149	*Dorcatragus megalotis.*	**Beira Antelope.** Africa. (A)

Tribe ANTILOPINI.

150►	*Antilope cervicapra.*	**Blackbuck.** S. Asia. (EM)
151►	*Aepyceros melampus.*	**Impala.** Africa. (EMH)
152	*Ammodorcas clarkei.*	**Dibatag.** Africa. (A)
153►	*Litocranius walleri.*	**Gerenuk.** Africa. (A)
154	*Gazella subgutturosa.*	**Persian Gazelle.** Asia. (EM)
155	*Gazella dorcas.*	**Dorcas Gazelle.** N. Africa and S.W. Asia. (EM)
156	*Gazella gazella.*	**Mountain Gazelle.** N. Africa and S. Asia. (EM)

157	*Gazella leptoceros.*	**Slender-horned Gazelle.** N. Africa and S.W. Asia. (EM)
158	*Gazella pelzelni.*	**Pelzeln's Gazelle.** Africa. (A)
159	*Gazella rufifrons.*	**Korin Gazelle.** Africa. (EM)
160	*Gazella spekei.*	**Speke's Gazelle.** Africa. (A)
161 ►	*Gazella thomsoni.*	**Thomson's Gazelle.** Africa. (A)
162	*Gazella tilonura.*	**Heuglin's Gazelle.** Africa. (A)
163	*Gazella dama.*	**Dama Gazelle.** Africa. (EM)
164	*Gazella granti.*	**Grant's Gazelle.** Africa. (A)
165	*Gazella soemmerringi.*	**Soemmering's Gazelle.** Africa. (A)
166 ►	*Antidorcas marsupialis.*	**Springbok.** Africa. (EMH)
167	*Procapra picticaudata.*	**Tibetan Gazelle.** Asia. (EM)
168	*Procapra gutturosa.*	**Mongolian Gazelle.** Asia. (EM)

Subfamily CAPRINAE.
Tribe SAIGINI.

| 169 | *Pantholops hodgsoni.* | **Tibetan Antelope.** Asia. (EM) |
| 170 ► | *Saiga tatarica.* | **Saiga Antelope.** Asia. (EM) |

Tribe RUPICAPRINI.

171 ►	*Naemorhedus goral.*	**Goral.** Asia. (EM)
172 ►	*Capricornis sumatraensis.*	**Serow.** Asia and Sumatra. (EM)
173	*Capricornis crispus.*	**Japanese Serow.** Asia. (EM)
174 ►	*Oreamnos americanus.*	**Rocky Mountain Goat.** N. America. (HK)
175 ►	*Rupicapra rupicapra.*	**Chamois.** Europe and E. Asia. (EM)

Tribe OVIBOVINI.

| 176 ► | *Budorcas taxicolor.* | **Takin.** Asia. (EM) |
| 177 ► | *Ovibos moschatus.* | **Musk Ox.** N. America. (HK) |

Tribe CAPRINI.

178 ►	*Hemitragus jemlahicus.*	**Himalayan Tahr.** Asia. (EM)
179	*Hemitragus jayakari.*	**Arabian Tahr.** Arabia. (EM)
180	*Hemitragus hylocrius.*	**Nilgiri Tahr.** S. Asia. (EM)
181	*Capra hircus.*	**Goat.** S. Asia. (EM)
182 ►	*Capra ibex.*	**Ibex.** Europe, Asia and N. Africa. (EM)
183	*Capra caucasica.*	**Caucasian Tur.** Asia. (EM)
184	*Capra pyrenaica.*	**Spanish Ibex.** S.W. Europe. (EM)
185 ►	*Capra falconeri.*	**Markhor.** Asia. (EM)
186	*Pseudois nayaur.*	**Bharal.** Asia. (EM)
187 ►	*Ammotragus lervia.*	**Aoudad.** N. Africa. (EM)
188	*Ovis aries.*	**Sheep.** (Domestic)
189	*Ovis musimon.*	**Mouflon.** Sardinia and Corsica. (EM)
190	*Ovis laristanica.*	**Laristan Sheep.** S.E. Asia. (EM)
191	*Ovis orientalis.*	**Red Sheep.** Asia. (EM)
192 ►	*Ovis ammon.*	**Argali.** Asia. (EM)
193 ►	*Ovis canadensis.*	**Bighorn Sheep.** N. Asia and N. America. (EM)
194	*Ovis dalli.*	**White Sheep.** N. America. (HK)

367

S I   Family SUIDAE

BUSHPIG

Potamochoerus porcus

(Forests of Tropical Africa and Madagascar)

The Bushpig is found throughout tropical Africa in all the most densely forested areas. Somewhat larger and heavier than the warthog, this pig often exceeds 200 lb. in weight and measures more than 30 inches in height. It varies a great deal in colour, but most individuals are a dark brown or black, with paler markings on the head. The tusks are far shorter than those of the Warthog, seldom measuring more than 6 inches.

Bushpigs are very retiring and largely nocturnal. During the day they lie up in tall grass or dense reed beds. They feed throughout the night in droves of anything up to twenty individuals. The main food consists of roots, berries and wild fruit, but they sometimes take snakes, insects and eggs. They feed by an extensive rooting process which often causes considerable damage. The species is seldom found far from water and is an excellent swimmer. The boar is reputed to be a very fierce antagonist and although Bushpigs are sometimes killed by Lions, the Leopard is seldom capable of tackling an adult pig.

Burrows are used only by the farrowing sow, which usually has a litter of five to six young in December or January. The young Bushpigs are born with a very marked brown and yellow striping. Their life expectancy is estimated at about 10 to 15 years.

A distinctive West African race known as the Red River Hog is strikingly marked with a white crest, black and white face markings, a rust-red body and long ear-tassels. Another race (sometimes referred to in earlier works as a separate species, *P. larvatus*) is found on Madagascar, being the only ungulate occurring naturally on that island.

368

WILD BOAR

Sus scrofa

(Woodlands of Europe, North Africa, Asia, Sumatra and Java)

The Wild Boar, once so plentiful in Europe, is now restricted to a few areas of woodland. The subject of a great deal of mythology and folk-lore, it has been intensively hunted for centuries on horseback and on foot, by hounds and by lance. Its range extends far beyond Europe, however, and there are still large populations left in various parts of Asia.

An adult male may be as much as 3 feet high and 5 feet in length and, if harassed, can be a dangerous adversary, inflicting severe damage with its 9-inch tusks that have been sharpened on the forest trees. Little is known of the behaviour of this wild pig. It usually keeps to the thickest undergrowth and travels in small parties called "sounders". An omnivorous creature, it eats most small animal and plant life that comes its way. It is known to be particularly fond of partially digested grass from the stomachs of ruminants.

The Wild Boar is an excellent swimmer and will not hesitate to cross a river or lake if pursued. It has large families, and there may be as many as twelve striped piglets in a litter. The gestation period is about 115 days. The piglets are very soon able to follow the sow.

Apart from man, the Wild Boar falls prey to Wolves and feral dogs, but the most serious losses to this species in recent years have been due to attacks of rinderpest to which they are particularly prone.

There are North African races of Wild Boar still to be found in Morocco, Algeria, and the Sudan, and island races on Ceylon, Sumatra, Java, Japan and Formosa.

369

S 6

WARTHOG

Phacochoerus aethiopicus

(Tropical Africa)

This warty-faced, heavily tusked animal is still fairly common over most of the open woodland of South and East Africa. The barrel-shaped body is supported on short legs and tipped by a long thin tail equipped with a terminal tuft of hair. This spindly tail is held stiffly erect like a flag while running. The body covering consists only of a thin, straggly coat with a mane or crest of long, coarse hair running from the top of the head back to the rump, and a fringe of white whiskers in the angle of the mouth. The face of the male is adorned with large wart-like protruberances, but that of the female is relatively clear. The curled upper tusks average 12 inches or more in length, with the record standing at 27 inches. The weight of an adult animal 30 inches high is about 200 lb.

The Warthog is largely diurnal, occuring in small family parties in sandy bush and close to a source of water. The old, darker coloured boars are usually solitary. Some authorities believe that this species is entirely herbivorous, rooting for bulbs and grazing on young grass, but others claim that it may also take carrion occasionally. Warthogs sometimes live in discarded Aardvark or porcupine burrows that they enlarge to some extent, and into which they retreat backwards in times of danger. The chief enemy of the species is the Leopard, although jackals may take an occasional young one.

The mating season is in May and June and after a gestation period of 4 to 5 months, three or four young are born in each litter. The sow has only four mammae.

370

Family SUIDAE

GIANT FOREST HOG

Hylochoerus meinertzhageni

(Forests of Central Africa)

The largest living pig is the Giant Forest Hog of Kenya and the Congo. The boar stands up to 3 feet high and may weigh over 300 lb. The overall length may exceed 5 feet. It was discovered in the Nandi Forest region of Kenya by Colonel Meinertzhagen as recently as 1904.

Giant Forest Hogs are a uniform brownish-black colour. They are sparsely haired except for a tuft at the base of each of the widespread ears, a tuft at the tip of the tail and a stiff crest. The boar has a saucer-like hollow on the forehead and a pair of extremely large, naked, facial processes in front of the eyes. The upper tusks may measure 9 inches and those in the lower jaw only slightly less. Both sets of tusks are kept sharp by grinding against each other. The muzzle has a very large terminal disc.

The Giant Forest Hog is a resident of the moist rain-forests, and was originally discovered at an elevation of 7,000 feet above sea-level. It associates in small herds which feed on low bushes, but are often almost predatory in habit. Like most pigs, it is omnivorous and has been known to hunt small mammals and birds. The herds feed in the early part of the morning and in the late afternoon and evening, and may be seen lying in the open glades in the sun after rain.

The nearest relative of the Giant Forest Hog is the Warthog (*Phacochoerus aethiopicus*). Both these pigs are preyed upon by the Leopard.

371

BABIRUSA

Babyrousa babyrussa

(Celebes)

The strangest member of the pig family is the almost hairless, wrinkle-skinned Babirusa. Its native name means "pig-deer" and was given to the animal because of its huge curved tusks that are reminiscent of antlers. These tusks (that can reach a length of 17 inches) represent an extraordinary development of a trend that can be seen in the Wild Boar and the Warthog, where the upper canines curve outwards and upward. In the male Babirusa this upward thrusting of "downward" teeth reaches a peak. Here the actual tooth sockets point upward so that the canines start out growing directly upward and penetrate the skin of the upper jaw. As they continue to grow they curve backwards more and more. The large lower canines grow upward outside them and also curve backwards, so that the face is virtually masked by a shield of enormous teeth. The female Babirusa lacks this weird development. It has been argued that if the tusks of the male act as a protection against rough undergrowth, then the female should also be similarly equipped. It seems likely, therefore, that they have some other function, although at present this is unknown.

The rather small piglets are unique in that they are unstriped. They are born in February and there are only one or two in a litter, the female having only two nipples.

The Babirusa herds prefer the damp regions of the forest, especially the banks of lakes and rivers, where they feed on the water plants. They are extremely good swimmers and, indeed, in some respects are rather like hippos in the making.

COLLARED PECCARY

Tayassu tajacu

(South and Central America)

The peccaries are the New World equivalents of the Old World swine. Although superficially very similar, they differ in a number of important details and are placed in a separate family. The upper tusks, for example, curve downward instead of upward, the hind limbs have three toes instead of four, and the stomach is more complex.

Peccaries have thirty-eight teeth and two pairs of tusks, the upper being short, with sharp cutting edges. The lower tusks curve upward to be received into notches in the sides of the upper jaw just in front of the upper tusks. There is a large scent gland in the middle of the back. When the animals become agitated the hair on the back is erected, exposing this gland. The ears are small and pointed and the body is covered with thick bristle-like hairs elongated into a slight mane on the neck.

The Collared Peccary ranges from the southern borders of the United States to Argentina, and acquires its name from the broad, yellowish stripe running from the hind part of the shoulders obliquely to the chest. It stands about 20 inches high at the shoulder. An omnivorous species, it feeds principally in the morning, moving about in small family groups.

The White-lipped Peccary (*Tayassu albirostris*) is also gregarious, but lives in larger herds, deeper in the forests. Its shoulder height is about 24 inches. This species consumes a variety of fruit and roots, but also eats carrion, worms and insects, and is reputed to hunt larger prey occasionally. It is found from Paraguay to Mexico. Its old name of *Tayassu pecari* is no longer acceptable.

373

HIPPOPOTAMUS

Hippopotamus amphibius

(Rivers of Tropical Africa)

Formerly far more widespread, the Hippopotamus is today confined to suitable rivers and estuaries in tropical Africa. An adult bull stands about 5 feet high at the shoulder and weighs up to 4 tons. The cow usually measures 4 feet high and weighs about 3 tons. The tusks, like those of rodents, show perpetual growth. A malformed tusk may be 6 feet long, but the usual length is 20 to 30 inches. The tail, the insides of the ears, and the muzzle, are the only parts of the body which show an appreciable growth of hair.

Hippos normally live in groups of about fifteen animals, but the herds may become much larger. They spend the day basking in the sun, or in the deep pools of the rivers, rising to the surface to breathe at intervals of about 5 minutes. At night they go ashore to feed, making their way to the grass patches along well-worn territorial paths. The herds will usually move only a short distance from the water, but even so, they may cover as much as 20 miles in a single night. Like the rhinoceros, the Hippo deposits its droppings in chosen spots, spreading the faeces by waggling its specially flattened tail rapidly during the act of dunging.

When disturbed, on land or in water, Hippos can be very dangerous and aggressive opponents, but they are normally rather placid. Although crocodiles may be able to attack a young animal, they have very few natural enemies. The bulls fight fiercely among themselves during the mating season. A single calf is born after a gestation period of about 240 days. It is usually suckled in the water.

374

Family HIPPOPOTAMIDAE

PYGMY HIPPOPOTAMUS

Choeropsis liberiensis

(West Africa)

Owing to its smaller head, much shorter body and relatively longer legs, the Pygmy Hippopotamus differs from its larger relative in shape as well as size. It stands about 2 feet 6 inches high at the shoulder and weighs about 400 lb., with a body length of 6 feet.

The eyes and nostrils are not raised above the plane of the head to the great extent characteristic of the common Hippopotamus. The nostrils are widely separated, oblique, valvular slits. The small external ears are furnished with three soft ridge-like thickenings which, when the ear is folded, are pressed together to block the orifice. The muzzle and 7-inch tail have short scattered bristles. The feet of both this and the larger species are of the most primitive type found in the artiodactyls, although the Pygmy Hippopotamus' are less compact. They are nearly symmetrical, the tips of the four toes all resting on the ground. There is only a single pair of lower incisors in this species, as opposed to two in the larger Hippopotamus.

The Pygmy Hippopotamus is a comparatively solitary animal and does not live in the large herds typical of the common Hippopotamus. It is less aquatic, and spends much of the night wandering in the dense forests of the coastal regions of Guinea, Liberia and Sierre Leone. During the day it lies up in the thick vegetation on the river banks. It is more pig-like in its habits than the other Hippopotamus, and, like the pig, suckles its young while lying down. Despite its smaller size, its gestation period is similar to that of the large species.

LLAMA

Lama glama

(South America)

The Llama is the best known of four camel-like animals indigenous to South America. Alpacas (*L. pacos*) and Llamas have been domesticated since the time of the great Inca civilization in Peru. Llamas were the Inca's beast of burden, a beast they valued enough to mummify in many cases.

Today there are no Llamas in the wild, but the Peruvian mountain Indian, living on the "altiplano" above 7,500 feet, still owns large herds of these creatures. They are the Indian's most important all-purpose animal. He makes rugs and rope from the fur, sandals from the hide, food from the flesh, candles from the tallow and even fuel from the droppings.

But the Llama's main use today is still as a pack animal, particularly in the ore-producing centres. Pack trains of Llamas travel 15 or 20 miles a day over mountain country that could support no other beast of burden. They need gentle treatment, eating and resting regularly, and will respond readily to a soft whistle, but spit and kick when annoyed and refuse to move with loads exceeding 100 lb. Only males over $3\frac{1}{2}$ years are used as pack animals. Females are kept on pasturage and used for wool and breeding. Neither sex is ever used as a saddle animal.

It is often claimed that the Llama is nothing more than a domesticated Guanaco (*L. guanicoe*), but recently this view has been rejected. It is now considered that many years ago, even before the Spanish invasion of the Americas, the wild Llama had become extinct. There are striking behaviour differences between the Llama and the Guanaco, of a type that do not normally accompany domestication.

376

Family CAMELIDAE

GUANACO

Lama guanicoe

(South America)

The Guanaco is the tallest South American mammal surviving in the wild today, standing 43 inches high and weighing 200 lb. The overall colour is pale brown with a darker face and white underparts. It is found from sea-level to 13,000 feet all along the west coast of South America, being most common in semi-desert and high altitude plains, but avoiding rocky country and never entering forests. Small herds of four to ten females are led by a single male. Young males unite into herds of twelve to fifty individuals. While females are grazing, the male stands at a vantage point and will attack an intruder, inflicting serious wounds with his teeth. During mating the male courts the female by circling, neck-pressing, snapping and grunting. He never goes far from the herd in case another male tries to steal one of his harem. During mating, the female lies on the ground.

Guanacos have a 30-year life span, but may fall prey to the Puma (*Felis concolor*), or at high altitudes the young may be taken by the Giant Condor. The herds were extensively hunted by the colonizing Spaniards, although the coarse hair has no commercial value.

The Guanaco has often been thought of as the wild ancestor of the Llama (*L. glama*) and the Alpaca (*L. pacos*), but recent evidence contradicts this. There are striking behaviour differences between the three species. The manner in which they deposit their droppings differs in the three cases. Their reactions to water also differ, as does their courtship behaviour. Also, male Guanacos differ from male Llamas in that they retain their dominance at all times of the year.

377

ALPACA

Lama pacos

(South America)

Despite its bulky appearance, the shaggy-haired Alpaca is smaller and weighs considerably less than the Llama. The usual colour is brown or black, but white and various other colours also exist. The Alpaca no longer survives in the wild. It has been domesticated since the third or fourth century B.C., but probably reached the height of its popularity during the eleventh to thirteenth centuries. The Incas considered it to be a gift of the gods and carefully segregated the herds into pure breeding types. White wool has always been the most valued. Even today, the Alpaca still provides the bulk of the wool for clothing the Indian peoples. Peru, with 2 million animals, is the chief wool producer. The wool is light and warm and very useful for rugged outdoor clothing. It easily sheds rain and snow, as the Alpaca lives most comfortably at altitudes exceeding 12,000 feet. The flocks are sheared every 2 years, each animal being shorn only three or four times in its life and yielding about 6 lb. of wool each time.

Alpacas have been successfully crossed with Vicunas to give an animal called a Paco-vicuna, which yields a lighter wool. Hybrids have also been produced between Alpacas and Llamas.

In the past the Alpaca has been thought of as merely a long-haired domesticated version of either the Vicuna or the Guanaco. It is now believed to have originated from a distinct species that became extinct even earlier than the wild Llama. As with most domestic animals, it is difficult to be certain of its exact origins.

378

VICUNA

Vicugna vicugna

(South America)

The Vicuna is the smallest representative of the South American camel-like group of animals. It still survives as a wild animal and resembles the Guanaco, but is smaller, more slender, and has a relatively longer neck. It stands only 30 inches high, weighs little more than 100 lb. and is golden fawn in colour with a white patch on its lower throat.

Vicunas are found in the Andes, on the high plateaux from 14,000 to 18,000 feet in Peru, Bolivia, Argentina and Chile. They thrive at these heights, near to the snow line, feeding on grasses and succulent broad-leafed herbs, and usually drinking only every 2 days. They are strictly territorial, living in small herds of eight to twelve, led by a single male. Young males are expelled from the breeding herd by their mothers when 8 to 10 months old and live together in groups often 100 strong. The average territory of a herd is about 32 acres and its boundaries are aggressively defended by the dominant male, which stands stiffly erect and attacks intruders by biting, or by spitting regurgitated food. Weaker males also spit, but never directly at the opponent.

The Colpeo Fox (*Dusicyon culpaeus*) and the Pampas Cat (*Felis colocolo*) are said to be the main enemies of the Vicuna. The single offspring, known as a "vicunita", is born after a gestation period of 10 months.

The wool of this species is probably the finest and lightest in the world. During Inca times, only royalty were permitted to wear Vicuna robes. The species has never been successfully domesticated. The Indians still obtain the wool today by driving the herds into corrals, shearing them, and then releasing them.

379

BACTRIAN CAMEL
Camelus bactrianus
(Cold deserts of Central Asia)

The two humps, distinctive of this species, are used as fat storage organs and are valuable to the animal when food is scarce. The Bactrian Camel feeds on the dry prickly scrub of the cold deserts, and although its divided upper lip is very sensitive, it does not appear to be injured by the thorns. The differences between the Arabian and Bactrian Camels are mainly adaptations produced by the surfaces on which they walk and climates in which they live. As the Bactrian Camel inhabits rocky deserts and snowy wastes, its feet are harder and more calloused, and the thick brown winter coat, which it loses in patches in the summer, enables it to work and live in extremely low temperatures. This camel can thrive even on the brackish water of the salt steppes.

During the pairing season in the autumn it can become dangerous. In some countries camel-fighting has been developed as a sport, with selected animals pitted against one another in a large, open space. Apart from biting and spitting, they also attempt to flatten and kneel on one another.

Domesticated at least by the year 857 B.C., the Bactrian Camel is principally a beast of burden, but it also provides hair for clothing, hides for leather, milk and flesh for food, and droppings for fuel. It travels in great caravans across the deserts, moving more slowly than the Arabian Camel.

There are very few truly wild Bactrian Camels left alive today. They were thought to be completely extinct, but in 1957 an expedition sighted a herd on the Mongolian side of the Altai Mountains. They had smaller humps, smaller feet, shorter hair and a more slender build than the typical domestic form.

Family CAMELIDAE

ARABIAN CAMEL
Camelus dromedarius
(Hot deserts of North Africa and South-west Asia)

The Arabian Camel is easily distinguishable from the Bactrian Camel by its possession of one hump instead of two. It also has longer, thinner legs and a more slender build. It is completely unknown in the wild state, but has been introduced in domestic form into the hot deserts of southern Africa, Australia and southern Asia. As a wild animal, it originally inhabited Arabia and the borders of the Sahara. There is evidence that it had been domesticated in Arabia by 1800 B.C.

This camel has become perfectly adapted to living under desert conditions. It is able to survive for considerable periods without water. It will, however, swallow as much as 15 gallons at a time when it is available. Other adaptations which are invaluable for its desert existence are the nostrils, which can close completely, and a double row of interlocking eyelashes that protect the eyes against sand and sun. The flat, broad feet prevent sinking into the soft sand, but the camel cannot jump and finds hilly country difficult. There are callosities on the chest and legs which take the weight of the body when the animal is resting. The Egyptian camels often carry loads of up to 1,000 lb.

Gestation lasts nearly 12 months, and a single offspring is the rule. The life-span is 30 to 40 years. A female breeds every second year and may produce ten to twelve calves in her lifetime.

The Dromedary is a special kind of Arabian Camel developed for racing and riding, with longer legs and a lighter body. Arabian and Bactrian Camels are capable of interbreeding, the best combinations being a Bactrian male and an Arabian female. This results in a one-humped offspring that is said to be heavier and more vigorous.

381

LESSER MALAY CHEVROTAIN
Tragulus javanicus
(Southern Asia, Sumatra, Borneo and Java)

The Lesser Malay Chevrotain, or Mouse Deer, is one of the smallest of all living hoofed animals, standing only one foot high. It is a timid forest-dweller, feeding on fruits, flowers, young leaves and green vegetables.

Superficially it resembles the agoutis of South America. It has the same shape and size and a similar way of life. It is interesting that both have also developed the same foot-stamping communication signals.

The male Chevrotain is remarkable for its extremely long upper canines (see photograph) that protrude below the lips. Neither sex, however, possesses either horns or antlers. Amongst the true deer there are only two species that exhibit this (fangs present, antlers absent) condition. They are the Musk Deer and the Chinese Water Deer.

The litter of one or two young is produced after a gestation period of 120 days.

There are four species in this isolated family: the Water Chevrotain of Africa, the spotted Indian Chevrotain from South Asia and, from farther East, the Larger and Lesser Malay species. The latter two lack the spots and dashes on their coats, the fur being a dark, rich brown, pale underneath and with a white throat and chest stripe and a white underside to the short tail.

The Larger Malay Chevrotain was once thought to come from Java and was then called *Tragulus javanicus*. It is now known that the only form on that island is in fact the Lesser Malay Chevrotain. The name *javanicus* has therefore been switched from the one species to the other. This can be particularly confusing when consulting older books on the subject.

382

MUSK DEER

Moschus moschiferus

(Mountains of Central Asia)

Musk Deer are diminutive, stockily built deer with small heads, big feet, and very coarse hair. The hind legs are longer than the fore legs, an adult Musk Deer measuring about 20 inches high at the shoulder and 22 inches at the rump. The tail is very short and the general colour of the fur is a rich reddish-brown. The rather pointed face and the large ears give it a head that is strikingly reminiscent of the kangaroo. Neither sex possesses antlers, but the male has long upper canine teeth which project well below the lips. The male also bears a musk-secreting gland, known as the pod, in the skin of the abdomen. No face gland is present in either males or females.

These small deer are usually found at high altitudes in Siberia, Mongolia, Manchuria, Korea, Tibet and from western China across to the Himalayas. They prefer wet, mountainous, forest regions and often occur above 8,000 feet in the summer. The hooves are well adapted to these conditions and are particularly efficient when the animal is fleeing rapidly over rough ground.

Musk Deer are chiefly nocturnal and solitary, though they may be found in pairs. They feed on leaves, flowers, grasses and lichens, and dart off in enormous bounds when disturbed. Their alarm call is a loud hiss. They have been greatly persecuted on account of the musk, which is used as a fixative in perfumes, and have been exterminated in many parts of their range.

Pairing occurs in January and the single white-spotted offspring is usually born in June. Musk Deer are mature at the age of 1 year.

INDIAN MUNTJAC

Muntiacus muntjak

(Southern Asia, Sumatra, Java and Borneo)

The Indian Muntjac, or Barking Deer, stands only 20 to 22 inches at the shoulder and weighs less than 50 lb. The antlers are short and simple, consisting of a short brow tine and an unbranched beam. They average about 5 inches long and are set on hairy pedicels which extend down each side of the face as ridges. This gives rise to the alternative name of Rib-faced Deer. The canine teeth are long and sharp and protrude slightly below the lips. There are several races in India, Burma, Malaya, Sumatra, Borneo and Java, but all of them are basically a chestnut colour with a white underside.

Muntjacs are usually found singly or in pairs in the thick undergrowth, but they may come out to feed on shrubs and grasses in the open clearings on the outskirts of the forests. The call of these small ungulates sounds very much like the barking of a dog and is usually heard in the early morning or late evening. When alarmed, they may utter a series of short, rapid barks which sound almost like the rattle of castanets.

The antlers are shed in May or June and the rut takes place mainly in the colder weather. One or two young are born in the rainy season. These are spotted with white markings until they are about 6 months old.

The Indian species and Reeves' Muntjac (*M. reevesi*) are very similar, but the latter, from China, is smaller (16 to 19 inches at the shoulder) and has a duller coat speckled with yellowish-grey. The rare Fea's Muntjac (*M. feae*) of Burma and Black Muntjac (*M. crinifrons*) of China are more darkly coloured.

384

FALLOW DEER

Dama dama

(Forests of Mediterranean Region)

The Fallow Deer, today very common in the parks and forests of Europe, originated in the Mediterranean countries. It is a medium-sized deer, standing about 3 feet high at the shoulder. The characteristic antlers of the common species are broadly flattened, or palmated, and are usually about 24 inches long. Those of the rare Persian species (*Dama mesopotamica*), although also ornamented with small tines, always lack this terminal flattening. The overall colour of the summer coat is a bright fawn with large white spots on the back and sides. In winter, Fallow Deer are uniformly grey. These colours of the wild animals have been considerably changed in many cases during domestication, and there are now herds of white, black, silver-grey and "blue" varieties in various park collections.

Fallow Deer are thoroughly gregarious, but during the summer the large herds consist almost entirely of females and immature males, the bucks remaining apart. Although predominantly grazers, Fallow Deer also eat the leaves of most deciduous trees, sometimes standing on their hind legs to do so. In winter they graze throughout the day, but feeding in summer is interrupted by two long rest periods.

Mating takes place during September and October, the buck's antlers becoming free from velvet in late August. The "adam's apple" of the male is extremely prominent and the rutting cry is a deep-toned grunt. Bucks lose their antlers at the end of April and one or occasionally two young are born in June or July. The fawns are only slightly spotted. Antlers first appear in the young males in their second year, at which stage the animals are known as "prickets".

385

S 45

Family CERVIDAE

RED DEER

Cervus elaphus

(Woodlands of Europe and Asia)

One of the best-known of all cervids, the Red Deer was once widely distributed throughout the woodlands and forests of Europe and Asia. The adult stag stands more than 4 feet high at the shoulder and may have antlers another 4 feet in length. The typical, or "Swedish" form has five tines on each antler. If a stag has twelve tines in all it is known as a "Royal", and if there are fourteen it is known as a "Wilson". The hinds are generally slightly smaller and, as in most species of deer, do not carry antlers. The summer coat is reddish-brown in both sexes and changes to a grey-brown in winter. The short tail is surrounded by a conspicuous, light-coloured patch. Stags mature at 6 years and hinds at 3.

During spring and summer the stags live alone, but in autumn when their antlers are free of velvet and the neck and shoulders bear a long fringe, they join the herd and form their harems. The gestation lasts about 250 days and a single calf is born, usually in May or June. The calf is able to run with the mother within a few hours.

Red Deer are very closely related to the Wapiti (*Cervus canadensis*) of North America, which derives its name from the Shawnee Indian. It is a massive animal, standing more than 12 inches higher than the Red Deer. Wapiti prefer mountainous districts and are gregarious at all times of the year. The mating call of the male is much more high pitched than the roar of the Red Deer.

386

PÈRE DAVID'S DEER

Elaphurus davidianus

(South-east Asia)

Père David's Deer, or Milou, now extinct in the wild, was discovered in 1865 by the French missionary Father Armand David in the Chinese Emperor's hunting park to the south of Peking. He sent specimens to Europe the following year, and a breeding herd was later set up by the Duke of Bedford at Woburn Abbey. The entire Chinese herd was destroyed during the revolution in 1900, but the Woburn herd has been so successful that there are today more than 300 of these deer in zoos and parks.

Père David's Deer is a large, long-tailed animal, standing 45 inches high at the shoulder. The general colour of the upper parts is a reddish grey, but the underside and a ring around the eye is white. The antlers of this deer are peculiar in that the front prong is forked and the hind prong is usually straight and slender. Another peculiarity is that two sets of antlers are sometimes grown in a single year. The first pair measure about 30 inches in length, while the second pair are much smaller. The hooves are very broad.

Nothing is known of the original habitat of Père David's Deer. The broad feet seem to indicate that the environment was probably marshy. In captivity these deer are very fond of water and swim well. During summer their food consists chiefly of water plants. Mating takes place in June and July, and the summer antlers are dropped in November. The winter antlers, when they occur, are hard by January and are dropped a few weeks later.

387

MOOSE

Alces alces

(North America and Northern Eurasia)

The American Moose, or Elk as it is known in Europe, is the biggest of all living deer. A mature male stands 6 feet high and may weigh over 1,200 lb. The American race, a young female of which is illustrated below, is slightly larger than the Eurasian form. The legs of the Moose are very long and the nose is extended and fleshy. Antlers are worn by the male only and are palmate, spoon-shaped, with a very short beam, and reach a maximum width of over 6 feet. The general coat colour is a greyish-brown.

The Moose, as is evident from its long legs and short neck, is poorly equipped as a grazer. It feeds either by browsing from trees and bushes, or, in the summer, by entering the water of lakes and rivers to obtain aquatic plants, especially water-lilies. The species is not strongly gregarious, living in small groups during the summer, but sometimes forming larger herds during the winter. These winter groups congregate in

"yards", special areas in which they have trampled down all the snow.

Moose are polygamous, the bull calling up any number of cows by a loud bellow. This sound is sometimes answered by an Indian hunter, who imitates the call of a cow with a birch-bark trumpet. Mating takes place in September and October when the bull Moose's antlers have been cleared of velvet and he has become very aggressive. The calves are born in the spring after 260 days' gestation.

An adult Moose will protect itself against predators by using both antlers and hooves, but in the deep snow of winter, Wolves and Pumas are likely to have the advantage.

388

Family CERVIDAE   S 61

REINDEER

Rangifer tarandus

(Arctic regions)

The Reindeer is the only species of deer in which both the male and the female are antlered. The two heavy main branches lead back from the forehead and then sweep upward and forward. The male stands about 4 feet at the shoulder and weighs approximately 250 lb.

Reindeer are the most northerly species of deer, feeding on grasses in the summer and lichens in winter. Their 1-inch long fur, with its dense, woolly undercoat covers even the nose and ears. During the cold season the coat fades from cinnamon brown to a dull white. The broad, round hooves are well adapted to snow conditions. In winter the frog becomes absorbed so that the hoof becomes concave. The sharp outer edges are then exposed and can grip the icy ground more efficiently.

This is the most migratory of all deer, huge herds of as many as 200,000 animals trekking for hundreds of miles between their summer and winter quarters. The rutting season occurs during the autumn migrations, and the antlers are shed in November. The remarkably precocious fawns are born during the spring migrations.

The sense of smell is very important to the Reindeer, as its sight and hearing are not keen. Alarm signals are given by holding the tail vertically and revealing the white rump patch more fully. It is a strong swimmer, noted more for endurance than speed, and can travel long distances in the water. Wolves are its chief natural enemy.

The Reindeer has been known to man since Palaeolithic times. The Lapps have domesticated it for centuries, principally for use as a draught animal. In America it is known as the caribou.

389

CHINESE WATER DEER

Hydropotes inermis

(Marshes of North-east China)

The Chinese Water Deer is a very small species confined to the marshes associated with the large rivers in north-eastern China. It is particularly common in the reed beds and low brush country along the shores and islands of the Yangtze River. This deer stands only 20 inches high at the shoulder and neither the male nor the female bears antlers. The upper canine teeth in the male have become enlarged to form long, curved and slightly convergent tusks which can just be seen in the photograph below. The coarse hairs of the coat are a yellowish-brown colour, slightly lighter on the centre of the back. The underparts are white. The tail is very short and, like those of other deer which live in swampy country, the hooves of this species are comparatively broad.

Chinese Water Deer live entirely on water plants which abound in the marshes. They feed during the greater part of the day, spending the night at rest in tufts of long grass or reeds. When disturbed they run only short distances, relying on their ability

to conceal themselves rather than on their speed. These deer are not gregarious. They are usually found singly or in pairs.

An unusual feature of the reproduction of the Chinese Water Deer is that three or more young may be born at a time. These are indistinctly spotted with white. The fawns do not follow the mother, but lie concealed, each in its own separate hiding-place, and are visited and suckled in turn by the mother.

Although it superficially resembles the Musk Deer (*Moschus moschiferus*) in appearance, the Chinese Water Deer is more closely related to the Roe Deer (*Capreolus*).

390

Family CERVIDAE

ROE DEER

Capreolus capreolus

(Temperate forests of Eurasia)

In spite of extensive hunting, the Roe Deer is still widely distributed throughout the woodlands of Eurasia. The presence of this species can often be detected by the circular, oval, or figure-of-eight tracks called "roe rings" which are made round certain bushes. These are formed during courtship pursuits, when the male chases the female repeatedly over the same route.

The roe is among the smaller of the deer, standing only $2\frac{1}{2}$ feet high at the shoulder. It seldom exceeds 50 lb. in weight and 4 feet in length. The three-tined antlers are knobbly at the base and only about 9 inches long. The winter coat, which is dark greyish-brown with a large white patch on the rump, is replaced in summer by a shorter-haired coat of reddish-brown with a white underside.

The Roe Deer is a forest-dweller and is mostly active at night, spending the day lying up in thick cover. Leaves, shoots and various fruits form its principal diet.

The rutting season is in July, when fierce fighting takes place between the bucks. There are usually twin fawns in the litter. They are born after a period of approximately 9 months, 4 months of which is a period of delayed implantation of the embryos and 5 months of which is the actual gestation. They have a life expectancy of 8 to 10 years. Unlike most deer, the Roe is seldom gregarious, living instead in pairs or in small family parties of only a few individuals. The natural enemies of this species are the Wolf and Lynx.

OKAPI

Okapia johnstoni

(Forests of the Congo)

"It has been one of the surprises of the twentieth century that a mammal so large and so eccentrically coloured could have remained unknown to science down to 1901." This remark was made by Sir Harry Johnston, Governor of Uganda, the man who first obtained material evidence (two skulls and a skin) that established beyond doubt that the Okapi really did exist. Although it is as big as a horse, its cryptic colouring, its gentle and retiring behaviour and the inaccessibility of its tropical forest habitat explain why it was undiscovered for so long.

The only living relative of the modern Giraffe, it inhabits the depths of the Ituri and Semliki Forests of the Congo. The body is a rich, dark reddish-brown with horizontal white stripes on the thighs, haunches and upper parts of the forelegs. The lower parts of the legs are white with black markings. In the male, which is smaller than the female, there is a pair of "horns". These are short pedicels of skin-covered bone, 3 inches long, rising from the frontal bones behind the eyes and directed backwards. The tips have naked, bony caps. The animal has large eyes, hairy nostrils, and a longish tail with a small black tuft at the extremity.

The Okapi lives singly or in pairs. A nocturnal animal, it has acute senses of smell and hearing. It is a leaf-eater and is very dependent on water, seldom straying far from it. The single offspring is born in May, after a long gestation period of 426 days. Okapis breed readily in captivity, and become so docile that they can be groomed regularly like horses.

392

GIRAFFE

Giraffa camelopardalis

(Savannah of Tropical Africa)

With a height of almost 18 feet, the Giraffe is easily the tallest of all the mammals. It has overcome the competition from all other browsers by an immense elongation of the usual seven neck vertebrae.

Twelve races are generally recognized. These range from the Nubian Giraffe of the Sudan which was the first to be described, to the rather more blotchily marked Cape Giraffe of Southern Africa. A form from East Africa known as the Reticulated Giraffe, with very narrow white lines between the rufous spots, has been considered by some to be a separate species, but this view is no longer generally accepted.

Giraffes avoid the closed canopy forest and live in the open savannah where they browse largely on the leaves and twigs of the acacia trees. The 17-inch tongue and the prehensile lips are well adapted to this mode of feeding. The Giraffe's sight is good and its speed, coupled with the tremendous force of a defensive kick from an animal weighing over 2,000 lb., makes it no easy prey for the Lion.

The small herds usually include only one mature male which, in an aggressive encounter with an intruding male, will use its long neck and head as a club. During courtship, a milder form of side-to-side neck-swinging may be employed. Contrary to popular belief, the giraffe is not completely voiceless. On rare occasions it can be heard to make a variety of whistling and gurgling sounds. A single young is born after a gestation period of 443 days. It is nearly 6 feet tall at birth.

Both sexes have short, hair-covered horns.

393

PRONGHORN

Antilocapra americana

(West of North America)

The Pronghorn is the sole living representative of an ancient family. It is not a true antelope; all those are found in Africa and Asia. Once very common in the west of North America, it is now restricted to certain limited areas. Pronghorns stand 36 inches high and weigh a little more than 100 lb. Both males and females possess branched, upright horns with a tine on the front. (The young specimen shown below has only partly developed horns.) These are hollow sheaths on a bony core. Like the deer, the Pronghorn sheds its horns every year, but, as with the true antelopes, the bony core is permanent. Horns are shed in October and the new growth is complete by July.

Pronghorns are found in wild, rocky desert country where their creamy colour blends in with the background, and the cartilaginous pads on their feet allow them to travel quickly and quietly. Speeds of 60 miles per hour have been recorded on salt flats. Pronghorns live in small herds, feeding on sparse, low-growing grasses, sagebrush and cactus. In winter they band together into larger groups.

In August the bucks start to accumulate harems of ten to fifteen does. Young are born in May or June after a gestation period of 240 days. Kidding occurs in open, semi-desert country. The life span is about 8 years.

Coyotes (*Canis latrans*) are their main enemies, particularly in the snow when the Pronghorn cannot move quickly. Bobcats (*Felis rufa*) may take young. A characteristic feature of the Pronghorn is the patch of white hairs on the rump which are raised when the animal is alarmed

394

BUSHBUCK

Tragelaphus scriptus

(Bush of Tropical Africa)

The Bushbuck is a small antelope inhabiting the dense bush and forests of most of Africa within the tropics. It is a delicately built animal, standing less than 3 feet high at the shoulder and weighing little more than 100 lb. The coat is a reddish-brown colour with a prominent white band across the chest, a few white spots on the body and white marks on the legs. In adult males there is a broad, almost hairless, circle around the neck. Females are smaller and, as a rule, paler than males. The male alone bears horns, and these are about 16 inches long.

The Bushbuck is a secretive species, living in pairs in thickly wooded ravines and along river banks. It is perhaps the most nocturnal of all African antelopes, lying up in the bush during the day and coming out in the evening to feed and drink. It browses on the leaves of small shrubs and trees and eats grass only when the blades are young and green. The males are sometimes very noisy, uttering a sharp bark when alarmed and using a rather more hoarse call in sexual encounters. The young are born in September and October after a gestation period of about 7 months.

The species is preyed upon by Leopards which carry off females and young. The male, however, is a most aggressive antagonist and, once he is aroused, can prove a match for even an adult Leopard.

The closest relatives of the Bushbuck are the Sitatunga (*Tragelaphus spekei*) and the Nyala (*Tragelaphus angasi*), both of which are shy and mainly nocturnal.

395

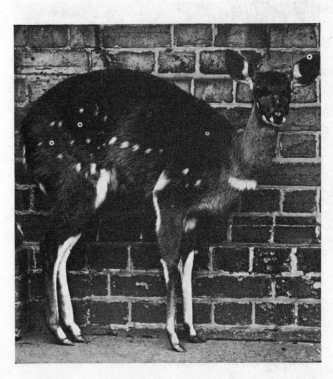

GREATER KUDU

Tragelaphus strepsiceros

(Rocky bushveld of Africa)

One of the largest and most striking of the antelopes, the Greater Kudu, or Koedoe, is found in the open forests and rocky bushveld of most of Africa. It stands 5 feet high at the shoulder, and is crowned by a pair of long, corkscrew horns which can measure more than 5 feet themselves, along the three turns of the spiral. The tips may be as much as 4 feet apart. (The animal shown below is a young male with rather small horns.) The hornless cows are very much smaller than the adult males, which may weigh 500 lb. Both sexes are a reddish-brown colour and have a number of thin, white, vertical stripes on the body. The male has a long throat fringe and a white chevron on the nose.

These antelopes are most often found in broken, hilly country. They go about singly or in small parties of cows and immature bulls. Adult bulls only join the herd during the mating season. Members of this species never stray far from water. They lie up by day in the thick bush and emerge in the cooler hours to feed. They browse on leaves and young shoots and are especially fond of leguminous seed pods. The deep, hoarse bellow of the Kudu is the loudest sound made by any antelope.

Young are born during the middle of the summer after a gestation period of about 7 months.

The Lesser Kudu (*Tragelaphus imberbis*) is similar to the Greater Kudu in appearance but is more colourfully marked, and, as the name implies, is much smaller, reaching a shoulder height of only 41 inches. It is confined to the north-eastern corner of Africa.

ELAND
Taurotragus oryx
(Thornbush of Africa)

The Eland is a heavily built creature, measuring almost 6 feet high at the shoulder and weighing up to 2,000 lb. Both males and females carry horns which are usually about 2 feet long and slightly spiralled. They bear a hump on the shoulders and a prominent dewlap. The overall colour is a light brown, but the dorsal line, the tail tuft, and the tip of the dewlap are all black. Most individuals have a small number of thin, vertical white stripes on the body. The striping is strongest just behind the shoulder region, fading away towards the rump.

These animals are found in small herds in thornbush cover on the edge of the grasslands in South and East Africa. In spite of their great weight, they are surprisingly agile, and it has even been claimed that they are capable of leaping over bushes more than 6 feet high. The herds travel long distances during their periodic migrations. They drink regularly when water is available, but can exist for long periods without it. Sometimes they graze, but the bulk of their food is made up of the young leaves of trees and shrubs. In their general behaviour they are more ox-like than any of the other African antelopes.

Calves are born during October and November. The gestation period is about 255 days.

The Eland is, as a rule, timid and inoffensive, and in many parts of Africa attempts are being made to domesticate the species. It tames easily and may be used as a draught animal as well as for food.

Even larger than the Common Eland is the Giant Eland (*T. derbianus*) of the Sudan and West Africa. This form has a more reddish tinge, longer horns, and lives in more wooded areas.

397

NILGAI

Boselaphus tragocamelus

(Indian peninsula)

The Nilgai is the largest of the Indian antelopes. Standing 54 inches high at the shoulder, it was once a favourite target of the Mogul emperors and is still extensively hunted by the local tribes today. It has, however, seldom fallen victim to the European's gun because of its poor trophy value, and is still fairly common in the northern states. Only the male bears horns and these are small, smooth, slightly curved structures which rarely exceed 9 inches in length. The name "Nilgai" means "blue cow", but the cow is in fact a brownish colour. The bull has a smooth bluish coat. Both sexes have a small neck mane and a white patch of hair on the throat. The bull also has a black tuft below its white throat patch. Other characteristic features are the white markings on the ears, nose and legs.

Small herds of Nilgai frequent the glades in open forest or parkland, browsing on the shrubs and fruit. They are most often met with in the low, hilly country at the base of the mountains. The herds of cows and calves are not at all shy and are easy to approach, but the small herds of old bulls are far more suspicious, soon making off with the ungainly gait occasioned by their strangely low hindquarters.

The cows produce one or two young after a gestation period of 247 days. The main enemy of the Nilgai is the Tiger.

The Nilgai is closely related to the Bushbuck (*Tragelaphus scriptus*), Nyala (*Tragelaphus angasi*) and Kudu (*Tragelaphus strepsiceros*) of Africa, but has no near relatives in India apart from the Four-horned Antelope (*Tetracerus quadricornis*).

398

Family BOVIDAE

ASIATIC BUFFALO
Bubalus bubalis
(Swamps of Southern Asia and Borneo)

The Asiatic Buffalo, Water Buffalo, or Carabao, has been extensively domesticated in many parts of southern Asia, but still exists in the wild state in parts of southern Asia and Borneo. A large, stockily built animal, it reaches almost 6 feet at the shoulder. The horns are black, back-swept and may reach 78 inches in length. Those of the cow are longer and more slender. In domestic breeds the horns are shorter than in the wild specimens. Both sexes are blackish-grey in colour.

In the wild they go about in large herds and, like the domestic breeds, carry their heads rather low. They are seldom to be found far from rivers or lagoons where they frequently wallow in the mud. Grass forms their chief source of food and they emerge from the tall, thick, reed-beds in the early morning and late evening to feed.

The wild Asiatic Buffalo has acquired a reputation for great ferocity and is regarded as extremely dangerous, particularly in dense cover. There are many accounts of fully-grown Tigers being defeated by large bulls.

The domestic breeds are very similar to the wild Buffalo in general appearance and are equally powerful, but considerably more docile. They are to be found today pulling ploughs and carts throughout southern Asia. The Buffalo's supply of milk is scanty and it has little importance as a dairy animal.

Both in the wild and in captivity, pairing takes place in the autumn and the young, which may be either one or two in number, are born in the following summer after a gestation period of about 10 months. This species will not interbreed with other domestic cattle.

399

ANOA

Anoa depressicornis

(Celebes)

The Anoa, Dwarf Buffalo, or Wood-ox, of Celebes is the smallest wild representative of the cattle tribe. It is also the most Eastern of all the tropical bovids. The height of an adult bull at the shoulder is only 40 inches. The body length is approximately 5½ feet. There is an 11-inch tail. The general build is sturdy with short legs and a rather plump body. The sparse coat of an adult Anoa is dark brown in colour, whilst that of the young is yellowish and altogether more woolly. Old bulls are often completely black. The horns are nearly straight and seldom more than 12 inches in length. The muzzle, like that of other cattle, is broad, naked and moist.

Because of its shy and retiring habits, very little is known of the Anoa in the wild. It usually goes about in pairs in the elevated woodland districts of the island and is seldom found far from water. Because the Anoa's flesh is very tasty, it is much sought after by the islanders. When pursued, it breaks into a clumsy trot, but relies largely upon concealment in thick undergrowth for protection. From specimens kept in zoos, it has been determined that the period of gestation is about 295 days.

The Anoa is closely related to the slightly larger Tamarou (*Anoa mindorensis*) of the Mindoro region in the Philippines. The Tamarou, unlike the Anoa, is an inhabitant of the lowland areas where it lives in small groups in the thick forest, emerging only at night to feed on sugar-cane and other crops.

GAUR

Bos gaurus

(Mountains of Southern Asia)

The Gaur, which is the largest of all the wild cattle, lives in the hilly forest districts of India, Burma and the Malay Peninsula. The bulls frequently measure more than 6 feet high at the shoulder. Both sexes are a uniform, dark olive-brown, although cows and calves inhabiting dry and open country are said to be lighter in colour. All individuals have vivid white "stockings". There is an elevated hump-like ridge on the back, formed by extensions of the dorsal vertebral spines. It ends suddenly midway between the shoulder and the tail. (This structure should not be confused with the well-known hump of the Zebu (*Bos indicus*), which lacks bony supports.) The strongly curved horns sometimes measure 30 inches in length. The small herds, numbering five to twenty individuals, feed and drink during the early morning and late evening, retiring to thick forest during the heat of the day. Grass forms their staple food and they are especially fond of young bamboo shoots. In spite of their great size, these cattle are said to be able to move very quickly across the rocky hills in times of danger. Their alarm call is described as a "whistling snort".

Mating takes place during the winter and calves are dropped during August and September. It is sometimes claimed that the Gaur has never been successfully domesticated. However, it is very closely related to the Gayal (*Bos frontalis*) of Burma, and some authorities believe that the latter is no more than a docile domestic version of it. The main difference in appearance is that the Gayal has a huge, bony forehead and wider horn-span.

S 84

BANTENG

Bos banteng

(Forests of South-east Asia, Java and Borneo)

The Banteng is easily identified by its sharply defined white rump-patch. It inhabits the forests of Java, Borneo, Bali, Malaya and Burma. Each island race differs very slightly from the others in appearance. Heights range from 60 to 69 inches at the shoulder, but the Banteng is considerably lighter than its close relative the Gaur (*Bos gaurus*). The ridge on the back, typical of the gaur, is almost completely lacking and no dewlap is present. The horns are comparatively small and slender, measuring only 20 inches in length. Bulls are dark brown in colour, but cows and calves are a more reddish-brown. As in the Gaur, the legs are marked with white "stockings". The Banteng lives in herds varying from ten to thirty in number, each group typically including one mature bull. Old, solitary bulls are very common. The herds are nearly always on the move, feeding as they travel, and only lying down during the heat of the day. When resting, they are reputed to lie in a circle with one of the cows standing as a sentry. It is claimed that a single stamp from the sentry's foot can send the whole herd stampeding away from the source of danger.

Banteng can go for long periods without water and are sometimes found in very dry districts. They are primarily grazers, living on young grass and bamboo shoots, but, owing to their shyness, they seldom invade cultivated lands.

A single red-coloured calf is born during September or October.

Domestic banteng in Java and Bali are sometimes interbred with domestic Zebu (*Bos indicus*).

402

Family BOVIDAE

YAK

Bos grunniens

(Uplands of Tibet)

The Yak has been domesticated in Tibet for centuries, but still exists in the wild state in small numbers on the plateaux of Tibet and the Chinese province of Kansu at elevations from 14,000 to 20,000 feet. A heavily built animal, it can reach a height of 65 inches at the shoulder. The wild colour is a blackish brown, with a little white on the muzzle. The coat is short and smooth on the back, but the hair on the flanks hangs down to the ankles in a long fringe. The smooth black horns may be 3 feet in length. Domesticated Yak (see above) are smaller and may be white, reddish brown or black.

Pasturage in the districts inhabited by wild Yak is limited to patches of coarse, wiry grass. But nonetheless they may be found in herds numbering from ten to a hundred head. Old bulls are, for the most part, solitary. The herds wander for considerable distances, feeding during the early mornings and evenings and sleeping on the steep slopes during the day. They drink frequently during summer and eat snow in winter. Calves are born in the autumn, after 10 months gestation.

The Yak is of great importance to the nomadic tribes of the region, who use them as beasts of burden and for riding and milking. Yak butter is very rich and the meat is excellent. In the highlands Yak dung is an important fuel. The horns are usually reduced in size and the hair much longer in the domestic breeds.

The Yak is to a considerable extent intermediate between the taurine oxen and the true bisons.

403

AFRICAN BUFFALO

Syncerus caffer

(South and East Africa)

The true Buffalo of Africa, once very numerous, suffered badly in the outbreaks of rinderpest which swept through the continent at the end of the last century. It is confined today to reserves and the fringes of thick bush along the eastern coast of Africa from the Sudan to Natal.

The Buffalo is one of the most heavily built and respected of African big game. The bulls and cows both bear massive, curved horns and can weigh more than 1,500 lb. Both possess a smooth black coat which, in the bulls, tends to become bluish with age.

The African Buffalo requires an abundant supply of water, grass and reeds; also, a closed canopy forest in the immediate neighbourhood of its grazing grounds, where it can seek shelter from the heat of the midday sun. In such areas it is found in large herds of anything up to several hundred individuals. The herds graze during the night and in the early morning, during which period they usually drink twice before returning to the thicker bush for the greater part of the day. Buffaloes are strong swimmers and will take to the water readily in times of danger. Their main enemy is the Lion, which will single out cows or calves that stray from the herd.

Mating takes place in January or shortly after and, following a gestation period of 11 months, the single young are born between December and February.

The common form of the African Buffalo is sometimes referred to as the Cape Buffalo in contrast to the smaller and rarer Dwarf Forest Buffalo (*Syncerus caffer nanus*) from Central and West Africa.

404

EUROPEAN BISON

Bison bonasus

(Eastern Europe)

The Wisent, or European Bison, is extinct in the wild and consequently little is known of its natural behaviour. Tsar Alexander I instituted game laws to protect the herds at Bialowieza on the Polish–Russian border, and in 1914 there were nearly 1,000 animals in the area; but all these were killed during the First World War. A second group in the Caucasus was protected by the Tsar in 1860, but these too were all dead by 1927. Three animals survived in the wild in Upper Silesia, and forty-five were safe in zoos. With these, breeding was started in earnest. By 1949 there were 119 pure-bred European Bison in the zoos and parks of the world, and the numbers have been increasing ever since.

In comparison with the familiar American Bison, the European species has longer legs, greater body length and a smaller head which is carried much higher. The hind-quarters are tall and thickly clad but the mane is comparatively short. Like the American Bison, it has a good sense of smell and weak eyesight, but it is an altogether wilder, more wary animal.

The single, yellow-coloured young are born in May or June after a gestation period of 276 days. The bulls reach maturity at 6 to 8 years, and the cows at 3 or 4 years of age.

The European Bison was a woodland animal, browsing on ferns, leaves and bark. Although gregarious, the herds usually numbered less than thirty individuals; solitary old bulls were not uncommon. Unlike the American Bison, there was only small seasonal movement.

405

AMERICAN BISON

Bison bison

(North America)

Formerly one of the most abundant hoofed animals of the New World, the American Bison is now found only in parks and reserves. The coming of the white man and the subsequent development of the railways almost spelled the extermination of the vast herds of so-called "buffalo" that roamed the open plains. They were hunted for their hides and their black tongues which were considered a delicacy.

The American Bison is a striking animal with its huge, low-slung head and massive hump, the latter supported by vertebral extensions. The bull may attain a height of over 5 feet at the shoulder, a length of 9 feet and a weight of up to 2,500 lb. The thick, dark brown winter coat (see below) is moulted in spring to be replaced by a lighter, shorter one.

Mating takes place in the autumn and a single, reddish-coloured calf is born in May or June after 274 days gestation. The calf develops the characteristic hump when about 2 months old.

Dust wallows on the prairie, sometimes 25 feet in diameter, bear witness to the bison's love of dust-bathing. It will also use trees as rubbing-posts, often destroying them in the process. Bison are grazers, feeding entirely on the prairie grasses and migrating in a southerly direction as these become sparse during the winter.

At the start of the nineteenth century there were still over 60 million bison in North America. By 1889 there were only 541 left alive. Hunters, like the famous "Buffalo Bill" Cody, were slaughtering them at a combined rate of thousands daily. Just before it was too late, protection was enforced and today the world population has risen again to over 20 thousand.

GREY DUIKER

Sylvicapra grimmia

(African Bushveld)

One of the most widely distributed of all the African antelopes, the diminutive Grey Duiker is found almost everywhere from the Cape to Abyssinia, and from Nigeria to Senegal. Although albino Duikers are often reported, their natural colour ranges from fawn to greyish blue. The male and female are similar in coloration and appearance, and both usually bear horns, although those of the female may be very short and thin and are sometimes absent altogether. The horns of the male are straight, closely set and usually about 6 inches long. The sexes are much the same size—about 24 inches at the shoulder—and weigh approximately 30 lb. The face glands are prominent and one can be seen in the above photograph as a black slit below the eye. Scent from these glands is deposited on twigs and branches by rubbing movements of the face. In this way a Duiker can leave its personal smell at various locations in its home range.

Grey Duikers occur in large numbers in the vicinity of streams and rivers where they drink regularly. They are essentially bush antelopes and avoid crossing open spaces. Mainly they are browsers, feeding on leaves, twigs and berries which they often reach by standing up on their hind legs. They also occasionally eat insects, snails and even frogs. The gestation period has been given as 121 days and also as 196 days; further information is obviously required.

There are sixteen distinct relatives of the Grey Duiker. They are found in all parts of Africa, the most common being the Forest Duikers of Central Africa and the Blue Duikers which inhabit the dense undergrowth in West Africa.

SABLE ANTELOPE

Hippotragus niger

(Forests of South and East Africa)

The Sable Antelope is a forest-living species found most commonly in the moist areas of East Africa from Kenya to the Transvaal. The fully-grown bull stands about 54 inches high at the shoulder, weighs 500 lb., and bears a pair of large, scimitar-shaped horns which are swept back in a curve measuring almost 4 feet. The females bear similar but shorter horns. Both male and female have a satiny black coat, which, in the old bulls, becomes a jet-black colour.

Sable Antelopes are found in herds varying from ten to fifty individuals. The herds usually consist of females and young led by an adult bull. "Surplus" bulls may sometimes be met with in groups of three or four. Young ones fall prey to packs of Hunting Dogs, but only Lions are capable of bringing down an adult.

They are chiefly grazers and drink regularly in the mornings and evenings. Sight, hearing and scent are well developed, but less so than in other African ungulates such as the zebra and kudu with which they associate.

The period of gestation in the Sable Antelope is very similar to that of man; about 270 days. The young, which are born from November to January, are a rufous colour which turns to black in their third year.

A notable race of this species is the rare Giant Sable Antelope (*Hippotragus niger variani*) of Angola, with horns of over 60 inches in length. The closest relative of the Sable Antelope is the fairly common reddish-coloured Roan Antelope (*Hippotragus equinus*), which has shorter horns.

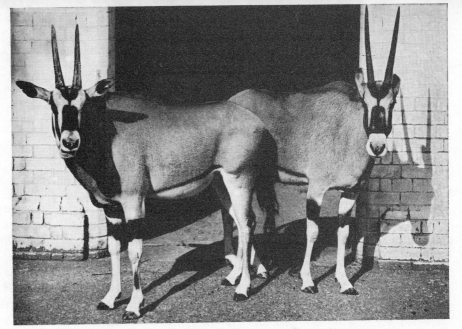

Family BOVIDAE

ORYX

Oryx gazella

(Deserts of South and East Africa)

There are three species of oryx surviving today: the rare, almost pure white Arabian Oryx (*O. leucoryx*) from the deserts of south-west Asia, the Scimitar-horned Oryx (*O. tao*, often incorrectly called *O. algazel*) from the North African deserts, and the common Oryx from the desert and scrub regions of South and East Africa. The latter exists as a cline, with a gradual increase in horn-length and in the black flank and leg markings as one travels south over its range. In the southern extremity of its distribution it has a broad black flank-band and is known as the Cape Oryx or Gemsbok (*O. gazella gazella*); farther north, in East Africa, the flank marking is a thin black line, the upper parts of the legs are white instead of black, and the animal is known as the Beisa Oryx (*O. gazella beisa*). The photograph above shows a male (left) and a female of the Beisa race.

The Oryx stands 4 feet high at the shoulders and weighs 450 lb. Living in large herds, these keen-sighted antelopes subsist almost entirely on seasonal grasses and on leaves and roots of stunted shrubs. They seldom drink and obtain most of their water from roots and tubers that they dig up with their hooves.

They frequently live in mixed herds with Springbok or Gnu and appear to benefit from the alarm calls of these species that herald the approach of danger. The Oryx is swift when fleeing and its straight horns are valuable defence weapons at close quarters against its enemies the Leopard and the Lion.

409

BLESBOK

Damaliscus dorcas

(Southern Africa)

The Blesbok (often referred to as *D. albifrons*) and its close relative the Bontebok (often called *D. pygargus*) are the smallest and most southerly members of their genus, and should be thought of as two races of a single species (correctly named *D. dorcas*). They stand about 40 to 42 inches at the shoulder and are easily recognized by the white blaze on the face of the adults. The Blesbok (seen below) differs from the Bontebok by having brown hair between the eyes dividing the white frontal blaze. It also lacks the pronounced rump patch and white tail of the Bontebok. Both forms have a deep purple-red coloured body. Their horns are lyrate and may measure as much as 18 inches.

The Bontebok was once considered to be the rarest antelope in the world, but careful conservation has ensured its survival, the numbers having risen from seventeen to about 350. The Blesbok herds have also decreased, although not so drastically, and this race still exists in fair numbers on reserves. Unlike the Bontebok, which comes from the south-western coastal belt of South Africa, the Blesbok is an inhabitant of the plains and hills of the Karroo, living on the coarse herbage found there.

The Blesbok is a gregarious animal, living in herds of eight to fifteen individuals. When disturbed, they usually run in single file upwind with their noses to the ground. The adult relies on its speed and wariness for protection, but in times of danger the young fawns conceal themselves in the grass. They are born from August to October, after a gestation period of about 230 days.

HARTEBEEST

Alcelaphus buselaphus

(Plains of Africa)

Weighing 400 lb. and standing 4 feet high at the shoulder, the Hartebeest is one of the larger antelopes. It has an elongated face topped in both sexes by upright, lyre-shaped horns. The limbs are thin and the plain, fawn-coloured body slopes rapidly down from the rump to the tail.

There are several closely related races of Hartebeest surviving today in the semi-arid areas of various parts of Africa. The most familiar is Coke's Hartebeest (*A. buselaphus cokei*) found on the plains of East Africa, from southern Kenya to central Tanganyika. It is often referred to by its Swahili name of Kongoni. Two extinct races are the Cape Hartebeest (*A. buselaphus caama*) which had dark shoulders and flanks, and the Bubal Hartebeest (*A. buselaphus buselaphus*), which was known to the Roman governors in North Africa.

Hartebeests are found on the thinly-covered plains and seem to be almost entirely independent of water. The herds are small; usually ten to twenty animals led by an old bull. They are grazers, feeding during the day, but frequently visiting salt-licks during the night.

They are often seen in mixed herds with gnu and zebra, and, like these, they produce young during the middle of summer.

The Hartebeest is a fast runner, and is closely related to the Sassaby (*Damaliscus lunatus*) which is reputed to be the fastest of all hoofed animals. Of all land animals, only the Cheetah (*Acinonyx jubatus*), can move more quickly. Hartebeests are reputed to post sentries that watch for danger from the top of a convenient anthill and in this way are said to avoid danger from their main natural enemies—the Lions.

BRINDLED GNU

Connochaetes taurinus

(Grasslands of Africa)

The Brindled Gnu, or Wildebeest, is found over wide areas of open savannah country in various parts of Africa. It is a sturdily proportioned animal, standing about 52 inches high at the shoulder and weighing approximately 500 lb. Both sexes have horns, which normally curve more strongly inwards at the tips than those of the animal illustrated below. The basically grey body colour is faintly bluish, but the long hair on the tail, shoulders and head is black.

There are two distinctive common forms, the black-bearded Blue Wildebeest (*C. taurinus taurinus*) of southern Africa, and the White-bearded Gnu (*C. taurinus albojubatus*) (see below) of East Africa. A second species of gnu, now practically extinct in the wild, is the slightly smaller White-tailed Gnu, or Black Wildebeest (*Connochaetes gnou*), which today exists mainly in protected areas of South West Africa.

The Brindled Gnu is highly gregarious and usually runs in herds of twenty to fifty individuals, though these groups may become very much larger in times of drought. They are very dependent on water and will travel great distances when their local sources become inadequate. They are wary creatures, grazing and drinking in the cooler hours and resting during the middle of the day. The herd is often led by an old cow and it is claimed that the group always posts sentries whose alarm snorts can send the whole population galloping off at high speed. They are often found together with groups of zebras.

The young are usually born during the first rains in October or November, after a gestation period of 8 to 9 months.

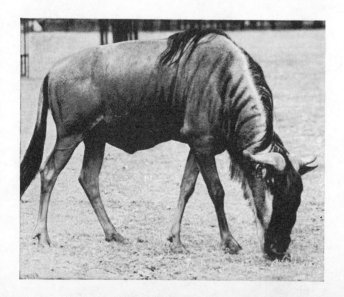

412

ORIBI

Ourebia ourebi

(Grasslands of Africa)

Once fairly common in the open grasslands of most of tropical Africa, the rather plain, fawn-coloured Oribi is today rare and disappearing very rapidly. Standing about 35 inches high at the shoulder, it has remarkably large ears and in spite of the slender legs the body is quite sturdily built. A female Oribi (see photograph below) may weigh as much as 40 lb. The horns, which are straight and spike-like, measure approximately 6 inches and are found in the male only. Distinguishing marks of the species are the tufts of hair at the knees and the characteristic bare patch on the head immediately below the ear. The tail is short and bushy.

Oribis usually occur in twos and threes, but on the more open plains they can sometimes be seen in small parties of as many as five to ten individuals. In the early morning and late evening they graze in the open, but during the major part of the day they usually lie low in thickets of grass. If approached closely, they crouch down and flatten their necks out along the ground. In this posture they are extremely cryptic. When disturbed in the open they run very fast with surprisingly large leaps and bounds. Their call is a thin-sounding whistle. Oribis are generally found within easy reach of water. Their haunts are characterized by accumulations of droppings in a selected bare spot.

The female isolates herself from the group when she is about to give birth. Young Oribis, which have very woolly coats, are born in July after a gestation period of about 7 months.

413

ROYAL ANTELOPE

Neotragus pygmaeus

(West Africa)

Typical mouse-deer being absent from Africa, their place in that Continent is taken by various minute species of neotragine antelopes. Dik-diks, the Steinbok, the Dwarf Antelope, the Beira Antelope and the Royal Antelope are members of this remarkable tribe.

The smallest of all these and, indeed, the smallest antelope in the world, is the Royal Antelope. It is found in the tropical forests of West Africa, and stands no more than 10 to 12 inches high at the shoulder. The male (see above) possesses simple, spike-like horns less than 1 inch long which scarcely project above the hair. The body, which is clad in rufous brown fur, is about 12 inches long from head to rump. The chin, throat and underparts are white, and there is a faint line on the hind surface of the limbs. The legs are as thin as one's little finger, and the hoof marks are the size of the little finger-nail. In spite of its size it has the reputation of being capable of covering as much as 9 feet in a single bound.

Little is known of the habits of this antelope, which not only lives in the thickest forests of the west coast, but is also nocturnal, making detailed observation of it extremely difficult. It is, however, established that it is not a gregarious animal, being either solitary or living in pairs.

Many legends surround this species. The Ashantis say "The Elephant is big-for-nothing, for the little Royal Antelope makes the best soup!"

In central Africa there is a close relative, Bate's Dwarf Antelope (*Neotragus batesi*), and in East Africa another pygmy species, the Suni (*Nesotragus moschatus*).

Family BOVIDAE · S 150

BLACKBUCK

Antilope cervicapra

(Indian grasslands)

The Blackbuck is the sole representative of its genus, and the most typical antelope to be found in India. The adult males are blackish-brown above, white below, and having a pronounced white ring around each eye. The females and young bucks are a yellowish-fawn above and white below. The male stands about 32 inches at the shoulder and weighs about 90 lb., with a body length of about 50 inches. His spiral, closely annulated horns are about 18 inches long. The spirals develop during the second year.

Blackbuck congregate in herds of ten or more in the grasslands, chiefly in the tall grass by the rivers and cultivated land, avoiding the hills and forests. The herd consists of females and their offspring, young males, and a dominant male in full colour. February and March are the main rutting times, with the males often fighting fiercely over the females. During aggressive encounters they approach each other with a peculiar mincing gait, uttering short challenging grunts, with the head thrown upward so that the horns lie along the back, and with the large scent glands on the face wide open. At other times they can be seen pressing these face glands on to the ends of branches and twigs in their home range, depositing scent secretions, and thus creating familiar landmarks.

These animals have a remarkable turn of speed and rely on this and their excellent eyesight for safety from predators. Like the African Springbok (*Antidorcas marsupialis*) they leap high into the air when fleeing. The young conceal themselves in the grass when danger threatens. Although intensively hunted by man, often with the aid of Cheetahs, their numbers have not been appreciably reduced.

415

IMPALA

Aepyceros melampus

(Savannah of South and East Africa)

The Impala is perhaps the most familiar and typical of all the antelopes. The horns in the male (see below) are gracefully curved in a lyre shape, inclining upward and slightly inward at the tips. The female is hornless. It is a fairly large antelope, measuring about 3 feet at the shoulder and weighing up to 80 lb. Both male and female have reddish-brown backs, a light fawn band along the sides and white underparts. The tail has a black line on the upper side and a white tip and underside. A characteristic feature of the Impala is the black tuft of hair which conceals a gland just above the heel of the hind leg.

This species, being a grazer as well as a browser, is plentiful almost everywhere within its range, in the open plains as well as in the thick thorny savannah. It is a regular drinker and is never found far from water. Essentially gregarious, it occurs in herds numbering from ten to several hundred individuals. Each herd is led by an old male and includes several young males that are reputed to act as sentinels, and whose sneezing alarm calls can send the whole group bounding away in leaps soaring 10 feet high and covering distances of almost 30 feet.

Intense threatening displays occur in the rutting season when the males strut around with the tail spread fanwise over the rump, displaying the vivid white underside. A single young is born in September or October.

The Impala is often to be seen in the company of zebra, gnu and even baboons, associations which afford it some measure of protection against its worst enemies: the Lion, Leopard, Cheetah and Hunting Dogs.

GERENUK

Litocranius walleri

(East Africa)

The Gerenuk, or Giraffe Antelope, is confined to scattered bush country in Somaliland and parts of East Africa. It is a delicately shaped animal with slender, elongated limbs and an extraordinarily long, thin neck. The head is small and the thick-boned skull (which gives rise to the generic name) has a greatly extended hind part. Horns are carried by the male only and are about 15 inches long, curving backwards for most of their length, but having a forward hook at the tip. Both sexes are a rich chestnut colour with fawn flanks and a white underside.

Gerenuks live in pairs or small family groups on stony ground in scattered bush country, often far from water. It has been claimed their drinking is confined largely to one another's urine, and that the males will only drink the urine of females, and vice versa. They are never found on the open plains, as they are specialized browsers, balancing on their hind legs to feed. In this vertical position their usual 39-inch height is extended to an advantageous 6 feet. The long neck is not only valuable when feeding, but also gives the animal a better view of an approaching predator. Their warning call has been described as a short, low "buzz". Alarm transforms the Gerenuk from a tall, elegant animal to a clumsy, crouching fugitive. It has a very peculiar evasive run in which the body is crouched low and the head is held out in front, parallel to the ground. It falls prey to both Lion and Leopard.

The nearest relative of the Gerenuk is the smaller and rarer Dibatag (*Ammodorcas clarkei*), which occurs in the same habitat and is of similar general appearance.

417

THOMSON'S GAZELLE

Gazella thomsoni

(East Africa)

The smallest of the true plains game of East Africa is the elegant Thomson's Gazelle, known affectionately as the Tommie, which stands about 26 inches high at the shoulder. The sandy brown colour of the body is divided from the white belly by a dark band along the flanks, and there is a white streak from the base of each of the 13-inch horns to the nose. The short tail, that is wagged rapidly if its owner becomes agitated, is conspicuously jet black on a pale rump.

It is a gregarious and polygamous animal. Parties of females are collected by a single adult male. Males over 8 months old are expelled and form "bachelor" herds of varying size. Solitary old males are frequently seen in their small territories. Groups of this species are often observed in company with the larger Grant's Gazelle (*Gazella granti*) and Impala (*Aepyceros melampus*).

Thompson's Gazelles migrate at the beginning of the dry season, sometimes travelling as much as 100 miles to better watered areas. At the onset of the rains they leave the district before it becomes too swampy. They feed and drink mainly in the early morning and late evening, resting during most of the day.

The young are born in the rainy season, and the female leaves the herd a few days before giving birth, remaining alone with her offspring for about 3 months. A female over the age of 12 months can breed twice a year.

When danger threatens, the young fawns may lie flat to conceal themselves, but the adults rely on their speed and eyesight for safety. The Spotted Hyaena (*Crocuta crocuta*) and the Cheetah (*Acinonyx jubatus*) are their principal enemies.

SPRINGBOK

Antidorcas marsupialis

(Semi-deserts of South Africa)

The national emblem of South Africa, the Springbok, is a medium-sized antelope, standing less than 3 feet high at the shoulder and weighing approximately 70 lb. Both sexes bear lyre-shaped, 12-inch horns. The sandy-coloured back and the white underside are separated by a dark lateral band similar to that of Thomson's Gazelle. There is a striking patch of long, white, erectile hair along the rump. This patch is normally concealed inside a fold of skin, but expands when the animal is frightened and flashes conspicuously like a white flag. When fleeing, the Springbok leaps 8 to 10 feet high into the air, often making a whole series of huge bounds.

Herds of these animals, many thousands strong, once used to undertake periodic migrations across the Karroo, leaving a frightening trail of destruction in their wake. They are far less plentiful today, but are still to be found in groups of anything up to 100 individuals. They frequent open grassland and arid plains, grazing on scattered saltbush and other low vegetation. Springbok dig up bulbs and water-roots with their hooves, and can exist for long periods without drinking water. They are swift (60 miles an hour) runners and can jump distances of well over 20 feet.

The single offspring are born around December after a gestation period of about 170 days.

Springbok are often found together with Oryx, Gnu and Eland, an association which affords them some measure of protection from their common enemies—the Lion, Leopard and Hunting Dog.

419

SAIGA ANTELOPE

Saiga tatarica

(Steppes of Southern Russia)

The peculiar bloated form of its nose renders this animal easily distinguishable from all other antelopes. Formerly common over most of the semi-desert area east of the Caspian Sea, its numbers were seriously reduced by extensive hunting. Careful protection has, however, saved it from extinction and it is now on the increase again. The male has a pair of slightly curved, amber-yellow horns 12 inches long, and stands about 30 inches at the shoulder. The female (seen below) is hornless. The summer coat is yellow-brown above and white below. In winter the coat grows much longer and becomes uniformly white.

The Saiga Antelope lives in the open desert and semi-desert country between the Don and Volga rivers, feeding largely on salt-loving shrubs and grasses. A gregarious species, it moves in small herds of a dozen or more individuals, each group being led by an old male. In winter the groups combine to form large assemblies and migrate southward ahead of the snows. As can be seen from the photograph, the scent glands beneath the eyes and inside the knees are well developed.

Pairing occurs in November and the young, numbering one to three, are born in May. They are able to run with their mothers after 1 week, and after 4 weeks are fully weaned. With the exception of a fly-maggot that lives in its fur, the Saiga Antelope today has virtually no natural enemies, but it must once have relied upon its great speed for protection.

The only close relative of the Saiga Antelope is the immensely long-horned Tibetan Antelope, or Chiru (*Pantholops hodgsoni*) from the high plateaux of Tibet.

420

GORAL
Naemorhedus goral
(Mountains of South Asia)

Slightly smaller than its close relatives the Serows (*Capricornis*), the Goral is found from the Himalayan Mountains east through the mountains of west China and north to Korea. It stands a little over 2 feet high at the shoulder and the small, conical horns are seldom more than 6 inches long. There are several races scattered along its geographical range. These differ somewhat in colour, but the general shade is a yellowish-grey suffused with black. The chin and throat patches are always white or yellow. Unlike the Serows, this species has no facial glands, but, like the Serows, it does possess foot glands similar to those found in sheep.

The Goral is sometimes called the "Himalayan Chamois". It is more often found in the open than are the Serows and frequents rocky hillsides from 3,000 feet to 14,000 feet during the summer. It grazes in small parties of half a dozen individuals, but the old bucks are more often solitary. Living entirely on the sparse vegetation of the rocky slopes, it feeds in the early morning and late evening. Easily the most agile of the goat-antelopes, it can make its way very rapidly across precipitous screes of loose rock with no apparent difficulty. During the day it can sometimes be seen, high up on a rocky outcrop, sitting on its haunches like a dog, or lying stretched out in the sun.

The period of gestation is about 6 months and the single offspring is born at the beginning of summer.

On characteristics of the skull, it has been argued that the Goral is more closely related to the heavily built Takin (*Budorcas taxicolor*) than it is to the Serow, but this view is not generally accepted.

421

SEROW

Capricornis sumatraensis

(Mountains of South Asia and Sumatra)

The Serow and the Goral (*Naemorhaedus goral*) with their large heads, donkey-like ears and thick necks are often known as the goat-antelopes. A fully grown Serow is larger than a Goral, being about 3 feet high at the shoulder and scaling almost 200 lb. The coat is coarse and varies in colour from black to reddish-grey. There is a varying amount of white on the muzzle, throat and lower legs. Both sexes bear horns which are about 12 inches long, black, conical, closely wrinkled and with a slight backward curve. Unlike the Goral, the Serow has well-developed face glands which exude a white secretion.

This species is found in thickly wooded gorges and on the boulder-strewn slopes of mountains in Malaya, Viet-Nam, Thailand, Burma, Assam, eastern China and Sumatra. It is more or less solitary, although four or five may sometimes be seen feeding together in the early morning or late evening. Much more secretive than the Goral, it spends most of the day in thick cover. When disturbed, however, it is extremely active, and can move rapidly over even the most difficult of rocky surfaces. While fleeing, it gives vent to a hissing alarm call.

The rut commences at the end of October and one or two young are born in June or July after a gestation period of approximately 7 months.

There is a smaller Serow in Japan (*Capricornis crispus*) which has a thick, woolly coat, and an even smaller race (*Capricornis crispus swinhoe*) that is confined to the island of Formosa.

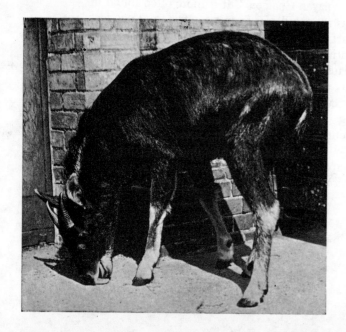

ROCKY MOUNTAIN GOAT

Oreamnos americanus

(Rocky Mountains of North America)

One of the "goat-antelopes" closely related to the Chamois (*Rupicapra rupicapra*) of Eurasia is the Rocky Mountain Goat of British Columbia, Alberta, Idaho and Montana. Looking more like a domestic animal than a wild species, this short-necked, large-headed, pure white creature has shoulders that are higher than its rump. A fully grown male mountain goat stands between 35 and 40 inches at the shoulder and weighs from 200 to 300 lb. Females are smaller than the males, but both sexes have horns and beards. The horns are black and upright, curving slightly backwards and seldom are more than 9 inches long. Rocky Mountain Goats are clothed completely in long, thick, white hair.

These goats prefer the steep mountain-sides and cliffs and never descend to the sheltered valleys, even in winter, finding protection beneath overhanging rocks. Their split hooves enable them to move easily along steep rock faces which provide no apparent support. Their sure-footedness has become legendary.

Food for this species consists of moss, lichen, grass, and the leaves and twigs of stunted bushes. They associate in small herds, the females retiring in groups to bear their one or two young in April or May. The kids are capable of following the mothers over difficult terrain when only a few days old.

Pumas and Wolves have been known to attack them, but their habitat is usually sufficient defence against all predators but the Golden Eagle, which occasionally manages to carry off a kid. The worst enemies of the Rocky Mountain Goats, however, are not other animals but the avalanches that sometimes sweep down the slopes in spring.

423

S 175

CHAMOIS

Rupicapra rupicapra

(Europe and South-west Asia)

Well-known because of its uniquely shaped horns and because its hide was used for making "shammy" leather, this increasingly rare animal can still be seen leaping about the steep slopes of the Pyrenees, the Alps, the Apennines, the Carpathian Mountains and the highlands of south-east Europe and south-west Asia. In every one of these regions special races have been named, there being nine distinct forms recognized at the present time.

Of all the acrobatic rock-climbers of the ungulate world, the Chamois is probably the most nimble. It is capable of leaps and runs along and across rock faces that would defeat even the best mountaineer.

During the summer they stay high up out of reach of predators, but in the winter they are forced down by low temperatures and the search for food. When they take refuge in the darker, more wooded areas they moult into a correspondingly darker winter coat (see photograph above) that helps to camouflage them against the new background.

In the spring, the pregnant female leaves the herd several weeks before giving birth and searches for a sheltered hiding-place, in a rock crevice or a thicket. When it is born, the young Chamois is capable of standing and walking, even before its fur is dry, and it starts to eat grass when only 10 days old. It becomes sexually mature at the age of 3 years. A wild Chamois has been known to live for as long as 19 years, although the large majority do not survive for more than 10.

They are no longer used commercially in the production of "shammy" leathers. These are now obtained from domestic goats and sheep.

424

TAKIN

Budorcas taxicolor

(Mountains of Southern Asia)

Superficially resembling the African gnus (*Connochaetes*), the Asiatic Takin is closely related to the only other "ox-sheep", the Musk Ox (*Ovibos moschatus*). Takins are short-legged and heavily built with a shaggy coat of hair. The typical form comes from the Mishmi Hills, north of Assam, and is brown with a black face and legs, but a race discovered in 1911 at 10,000 feet in Shensi, China, (*B. taxicolor bedfordi*), the Golden Takin, is a rich golden yellow colour. The horns of the males and females are similar in appearance. The tail is short and broad and concealed beneath the fur. Full grown bulls stand about 50 inches at the shoulder.

Takins live in small groups of up to eight animals in the thickets of rhododendron and bamboo near the timber line in the mountains. In summer they sometimes collect into large herds of several hundred individuals. Remarkably shy and secretive in spite of their heavy build, they can cover rough ground with extraordinary agility when fleeing from enemies. They usually move with head and bulbous nose held rather low. Seldom moving far from their usual haunts, they feed in the evening and early morning, emerging from the thickets to graze on the near-by slopes. Their senses do not seem to be especially acute and they are frequently trapped by the Chinese for food.

When suspicious, Takins utter a warning cough and, during the rut, a low bellow. Rutting takes place in July and August and the single calves are born in March or April. The cows at this time travel alone with their calves which can walk well at 3 days old and are weaned at 1 month.

425

MUSK OX

Ovibos moschatus

(Tundra of Canada and Greenland)

The Musk Ox of the windswept tundras and snowfields of Alaska, Canada and Greenland is the most northern representative of the Bovidae. It is a medium-sized animal, stoutly built with a short neck and a very broad head. The male stands about 4 feet high at the shoulder and has enormously expanded horns, flattened at the base and measuring about 24 inches in length. The whole animal is covered with a dense coat that hangs down from the body rather like that of the Yak. The colour of both sexes is a dark brown with buff-coloured saddle and lower legs. The feet are huge and widely splayed, a design that is of great assistance when moving over the snow. The name Musk Ox is derived from a musty odour emanating from the fur.

Musk Oxen associate in herds numbering from 20 to 100 animals in winter, but these split up into smaller groups in the summer. Their food in summer is mainly the leaves of a small stunted willow which grows on the tundra, and in winter, moss, lichens and bark, which are scraped out of the snow by hoof and horn.

Their main natural enemy is the wolf, against which their defence is to form a hollow circle with the young animals in the centre. In spite of their short legs, they can run with considerable speed, but neither of these defence mechanisms are of much assistance against the Eskimoes or the Indians, who hunt them for their meat and fur.

A single offspring is born in May or June, each cow producing a calf only once every 2 years.

426

HIMALAYAN TAHR

Hemitragus jemlahicus

(Mountains of Southern Asia)

The Himalayan Tahr stands about 3 feet high and, with its long narrow face, looks rather like a sheep wearing someone else's fur coat. The small horns grow close together and are almost semi-circular in section. There is no beard, the whole head region being extremely short-furred. Contrasting strongly with this, the males have a long, soft mane. Both sexes are reddish-brown in colour. They are found south of the main range of the Himalayas, from Bhutan to Kashmir.

Close relatives are the Nilgiri Tahr (*Hemitragus hylocrius*) of the mountains of southern India, which is slightly larger and has short, stiff, brown hair; and the Arabian Tahr (*Hemitragus jayakari*) which is much smaller than the other two, more grey in colour and has more slender horns.

These three species are more forest-dwelling than either the Markhor (*Capra falconeri*) or the Ibex (*Capra ibex*), and although they sometimes resort to the rocky summits, they prefer steep, more-or-less tree covered slopes. Like other goats, they feed during the mornings and evenings, reposing beneath the shelter of rocks during the day. The herds are very active and wary, with several females always acting as sentinels. The old males herd separately during the summer, living in the least approachable places, and returning to the main groups only in winter when pairing takes place. The young are born in June or July after a gestation period of about 6 months. Their chief enemies are Leopards, although a few fall prey to Tigers.

Along with the Wild Goat (*Capra hircus*), the Tahr is sometimes considered to be an ancestor of our common domestic goats, but this is highly unlikely.

427

IBEX

Capra ibex

(Europe, Asia and North Africa)

The typical form of the Ibex is nearly extinct. It once occurred widely through the Alps, but was completely exterminated except for a colony in North Italy. It has since been re-introduced to several reserves in Switzerland and elsewhere. It is a brownish-grey colour and stands about 40 inches high at the shoulder. The mature male has a small, short beard and dramatically curved horns of about 30 inches in length. The female's horns are small and upright and usually less than 8 inches long.

There are a number of races closely related to the Alpine Ibex (*C. ibex ibex*). The Nubian Ibex (*C. ibex nubiana*) is brown in colour but has white hooves, a long, full, beard and longer, slimmer horns, sometimes as much as 4 feet in length. The Siberian Ibex (*C. ibex sibirica*) (see photograph below) also differs from the Alpine form in that its horns and beard are longer, but it possesses a dark stripe along the middle of its back.

There are several other species which are also called Ibex. These include the Tur, or Caucasian Ibex (*C. caucasica*), from south-east Russia and the Spanish Ibex (*C. pyrenaica*) from the Pyrenees (where it is now extinct) and other mountainous parts of Spain, to the west of Madrid and in the south-east.

The habits of all these goats are very similar. They live on cliffs and crags close to the snow line throughout the year. Their senses are acute and they are extremely agile and sure-footed. Mating takes place in October, when the males descend from the crags, and the young are born in the spring, after a gestation period of 158 days.

MARKHOR

Capra falconeri

(Himalayas)

The Markhor is the largest of the wild goats, standing 40 inches high at the shoulder and weighing more than 200 lb. The hair is short in summer and long and silky in winter. The old males (see above) have a long beard which covers their throats throughout the year. The horns, which are close together at the head, spread out in a heavy corkscrew more than 4 feet in length. There are four distinct races which occur throughout the Himalayas from Kashmir to Afghanistan. These are separated largely on the number of turns in the screw of the horn. All are a rich reddish-brown colour that turns to grey in winter.

They are extremely agile creatures despite their appearance and inhabit the most difficult and precipitous ground along the margin between the deep forest and the higher snow-capped peaks. They congregate for part of the year in large herds, but in the summer the males restrict themselves to the higher ground, coming down to graze only in the morning and the evening. The fur of the Markhor is not as thick as that of the Ibex (*Capra ibex*) and these animals are far more susceptible to severe cold. In some parts of the Markhor's distribution they may be seen feeding together with the Ibex.

The name Markhor is derived from the Persian for "snake-eater", but there is no evidence to support the contention that snakes form part of their diet.

They fall prey to the Snow Leopard and Asiatic Wild Dogs and have been extensively hunted by man for the great trophy value of their horns.

429

AOUDAD

Ammotragus lervia

(Mountains of North Africa)

The Aoudad, Udad, Arui, Fechstal, Maned Sheep or Barbary Sheep, is the only wild sheep found in Africa. It stands about 40 inches at the shoulder and has smoothly curved semi-circular horns measuring up to 30 inches in length. The horns of the female are only slightly smaller than those of the male. The head is long, without any face glands, and the ears are relatively large. Aoudads are of a uniform tawny colour and the adult males have a fringe of long hair hanging from the throat and chest extending down to include the front legs. Although short by other standards, the tail is unusually long and hairy for a wild sheep.

They are found in bare, sandy and rocky districts of north-east Africa, Morocco, Algeria, Tunis, Libya, Sudan and Egypt, where their tawny colour renders them almost indistinguishable from their background. Seldom drinking more than once in every 4 or 5 days, these sheep move about in small family groups. They travel a great deal in search of water, avoiding as much as possible the tribes of nomadic Arabs. The groups often consist of a number of ewes and their young, as the older rams tend to be more solitary, joining up with the flock only in the breeding season during October and November. The gestation period is 160 days and either one or two lambs are born to each female each year.

The Aoudad is sheep-like in some respects and goat-like in others, but its closest relative is probably the wild Blue Sheep or Bharal (*Pseudois nayaur*) of the Himalayas.

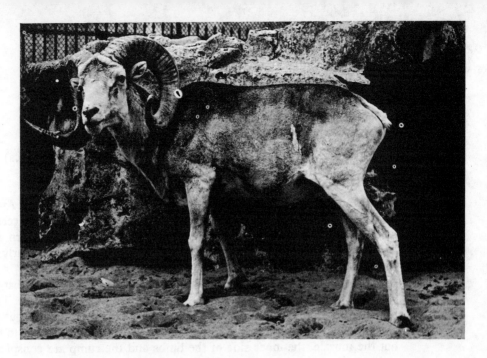

ARGALI

Ovis ammon

(Semi-deserts of Central Asia)

The largest of all the living sheep is the Argali which frequents the semi-desert countries bordering the Gobi Desert in Siberia, Mongolia and Tibet. This species may attain a shoulder height of 4 feet and a weight of 350 lb. The horns of the ram are massive, curling outward from the side of the head, sometimes making more than one complete turn, and measuring 60 inches along the curve. The winter coat is a light brown, but this tends to become even lighter during the summer.

The typical Siberian Argali (*Ovis ammon ammon*) is closely related to the Marco Polo's Sheep (*Ovis ammon polii*) of the Pamir Plateau in the south, which has longer, more slender horns, and paler underparts. (The photograph above shows the male of the Marco Polo race.) Fifteen races have been named altogether.

These powerful sheep live in large herds in the lower and more protected valleys, where snow does not accumulate to any great depth, but in summer the old rams separate from the group to live singly at higher levels. Young males stay with the herds of females until they are about 5 years old. Living in rough, rocky country, they feed in the morning and evening on the isolated tufts of grass. They have very keen senses of sight and smell and strike the ground with their fore-feet as a warning of danger. In an aggressive encounter, rams not only butt but may also run alongside each other striking sideways with their horns.

They mate during the winter months of December and January and the young are born during May or June.

431

BIGHORN SHEEP

Ovis canadensis

(Mountains of North-east Asia and North America)

The Bighorn Sheep probably originated in Asia, entered the North American continent via the Bering Peninsula and in its wanderings south underwent certain geographical modifications. A number of local races are recognized from eastern Siberia and from British Columbia through to Arizona and Mexico. These are nearly all separated on the basis of colour, horn structure and ear shape.

In all these regions, however, the males possess massive horns that are curled into a full circle which may measure as much as 36 inches in circumference. The female usually has small upright horns. Bighorns are heavily built, standing about 38 inches at the shoulder. The fur is short and tight and commonly greyish-brown to black in summer, but the muzzle, the inner side of the limbs and the rump are conspicuously white.

They are gregarious, living in flocks of up to fifty individuals. Vigorous fighting

between mature rams takes place in November. The victors collect five to twelve ewes which they keep for the breeding season, subject always to a constant challenge from solitary rams. One- and 2-year old rams remain with the ewes. They are unable to breed until $2\frac{1}{2}$ years old. The young are born in May and take an active part in flock life when only 1 week old.

Bighorn Sheep are grazers, living on the sparse vegetation in their rocky mountainous habitats. Their hooves are straight-edged and sharply divided, and grip the rock securely. Their sure-footedness, coupled with remarkable leaping powers, makes any but the youngest Bighorn Sheep a difficult prey for the Puma which, in the New World, is their only natural enemy.

PHOTOGRAPHIC CREDITS

I am extremely grateful to the following for making photographs available:

GRANADA TV (Photographer, Frank Pocklington):
- A 2.
- B 64, 107, 151, 164, 192, 216, 219, 224.
- C 4, 55.
- E 59.
- F 21, 22, 24, 40, 41, 43, 44, 45, 79, 81, 82, 88, 95, 100, 129, 134, 140, 146, 147, 148, 155, 156, 160, 179, 182, 189, 190, 192.
- G 1, 11, 17.
- I 65.
- J 2, 10, 31, 62, 67, 135, 193, 304, 308, 317, 321, 330.
- L 1, 3, 5, 9, 11, 19, 22, 33, 35, 36, 38, 39, 40, 41, 42, 44, 53, 54, 57, 61, 62, 74, 85, 87, 94, 96, 104, 126, 136, 197, 229, 235, 245, 246, 247, 248, 249, 250, 251, 252.
- M 9, 17, 21.
- O 1, 2.
- Q 2.
- R 1, 3, 7, 8, 9, 12, 15, 16.
- S 1, 2, 9, 11, 12, 13, 14, 15, 16, 17, 18, 23, 24, 30, 45, 47, 60, 61, 62, 65, 73, 76, 84, 87, 88, 89, 90, 107, 120, 126, 131, 150, 151, 161, 170, 187, 192, 193.

ZOOLOGICAL SOCIETY OF LONDON:
- A 3, 6.
- B 2, 32, 89, 111, 112, 117, 145, 173, 235, 240.
- C 51, 71, 360.
- E 14, 24, 29, 40, 123.
- F 1, 32, 39, 51, 54, 56, 64, 66, 72, 98, 99, 126, 132, 141, 149, 158, 174, 188.
- G 3, 4, 28.
- H 2.
- I 57.
- J 1, 32, 33, 34, 59, 123, 146, 151, 154, 163, 178, 207, 241, 247, 279, 280, 297, 307, 311, 315, 323, 325, 337, 353.
- L 34, 37, 43, 68, 89, 91, 101, 143, 154, 156, 172, 212, 214, 216, 217, 230, 232, 237, 243.
- M 14, 31.
- N 1.
- P 1.
- R 5, 6, 6a.
- S 6, 7, 8, 64, 70, 72, 80, 82, 119, 128, 133, 140, 153, 166, 171, 172, 175, 176, 177, 178, 182, 185.

PAUL POPPER LTD:
- C 1, 94, 138, 358.
- E 123.
- I 14.
- J 319, 356.
- K 42, 64.
- L 45, 63, 67, 95, 213.
- M 25.
- S 22, 66, 78, 174.

433

MARINELAND OF THE PACIFIC:
   K 47, 69.

FOX PHOTOS LTD:
   L 161.

SHAMROCK FARMS LTD:
   L 97.

COLOGNE ZOO:
   L 124.

WOODLAND PARK ZOO (Photographer, Stuart B. Hertz):
   L 130.

SAN DIEGO ZOO:
   F 178.

I am also particularly indebted to the private individuals who have supplied the following photographs:

DAVID ATTENBOROUGH:
   F 37, 38.

J. H. CALABY:
   B 113.

R. C. LEIGHTON-HERDSON:
   F 136.

MALCOLM LYALL-WATSON:
   J 322.

RAMONA MORRIS:
   I 26.

N. PELHAM-WRIGHT:
   G 31.

ALAN ROBERTSON:
   L 59.

ERNEST P. WALKER and JOHN N. HAMLET:
   D 2.

G. KENNETH WHITEHEAD:
   S 63.

APPENDIX OF RARE SPECIES

The following 118 species of mammals are at present listed as being rare or in danger of extinction. I am extremely grateful to the I.U.C.N. (International Union for the Conservation of Nature) for permission to include this list, which is based on their most recent surveys. They stress that it is incomplete and that when more information becomes available additional species will undoubtedly have to be added to it. In the meantime it can serve as the best preliminary guide to the current situation.

MARSUPIALS: B 80, 81, 84, 94, 99, 105, 112, 114, 119, 129, 130, 132, 162, 171, 178, 198, 209, 210, 215, 241, 242, 243, 244, 248.

INSECTIVORES: C 1, 2, 357.

PRIMATES: F 19, 20, 25, 27, 28, 31, 33, 34, 37, 38, 39, 175, 189, 191.

EDENTATES: G 17, 31.

LAGOMORPHS: I 15, 21, 66.

RODENTS: J 2 (*kaibabensis*), 31 (*parvidens*), 59 (*elephantinus* and *elator*), 81 (*raviventris*), 151 (*breweri*), 327 (*browni*), 329 (*aedium* and *hylaeum*).

CETACEANS: K 84, 85, 87, 88, 89, 90, 91.

CARNIVORES: L 33, 42, 62, 66, 124, 215, 252.

SEALS: M 19, 24, 27, 28, 29.

SIRENIANS: Q 1, 2, 3, 4.

ODD-TOED UNGULATES: R 1, 10, 11, 12, 13, 14, 15, 16.

EVEN-TOED UNGULATES: S 3, 12, 27, 28, 31, 34, 42, 44, 47, 57, 58, 59, 68, 79, 80, 86, 89, 94, 103, 121, 122, 123, 127, 130, 149, 157, 158, 173, 176, 179, 180, 185.

INDEX OF POPULAR NAMES

Numbers in italics indicate that there is a full description and a photograph. Other numbers refer to the classification lists. Where certain animals in a group share a popular name, a general reference is given. (e.g. There is no advantage in including every species of Armadillo in the index when all are to be found together on two pages of the classification list.)

442

443

447